A PRACTICAL GUIDE TO N.F.T.

C. J. MOLYNEUX

ACKNOWLEDGEMENTS

The author wishes to acknowledge the kindness of the United Kingdom Ministry of Agriculture Fisheries and Food in permitting the use of tables and substance material from their work previously published in GCRI Growers Bulletin No. 5 (2nd edition). Likewise, the Institute of Horticultural Research for allowing the use of material originating at the Institute and previously published in the same work.

The author wishes to thank the Small Farms Association, Home Farm, Widdington, Saffron Walden, Essex, for helpful advice. He is greatly indebted to Barry Wearing, his dedication and inspiration have produced the illustrations which so enhance the text. He is indebted also to Hewitt Roberts Design, whose efforts have made this publication so presentable.

The author also wishes to thank Tony Tollitt for his skill and professionalism in producing photographic material. Finally, would Geraldine accept his sincere thanks for her generous assistance.

Published (1988) by Nutriculture Ltd., Mawdesley, Ormskirk, Lancashire.
Reprinted February, 1993.
Reprinted March, 1994,
Reprinted July, 1996.
Reprinted September, 1998.

ISBN No. 0 9513519 0 7

Phototypeset and Printed in Great Britain by T. Snape & Co. Ltd., Preston, Lancashire

All rights reserved. No part of this publication may be reproduced, stored in a retrieval system or transmitted in any form or by any means electronic, mechanical, photo-copying, recording or otherwise, without the prior permission of the publishers.

A PRACTICAL GUIDE TO NFT

CONTENTS Page

INTRODUCTION

When I first encountered the hydroponic technique dubbed NFT, I was convinced that it would never be of interest to the amateur gardener. It was one of my more notable mistakes!

Nonetheless, I hope you'll agree that there was some justification for that impression.

I saw it first at the Glasshouse Crops Research Institute in Sussex, where Dr. Alan Cooper was developing a system for the commercial grower. Certainly it was a fascinating set-up and it was producing some very acceptable crops. Miles of plastic ducting was used to carry a solution of plant food over the roots of plants. There was not a sign of anything so old-fashioned as peat or soil, yet tomatoes, cucumbers and courgettes were producing fine yields of fruit. So far so good.

The problem was that the whole set-up was run by a complicated computer system which carefully controlled the level of nutrients and acidity of the solution. This electronic brain monitored the mixture every few seconds and a robot corrected it if necessary. Not, I thought, ideally suited to the back-yard gardener. Anything that demanded that level of accuracy, to say nothing of the capital cost, was never going to appeal to your average amateur.

So, it was with some reservation that I visited Robert Irvine's "Hydroponicum" in the north of Scotland. What I saw there astounded me.

His set-up was on two distinct levels. With the help of John Molyneux, he had started a pilot scheme in an ordinary, garden sized polythene tunnel - the kind of structure anyone could buy for less than a hundred pounds. In it were rows of tanks bubbling with solutions of plant food, all circulating by means of a small pool pump. Mind you, it took a while to find the tanks because they were hidden by a jungle of verdent foliage.

There in the very north of Scotland, all most folk grew were potatoes and turnips, yet this was as productive as the most luxuriant valley in the south of France. Encouraged by his results, Robert had then expanded to a fully fledged commercial unit, but still run on John Molyneux's simple system.

There were no computers installed here, no robots and not even a white coat to be seen. It was simple enough for any good gardener to follow and without the enormous expense of the alternative commercial system. And by golly it worked! Robert was growing everything from beans to beetroot with astonishing success.

Now, John Molyneux has put down the method for all to see in the most comprehensive book yet written on NFT for all, from the amateur to the most polished professional. Here is all you need to know about a new method of growing that is not only highly productive wherever you may live, but a lot of fun too. I can thoroughly recommend it.

Geoff Hamilton,
Barnsdale 1987.

CHAPTER ONE

THEORY OF NUTRIENT FILM TECHNIQUE (NFT)

It has become plain from simple observations that all plants require plant food, essentially inorganic nutrient ions, and water. Although the former has been successfully introduced to plants in minute quantities through the leaves (foliar feeding) it is clear that with very few exceptions e.g. carnivorous plants, it is the roots of plants which are principally involved in nutrient and water uptake. It follows that if we can improve nutrient and water uptake we stand a good chance of improving yields and quality.

It is less well appreciated that plant roots also take up oxygen. Oxygen is as essential to plants as air is to humans. We need not unnecessarily concern ourselves with what happens to the oxygen once it is absorbed by the plant, suffice it to say that if we can improve the oxygen uptake by the plant roots we stand a good chance of improving nutrient and water uptake.

Where people have concerned themselves with improving plant performance by cultural techniques they have very often, knowingly or unknowingly, attempted to provide conditions for the plants which maximise the plants ability to take up water, nutrients and oxygen. Most of us are familiar with the difficulties of various soils and composts and accordingly it is hardly surprising that over many years a considerable effort has been made to attempt plant cultivation using hydroponic techniques; i.e. using water to replace solid material as the carrying medium for essential plant nutrients.

CONVENTIONAL HYDROPONICS

A good level of success has been achieved. Many gardeners will be familiar with "ring culture" technique for growing tomatoes and others with "Hydropots" widely used to grow decorative plants. In these cases a solid component is used to provide surfaces for root growth and a degree of anchorage but not as the prime carrier of plant feed. Because the solid component is relatively coarse, there is excellent permeability of the medium by air and oxygen uptake is potentially good. More elaborate hydroponic growing units using a wide variety of solid components have been established for commercial plant production and some have had outstanding success. All these systems of hydroponic cultivation are known collectively as aggregate systems, this term referring, of course, to the relatively large granular medium which is employed. Briefly the principal problems encountered with aggregate systems are:—

1. High initial cost.
2. Complicated feeding and watering programmes giving cyclical availability of water and nutrients.
3. Breakdown of the granules leading to poor aeration.
4. Naturally poor aeration in those areas of the unit where water collects.
5. High work load in non-automated units or conversely high cost and difficulty of automation.
6. Ability of the aggregate to become contaminated with root disease organisms i.e. soil borne disease.
7. Inefficient use of space especially in large production areas.

For these reasons aggregate hydroponics has remained largely a technique favoured in certain difficult situations, or used only by the very able and inventive grower.

NUTRIENT FILM TECHNIQUE

Nutrient Film Technique (NFT) is a hydroponic growing method. Surprisingly it did not arise as a refinement of conventional "aggregate" systems but instead was developed from observations of the growth of certain plants which, more by accident than design, had been placed in an NFT like unit at the Glasshouse Crops Research Institute at Littlehampton in Sussex. Very soon the basic principles of a hydroponic system now known as Nutrient Film Technique were established. These are:

1. A nutrient solution is circulated past the roots of the plants.
2. No solid root zone material is necessary for the system.
3. The plants are grown on a slope.

It is 1. above which differentiates NFT from other forms of growing plants, the essential substance of the technique being the circulated nutrient solution. As this solution is necessarily very shallow the phrase 'nutrient film' was evolved. Figure 1/1 shows the principal components and layout of a simple NFT system.

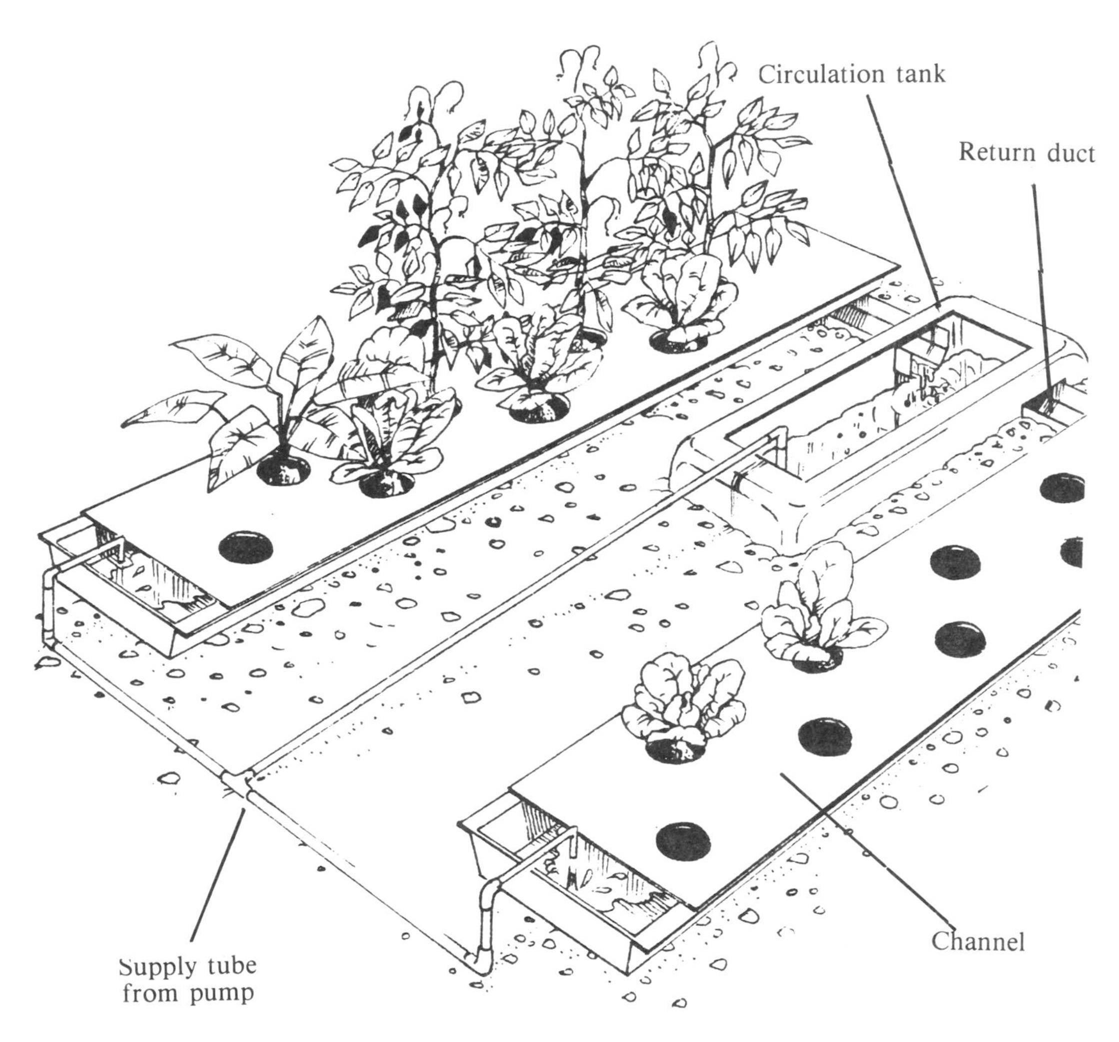

Fig 1/1 Basic NFT layout

IMPACT OF NFT

It is immediately obvious that the three essentials of plant root performance are at once satisfied by the simple innovation embodied in NFT. Water, nutrients and oxygen are always available to the plant roots, let us briefly examine how this comes about.

Water:

In the soil, plant roots extract the moisture from an area immediately surrounding the individual root axes. Once the water in any locality is depleted the plant must find more water at another locality or wait for water in the initial locality to be replenished. Root extension growth provides the former whilst rain or irrigation and, to a lesser extent than might be imagined, sideways movement of water in the soil provide the latter. This situation is illustrated in Figure 1/2.

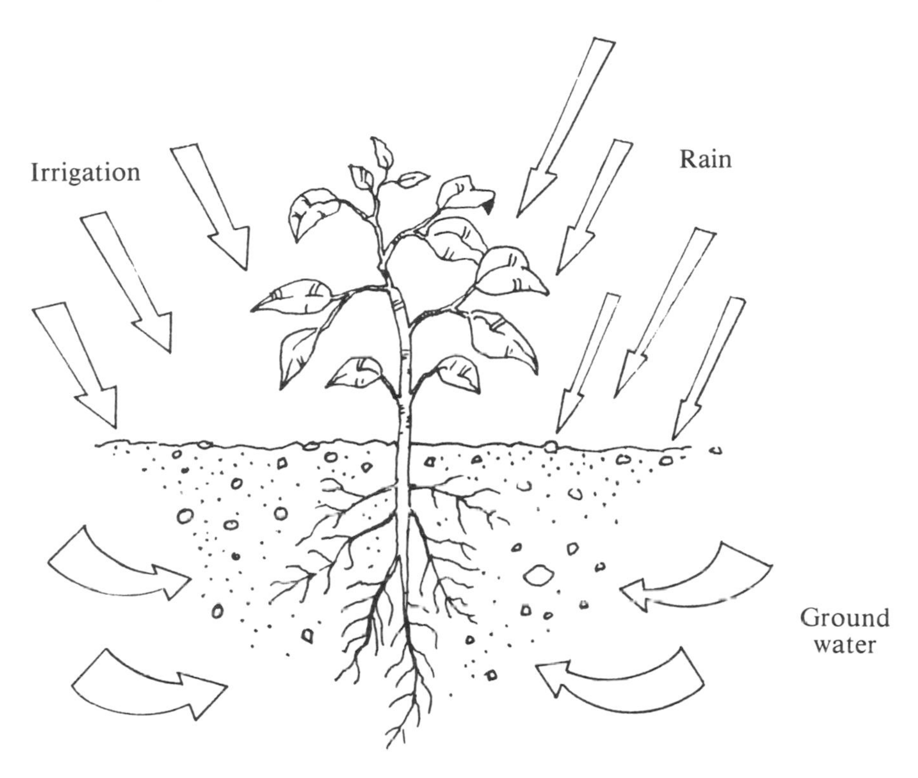

Fig. 1/2 Water supplies to soil grown plants

This arrangement is always less than perfect because it means that at one time or another water is in short supply or is supplied in such quantities that waterlogging occurs. This latter is especially significant because waterlogging is the exclusion of air from the root zone. In NFT water is taken up by the plants from the stream which passes by the plant roots, as shown in Figure 1/3. Provided this stream flows at a rate in excess of the rate at which plants can absorb water then the plants are never short of water and do not have to rely on root extension growth to tap new sources of water.

Nutrients:

Some controversy exists in scientific circles regarding the nature of nutrient uptake. Is it passive, i.e. are nutrients absorbed with water at a rate according to the concentration of the nutrient in the surrounding water, or is it active, i.e. does the plant specifically absorb some nutrients from those present in the water whilst blocking the uptake of other nutrients? This discussion need not confuse us, provided we bear in mind at all times that only soluble plant nutrients are taken up by the roots. It follows then that if water is scarce in the locality of the root axes then plant nutrients are also likely to be scarcely available to the plant, whilst if waterlogging occurs, both nutrients and water will be available to the plant, but the plant will be unable to absorb either. This is the situation often existing in the soil. In NFT the advantageous position of the plant in

Fig. 1/3 Water supply to NFT grown plants

relation to its supply of water is also a feature of its supply of nutrients. Provided the stream of nutrient solution at once provides an excess of water and of all the essential plant nutrients, it makes no difference whether nutrient uptake is passive or active as the plant will always have access to excess supplies of plant nutrients.

Of course this arrangement is satisfactory only within certain limits of nutrient concentration. High nutrient concentrations are injurious to plants as they inhibit water uptake. In practice it is not difficult to keep the nutrient concentration in the solution at such a level that all nutrients are available to the plant in excess of requirements, whilst the total concentration is lower than the level at which injury occurs. Nonetheless total nutrient concentration is an important issue and later it will be shown how to make use of it in improving growth and performance.

What of the possibility of nutrients being provided at a level lower than their take-up by the plant? Experimentation has shown that very low concentrations of nutrients, far lower than might have been guessed at, are sufficient to enable a satisfactory rate of uptake. Remember that new nutrient solution is continually arriving at the plant roots. This situation appears to be slightly analogous to the situation in soil where the soil nutrient solution concentration is weak but nutrient losses due to uptake by the plant are continually made up, subject to availability, by new nutrient ions being released from the soil particles. Whatever the similarities, this feature is important because it widens the band of nutrient solution concentration which is acceptable for successful NFT and this immediately simplifies the design of systems and their operation especially in the area of home and garden use where complicated or expensive nutrient control equipment would be out of the question.

Oxygen:

We have already seen how the application of water, either as rainfall or blanket irrigation, tends to drive air from the soil leading to low activity of the root system. It is the object of good cultivation to provide a soil structure which minimises this effect while allowing satisfactory quantities of water to be made available to the plant. It is fortunate indeed that plant roots totally immersed in water at one point appear to be able to function satisfactorily using a supply of oxygen absorbed elsewhere in the root system. It is this aspect of plant physiology which is used with great success in NFT.

Remember that using NFT only a thin film of nutrient solution is introduced to the channel. Accordingly, when root axes emerge from the propagation block and enter the nutrient solution they do so, at once, in contact with the solution and at least in part in contact with the atmosphere. Subsequently emerging root axes may indeed cause a part or all of the original axes to submerge by pressure of their own weight and/or by the build-up of the nutrient solution behind the increasing dam of roots occupying the channel. However, these roots in turn maintain a part of their surface exposed to the atmosphere.

ESSENTIAL FEATURES OF NFT

As described, plants grown in a NFT system are simultaneously exposed to effectively unlimited supplies of water, plant nutrients and oxygen. It is this feature which gives NFT its growth advantage over alternative methods of cultivation. In subsequent chapters, it will be shown how to realize this advantage, but first it is necessary to consider further elements of NFT which are essential foundations for success.

On careful examination of Figure 1/1, it is apparent that certain features are essential components of the NFT system. These are:—

1. The channel and the flow in the channel.
2. Solution volume.
3. The composition of the nutrient solution.

The channel and flow

Channels are the structures or vessels which accommodate the plants. They may be simple or somewhat complex and they may be made of a wide variety of materials which will be examined later. To be successful in NFT the channels must be laid on a firm and regular slope, and be of a shape and size compatible with the correct flow of the nutrient solution and the growth of the plant roots. Flow rate, slope and channel dimensions are intricately related. If a nutrient solution is introduced at the end of a channel, at what rate must it be introduced, at what slope, and in what width of channel, in order to achieve the desired aim of unrestricted access to water, nutrients and oxygen? Values must be found for these variables.

Channel Width:

Suppose a tomato crop is to be grown. If the root system of a soil grown tomato plant is examined it will show that roots are freely produced and abundant. Accordingly narrow channels can be dismissed, simply because accommodating the root would require at least 20 cm. width at normal spacing. In practice 20 cm. might be considered a minimum for a single row of tomatoes whilst plants at greater density and larger rooted species would demand wider channels and smaller plants might be accommodated in somewhat narrower channels.

Flow Rate:

Again using the tomato plant as an example, a healthy plant in good growing conditions may take up 2 ml. water/minute. A run of 10 plants would require a flow of 20 ml./minute to satisfy the water requirements of the plants. At this rate the solution would have to be finely distributed along the root axes and this would present a problem.

It would be prudent on this count alone and working with a perfect slope to provide at least 100 ml./minute, so that the last plant in the row had equal chance of access by its entire root system. However, there are two further points of consideration. Firstly, the water is the carrier of the nutrients. Already it has been shown that a wide band of nutrient concentration is acceptable, but in practice the solution should be approximately the same strength to all plants in the system irrespective of the number of plants in the row. To guard against along the row depletion of nutrients by selective uptake, or concentration of the nutrient solution by preferential extraction of water, an increase in flow rate is generally desired. This might be to 200 ml./minute.

Secondly, it is unlikely that the flow along the channel would take the form of a perfect film. In the first instance slight across channel uneveness allows the solution to flow away on one side or the other, whilst subsequently, development of the root system displaces the nutrient stream. For these reasons a flow rate of less than 200 ml./min. in a 20 cm. channel would not normally be desired and in most cases a significantly higher flow could be introduced with advantage.

Channel Slope:

Now with flow rate at say 400-500 ml./minute and channel width of 20 cm. the task of determining slope is straightforward. Experiments show that good flow characteristics can be achieved with a slope as gentle as 1:150 but practical considerations demand that this be much increased because of the difficulty and avoidable expense of preparing a perfect slope. A minimum slope of 1:50 has received widespread acceptance. It should be emphasised that the slope of 1:50 is a minimum practical figure and that if circumstances allow it may be slightly advantageous to construct a rather greater slope, and as will be seen later there are certain sites and conditions where a greater slope is highly desirable. In practice, even on a small scale, it is not always easy to construct a slope much steeper than 1:50 because of the extra lift required of the pump and because benches etc. may become unstable. Nonetheless there is no upper limit to the slope and in fact vertical systems have been installed and run effectively. The principal disadvantages of such systems being, holding the plants in position and the extra cost of pumping the solution.

Any slope used for NFT channels must be firm and regular. This will avoid the formation of pools of nutrient solution. In these pools plant roots lose contact with the atmosphere and show the symptoms of waterlogging. Any work spent on stabilizing the slope will be rewarded by results.

Variations of flow rate and channel width are common. In either case variations are inspired by practical considerations. For example; a 20 cm. channel width is barely sufficient for tomatoes, whilst it is definitely too narrow to accommodate the expected root growth of cucumber or marrow plants, when 25 cm. minimum is considered much more appropriate. For smaller plants generally not less than 12 cm. is provided. At first this seems rather large, but some of the channel is occupied by the propagation block which restricts the flow.

As regards channel shape, many forms have been proposed and used. It is apparent from that which has already been discussed that the channel must not interfere with the smooth uninterrupted flow of the nutrient solution. Not surprisingly then channels with bases smooth and flat are normally employed whilst uneven surfaces, especially anything with transverse raised pieces, should be avoided.

The Importance of Volume:

Volume is important to the smooth and effective running of NFT systems. Continuing with tomato plants as an example, a row of 10 plants might use in the order of 9 litres per day. Clearly from the point of view of water supply only, a volume of something over 9 litres assuming daily topping-up, would suffice. Further consideration of the example reveals that after half a day the volume in the unit will be reduced to 4½ litres. Assuming no nutrients but only water has been removed, this would result in a doubling of the nutrient concentration. Notwithstanding the relatively wide band of nutrient concentration which may be tolerated, significant uncontrolled nutrient concentration increases may be injurious. Of course, in practice, the plants would take up some nutrient and the actual changes would not be so dramatic in such a short space of time, but the tendency for uncontrolled nutrient concentration changes must be avoided and it is achieved by adding volume to the unit. Subject to the assumption that the NFT unit could be topped-up at least every 2-3 days during periods of high water usage, a figure of 5 litres per tomato plant has been found to give practical advantage. Note that it is generally agreed that a tomato plant requires an air space of around 50 cm. × 50 cm., say 4 plants/sq. metre. It is in order, quite irrespective of the plant type, to calculate acceptable tank volume by reference to the air space occupied by the cultivated plants.

It may be necessary or desirable to adjust the volume to allow for particular conditions. In the case of the use of very hard water it is prudent to provide for double the calculated volume in the system. This is so, because the massive presence of non-nutrient elements in the water limits the quantity of plant nutrients which may be added without the risk of the total solution concentration going outside of the acceptable band.

Very often NFT systems are fitted with a device to make up the volume lost by transpiration and evaporation i.e. an automatic top-up system. In these cases the suggested minimum volume arrived at by calculation may be reduced by up to 50%. This is because automatic top-up stabilises the nutrient concentration where the tendency would otherwise be towards solution nutrient concentration increase.

Whatever figure for tank volume is arrived at by reference to the above must be subject to a minimum volume requirement. Of course this will only be applicable in the smallest systems but it does appertain particularly to home built 'trial' units, when it might be supposed 'practical' to dispense with some volume. 20-25 litres is considered the minimum volume which will eliminate a phenomenon of dry powder nutrients known as "sampling error", by which it is potentially possible to measure a nutrient dose which would be so at variance with pack analysis as to be toxic or deficient in one or more essential elements. Similarly low volumes tend not to be amenable to the adjustment of nutrient concentration and solution pH using standard equipment. There is no theoretical upper limit to the volume of an NFT system.

The nutrient solution:

It has already been shown that the total nutrient concentration may be acceptable within wide limits. The same can be said of the individual nutrients ions where concentration will vary markedly with total nutrient concentration and with differential uptake by the plants, and sometimes with differential additions. Remember that, as shown, it is an embodiment of NFT that all essential elements are supplied in excess of requirements and accordingly variations do not threaten the success of the system. It follows that the use of a properly formulated nutrient solution demands a degree of confidence by the user. A practical example will emphasise the point. If plants growing in an NFT system show symptoms of iron deficiency, then as iron has been supplied in excess of requirements it is most likely that the deficiency is due to poor uptake of iron. The problem can be solved not by increasing the iron concentration in the nutrient solution but by improving the conditions for iron uptake.

OBSERVATIONS CONCERNING THE HEATING OF THE SOLUTION

Having examined the circulating system as supplier or provider of water, nutrients and oxygen, it is worthwhile spending a little time considering the effect of temperature on plant growth and in particular special aspects arising from the use of a circulating solution.

Heat fundamentally affects the rate of metabolism, essential "life activity", of all living things. It is abundantly clear from every day observations of native plants that growth is massively affected by temperature and it is not hard to deduce that there is an optimum temperature range above and below which growth will be adversely affected. It is not so well understood that for optimum growth both the shoots and roots should be as close as possible to optimum temperature and that this optimum is not necessarily the same for the shoots and roots of the same plant. The operation of a circulating nutrient solution provides an easy opportunity for the direct application of heat almost exclusively to the root zone. It is interesting and pertinent to compare the performance of "soil" and "water" in terms of heat. Soil is a reasonably good insulator, it is slow to warm up but once warmed is slow to cool down. Water is a good conductor, fast to warm up but equally fast to cool down. Wet soil would function very much like water. Soil might have the advantage in natural summer and autumn conditions when excess heat absorbed during the day may be useful at night, but might suffer disadvantage compared to water in natural spring conditions, when it would be slow to respond to good day time increments of air temperature. If there is any decisive advantage of one over the other it would clearly be in 'artificial' conditions, where the ease with which water can be heated and the heat controlled is potentially so useful.

What are the possibilities of benefit from the application of heat to the root zone? There are two classes of possible benefits. Firstly, to increase the growth of the root system, secondly, to increase the activity of the root system. In the case of the former, the application of heat to the root zone, thereby raising the root zone temperature closer to optimum for root growth, is used to improve either the rate at which roots emerge from the propagation block into the circulating solution or to increase the quantity and extent of the roots occupying the channel. There are various circumstances in NFT cultivation where such heat applications are made. In the case of the latter a further division is called for. In the first place, solution heating is applied so that root zone temperature increases and with it root activity, with the aim of balancing the activity of the roots with that of the shoots. It has been shown that shoot activity is more or less exclusively influenced by the temperature of the shoot environment and hardly at all by the temperature of the root zone. Accordingly, if there is a great disparity between the rate of activity of the shoot and the rate of root activity caused by the shoot being closer to its optimum than the root is to its optimum, then the plant may not perform to expectations. Consider the case of glasshouse tomato plants, subjected to a series of days of particularly fine weather giving rise to high air space temperatures and high light levels, themselves promoting a high degree of shoot activity. But commonly growth is poorer than expected. The problem may be that the shoot demand for water is greater than can be met by the activity of the root system. In certain cases raising the solution temperature, increasing root activity, improves water uptake and results in better growth of the shoot.

In the second place the question raised is:— Can the uplift of root zone temperature offset shoot zone (space) heating with no loss of growth performance and at the same time save heating costs? This subject has been closely studied at research establishments, particularly in recent years, when the need to save glasshouse heating costs has become paramount. The resulting evidence is somewhat confusing. The most satisfactory conclusion is that generally it is not possible to maintain the growth rate of plants by offsetting heat to the root zone from the shoot zone, but it may be possible to maintain the quality of growth by this method. Accordingly there may be some scope for cost savings. For example, in the early spring the quality of shoot growth of early planted crops may be maintained at lower than usual night time temperatures if heat is applied to the roots. Again, in the autumn, plants may require "finishing" i.e. the crop is present but needs to be enlarged and ripened while air space conditions are deteriorating, root zone heating may allow this process to continue.

Let us consider briefly some dynamics of solution heating. In any body of material the amount of heat it contains is proportional to its volume. It follows that in a circulating solution the amount of heat available to the plant roots is proportional to the flow rate of the solution. The higher the flow rate the more heat is applied at constant temperature. It is worth examining a practical example. With maize (sweet corn) it is generally agreed that significant root growth commences at 10°C. If the circulating solution is heated to 12°C more heat is applied to the plant roots at a flow rate of 1 litre/min. than at 250 ml./min. since 1 litre of water contains more heat than 250 ml. Similarly, if the temperature of the solution drops to 8°C then the cold shock to the plants will be greater at flow rate of 1 litre/min. than at 250 ml./min. and more harm will be done. We have already seen that flow rates above certain rather low levels perfectly satisfy the plants nutrient and water requirements but higher flow rates may be required to obtain practical advantage.

CONCLUSIONS FROM THE THEORY

I hope and trust that the foregoing essential theory has proved useful. There have been quite a number of conclusions drawn which should help in the practical applications of NFT. There are three additional points I regard as opportune to make at this stage. Firstly, though NFT is easy and simple it cannot be easier or simpler than neglecting plants grown conventionally. More appropriately NFT is an easy and simple method of improving performance. Clearly NFT is likely to be of use only if there is an earnest desire to improve. Secondly, from that which has been discussed, it follows that the performance of a range of species is adversely affected by difficulties of water, nutrient and oxygen uptake. If none of these factors are limiting performance of a particular species in conventional culture then it is unlikely that NFT will improve performance directly because NFT has no influence on light, humidity etc. Of course the benefit of lower work load may still be available.

Finally, in general, it appears to be easier to obtain the benefits of improved water, nutrient and oxygen uptake when using plants with vigorous root systems. Actually this subject is rather interesting in itself because research has suggested that modern plant varieties, especially but not exclusively, of crop plants, though selected by plant breeders for their shoot performance e.g. weight and numbers of peas, have more vigorous root systems than their poorer performing predecessors.

CHAPTER TWO

MATERIALS AND THEIR USES IN NFT

All NFT systems are basically systems for circulating water. In our society such systems are commonplace in the house, in the construction industry, in agriculture and throughout manufacturing and applied technology. It is fortunate that this is so because it means that there are available an abundance of suitable materials and items of equipment and that they should be competitively priced.

METALS

Metals are used extensively in the supportive structures of NFT systems and much less so in those positions were they would come into contact with the circulating solution. This is because some metals are toxic, dependant on concentration, to plants and small amounts of metal are released into the nutrient solution by contact with the solution. Let us consider a few common metals.

Galvanised Steel

Galvanised steel is often used to manufacture stands and trays which are widely employed in commercial horticulture to construct the slope and upon which flexible channelling is laid. It is relatively inexpensive and in sheet form can be bent and formed fairly readily. Alternatively, manufactured steel can subsequently be galvanised. Galvanised steel is unsuitable for use where it may come into contact with the nutrient solution because it releases zinc which may well prove toxic. Approximately 20 parts per million (ppm) of zinc is believed to be toxic to many plants whilst about 0.1 ppm is necessary for nutrition. Galvanised steel tanks should be avoided unless they can be adequately sealed; e.g. with a plastic liner.

Brass and Copper

Brass and copper are common materials of the plumbing industry but they can release toxic levels of metal into the solution if used extensively. These materials are however well distributed in plumbers and builders merchants and DIY stores, and this accessability is useful in emergencies especially in difficult pipework. Materials so used should be replaced with suitable materials as soon as practicable. Brass and copper fittings may be used occasionally in the fitment of auto top-up facilities, the important distinction being that they are not in contact with the circulating solution.

Aluminium

Aluminium is quite unsuitable for use in contact with the nutrient solution. It has been used to form stands and trays for channel supports where its lightweight and great longevity are advantageous. However it is expensive. Problems have arisen when water draining from aluminium glasshouses has been used in NFT. This is a problem confined to new aluminium since subsequently a "skin" forms which prevents heavy releases of metal.

Mild Steel

The problem with mild steel is that the nutrient solution, being slightly acidic, causes fairly rapid corrosion where contact is prolonged. Its main use is in self constructed systems when, because it is readily available as scrap, it may be put to excellent use as channel supports even if it does look rather unsightly.

Cast-Iron

Cast-iron is highly suitable but not widely used. It is most commonly employed as pump housings.

Stainless Steel

Common uses of stainless steel in NFT applications are in pump components and sink wastes. Elsewhere this highly suitable material is only occasionally employed on account of expense.

Chrome and Nickle Plate

Chrome and nickle plate are best avoided in positions where they may contact the nutrient solution. Be careful not to confuse these finishes with stainless steel.

Painted/Coated metals

These compositions are as good as the material which covers them. The best advice is to avoid them in uses where they come into contact with the nutrient solution unless you have sound advice as to suitability.

PLASTICS

As described metals have a limited application in NFT systems. By far the largest proportion of components are fabricated in plastic. This is hardly surprising as it reflects the inexorable trend towards the replacement of metals by plastics in liquid transport facilities. As there is general unfamiliarity with the various plastics it is worthwhile spending a little time in description. Plastics are neatly divided into two groups; construction plastics and engineering plastics. Considering first construction plastics, these are bulk materials used as replacements for the cheaper metals. They are polyvinyl chloride (PVC), polypropylene and polyester.

Polyvinyl Chloride (PVC)

There are two groups of PVC namely uPVC, the 'u' meaning unplasticised and also known as rigid PVC, and plasticised PVC usually referred to simply as PVC.. uPVC is highly suitable for NFT use either with or without contact with the solution, whilst plasticised PVC is unsuitable for use in contact with the nutrient solution but may be used where no contact is made. Amongst the useful materials manufactured in uPVC are:—rigid drain pipes and guttering and associated fittings, domestic waste pipes and fittings, and additionally there is some sheet construction of troughs and tanks. uPVC has two great advantages, firstly, it is relatively inexpensive, probably the least expensive of all plastics. Secondly, it is easily and permanently bonded using a solvent cement. This means that cracks are repairable and joints made watertight without the need for specialist skills. uPVC is somewhat brittle and is subject to fracturing on receipt of a sharp blow or if water is frozen inside a uPVC pipe.

As its name suggests plasticised PVC has plasticisers added to give flexibility to the material. Many plasticisers are easily leeched from the surface of the material and many are seriously phytotoxic. How can the layman tell plasticised PVC from uPVC? The rule is simple. If it is flexible and PVC it is plasticised PVC and should be avoided. The most common garden product which may be made in plasticised PVC is garden hose.

Polypropylene

In this group are included polythenes. Polypropylenes are the most common plastics in everyday use. This is not surprising since from a manufacturing angle they are easy to use, highly versatile and relatively inexpensive. Additionally they are non-toxic to humans and plants alike. Accordingly products manufactured in polypropylene are used extensively in NFT systems, chiefly as tanks, flexible pipes and fittings and as channelling. The main disadvantage of polypropylene is that it is difficult to repair and therefore on-site repair is unlikely to be successful or economic. A slight exception is polythene sheet which will take a reasonably permanent repair with electricians tape, or a specialist tape designed specifically for the purpose. Fortunately repair of polypropylenes is not often necessary as they do not corrode, they are flexible and they have good impact resistance.

Natural polypropylenes suffer deterioration by ultra violet light which is contained in sunlight. To overcome this an ultraviolet inhibitor (UVI) is mixed in manufacture. It is essential to use UVI polypropylene products for normal NFT purposes. In fact most products are UVI and the benefit is enhanced if black material is used. Black has the dual benefit of absorbing more heat and ordinarily being better UV stabilised.

Because polypropylene cannot be readily bonded a potential problem occurs when attempting watertight joints. In practice this is less of a difficulty than might be imagined because the flexibility of polypropylene, coupled with a surface characteristic known as greasiness makes watertight friction joints very reliable. Note that the manufacturers of domestic waste systems sometimes employ this jointing technique, and do so with complete confidence.

A special word on polythene is appropriate. For practical purposes polythenes are sheet forms of polypropylenes and they are so useful because they do not have ready alternatives in other materials. The principal use of polythene in NFT is as channelling. More often than not this is the material upon which the plants grow and the solution flows. It is often employed as a disposable item being renewed annually.

Can the layman tell the difference between plasticised PVC and polypropylene? It is not always easy. PVC cement will not stick to polypropylene, on drying it peels away. PVC burns poorly with an acrid smoke, whilst polypropylene burns fiercely with a black smoke. Polypropylene has surface greasiness but it is not always so obvious. Sometimes PVC is labelled as such but polypropylene rarely is.

A further confusion is caused by the availability of reground plastics, that is recycled plastics. There is a considerable growth in products manufactured from these in both PVC and polypropylene. They are best avoided for use where contact with the nutrient solution would occur. Again manufacturers do not usually state that reground material has been used. Clearly products made in reground tend to be cheaper. Look for a uniform 'non-colour' i.e. that which you would expect if all colours were mixed together.

Polyester

Polyester is another widely used plastic. Most of us are familiar with polyester fabrics. In NFT it is most widely employed as the plastic in glass reinforced plastic (GRP), better known as fibreglass. Polyester is very tough.

Tanks and channels are likely uses for GRP products. Additionally there is some scope for home construction using fibreglass kits. GRP can be repaired with some, not guaranteed, success using more GRP or possibly by polyester resin alone. Polyester cannot be joined by common bonding materials, glues or PVC cement. Complete curing of GRP takes several days to several weeks depending on light, heat and other variables and it is advised to allow ample time before using the product.

Engineering Plastics

Engineering plastics are a new growth industry. Traditional types include "nylon" and the similar "ryton" but the range is massive. They tend to be used in high duty applications and in NFT these are found chiefly in the working parts of pumps, filters and valves. There are three engineering plastics which may become more widely used in non-specialised applications. These are: polycarbonates, ABS and PET. All are suitable for NFT purposes.

Other Materials

Other materials of occasional use in NFT are glass, used as tubes and vessels, and asbestos as channel supports. More widely employed is wood from which channel supports and even channels may be fashioned. In spite of its well known limitations, namely rotting and warping, wood should not be dismissed as unsuitable. Not only may preservatives be used to prolong life, but wood is immensely adaptable and can be worked with common tools and yet it is still usually inexpensive.

CHAPTER THREE

COMPONENTS. HOW TO SELECT AND USE THEM

CONSTRUCTION OF THE SLOPE

The first essential of any NFT system is the slope. The specifications are that it must be firm and regular and not less than 1:50. As NFT systems may be 'ground' or 'bench' types it is useful and convenient to look at these separately.

Ground slopes

A practical advantage accrues from keeping NFT channels as low as possible since height in the greenhouse is very often at a premium. Accordingly ground slopes are popular whenever it is proposed to grow plants such as tomatoes or cucumbers and the like. Most level or nearly level sites can be converted to slopes without inordinate work or expense, but these should never be underestimated. Sites with an existing slope are the easiest to convert if the direction of the slope is unchanged but if, unusually, the slope direction is reversed very considerable work and expense may be involved. Sites with peaty subsoil are unsuitable for conversion to ground slopes except where a better than 1:50 slope is produced and even then expect settling, requiring significant annual repair, to occur.

The most common slope construction material is the existing earth which can be formed up by spade and tamped down, but there are snags. Ordinary garden soil, especially that to which organic matter has been added is unstable and no matter how well the slope is formed in the first instance it will fairly quickly misform. Heavy clay soils are less unstable but they are inclined to be sticky and provide a poor surface on which to stand and work. The conclusion is that except on very short runs where a slope in excess of 1:50 is easily constructed, earth alone is not recommended. An exception is a site on a steep existing slope where the soil can be easily smoothed off, perhaps with a filling of sand in small depressions. Figures 3/1 and 3/2 illustrate alternative methods of forming slopes from earth.

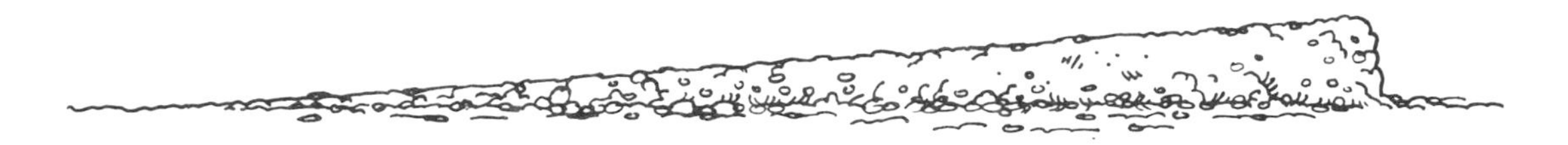

Fig. 3/1 Slope built up from earth

Fig. 3/2 Excavated slope - prevents loss of headroom

Sand and particularly sand/stone mixes, termed aggregates, are useful for consolidating slopes as shown in figure 3/3. Material may be found at builders merchants when ordinary concreting ballast may be employed. A mix of 2 stone to 1 sand being most usually used. Alternatively stone may be supplied directly from stone merchants or quarries when "crusher run" may be specified. This contains a mixture of various stone sizes together with sufficient fine particles to effect good binding of the material when compacted. In order not to lose height the existing earth should be removed to leave a rough regular slope. On large sites it is appropriate to mechanise the job with earth moving equipment and roller. On small sites a lawn roller is ideal for compacting added material. If a good job is done sand and sand/stone mixes make excellent slopes. Very often an insulating layer of 25mm of polystyrene is added and upon this the channel may be laid. This arrangement is shown in figure 3/4.

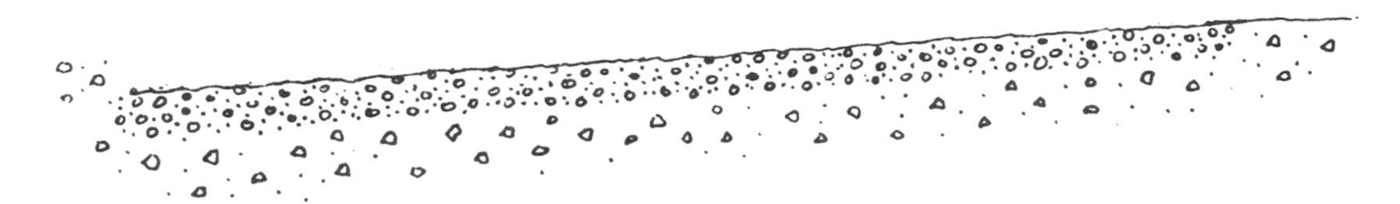

Fig. 3/3 Slope stabilized with stone and sand

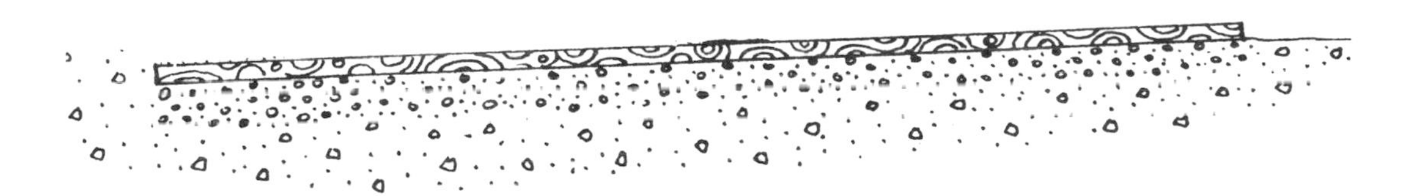

Fig. 3/4 Semi-permanent slope using insulation board

Permanent slopes have advantages. Firstly they provide reliability, secondly they encourage the use of flexible channelling which may be an important cost saver. Finally they provide excellent surfaces upon which to stand and work if they are extended beyond the sideways limits of one or more of the channels. This latter being hugely encouraging to continuing work in a greenhouse during the more forbidding months of the year.

Amongst the materials used to form permanent slopes are garden paving, as shown in figure 3/5, house bricks (new and second hand) and all the blocks and bricks used in the construction industry. With all these materials the resultant slope is permanent only if they are laid to a fair standard. Soil must first be removed and replaced with sand, sand/stone or rubble. Again where possible ensure no loss of air space.

Laying concrete in-situ is another alternative and here again removal of the existing soil is necessary. Several commercial growers have, on converting their holdings to NFT, used concrete to form the slope. Two advantages are claimed for this construction. Firstly, channels can be formed in the concrete during construction, providing sites for flexible channelling or subsequently lined with waterproofing resin so they can be used permanently as channels. Secondly, insulation can be bedded into the concrete as a

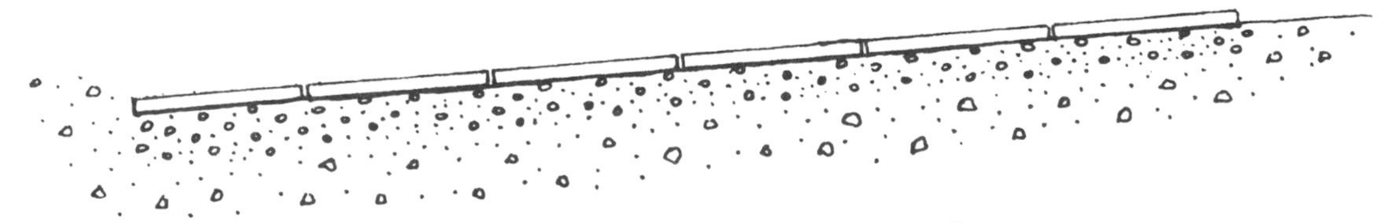

Fig. 3/5 Permanent slope using paving

Figure 3/5
sandwich as shown in figure 3/6, use either polystrene or closed cell styrene. Alternatively polystyrene granules can be added to the concrete mix. The use of concrete in which channels are formed sounds a good idea but in practice it is only recommended for the semi-commercial house at the smallest, because on smaller sites flexibility as to the position and number of channels might be important. A flat floor sloped 1:50 upon which non-permanent channels can be laid is highly advantageous. In any season sites not taken by NFT could be used to site tubs, pots and bags, whilst working conditions in the greenhouse are also enhanced. If laying concrete do not lay too thick a slab so that subsequent excavation, e.g. to move a tank site, is not so painful an experience.

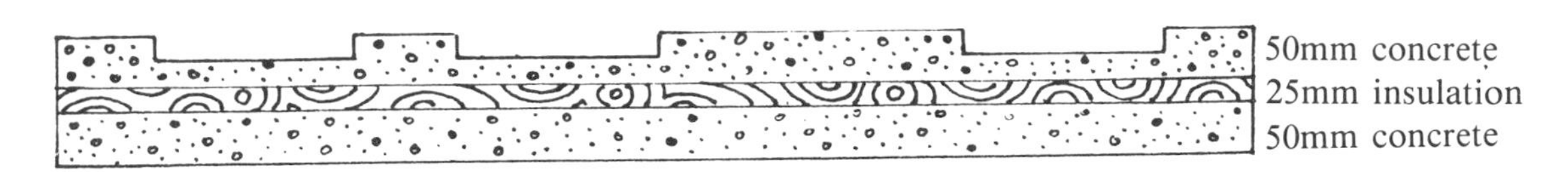

Fig. 3/6 Section showing a use of concrete and insulation to form channels

The importance of not losing height in the small greenhouse has been emphasised but what of the possibility of gaining headroom? The entire top soil can be removed and probably used profitably elsewhere in the garden. A permanent slope being formed at the level of the sub-soil. This idea has been used but note the following objections. First, with an existing greenhouse removal of the soil can lead to instability of the structure if there are no foundations or the foundations become undermined. Second, in sites characterised by wetness and poor drainage the removal of the earth may lead to flooding. Having stated these objections if they are not applicable the idea is sound. 20-22cm + may be gained but a compromise gain would still be very useful if the objections where considered restrictive.

The normal practice of subsequent insulation of ground slopes by using an insulating board has prompted the suggestion that "two birds may be killed with one stone", if a rigid insulating board replaced concrete bricks or other slabs or blocks. Ordinary polystyrene is probably unsuitable except in large thicknesses, but a heavier grade is available. Better still is closed cell styrene available under several trade names and quite rigid and also polyurethane board. These are not as widely available as polystyrene - try specialist insulation suppliers, and they are also considerably more expensive, but they have been effectively used especially, but not exclusively, on small sites.

Bench Slopes

In practice there are two types of bench slope. Firstly, where the channels are laid on existing benches, secondly, where purpose built benches specially designed for NFT are employed.

If an NFT channel is to be sited on an existing bench it is often a simple enough job to raise the legs with blocks such that the correct slope is obtained. The same applies to benches hung by special fixtures to the walls of greenhouses, particularly some neat modern benches. Existing bench tops are usually easy to convert to NFT being sufficiently solid to take any preferred channelling. If the top is insufficiently solid to accept flexible channelling some suitable solid material must be laid if the same is to be employed, but if a rigid channel were to be used it is unlikely any extra work would be necessary.

Where purpose built benches are employed there is a great variety to choose from. Amongst commercial growers purpose built benches are generally argued to offer the best combination of efficiency and economy, so that on the commercial holding the slope may be formed by differentially raising trays on stands. Typically the grower would use galvanised steel trays on suitably distanced adjustable stands, also of galvanised steel. Tray lengths vary but are usually 2.4 - 3.O metres. Successive trays interlock and overlap. Tray widths are manufactured according to the needs of the crop but 275mm is common, the next most popular being 300mm. An arrangement of galvanised stands and trays is illustrated in figure 3/7. Other trays are multiduct giving combinations of parallel channels. Multiducts of 2, 3, 4, 5 and 6 channels have been produced. Installation of these raised systems is rapid and of course, unlike concrete, stands and trays can be removed as and if it becomes necessary.

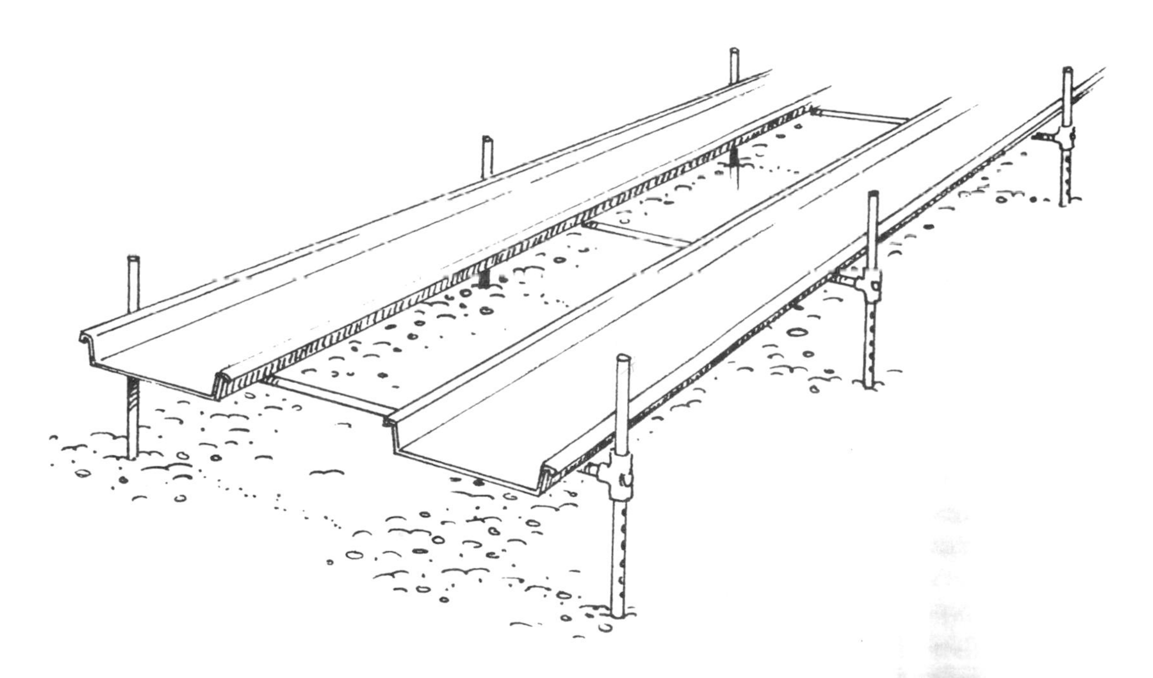

Fig. 3/7 Bench slope formed from purpose designed trays and adjustable stands

Using galvanised steel, slope formation is clearly economical on a large scale but much less so for the small private gardener because the cost of bending and transporting the few sheets required is so high. For the middle size system and small commercial and semi-commercial growers galvanised steel may well be worth costing.

Though galvanised steel may prove too expensive, the raised trays on stands method may be adopted by the private gardener using a range of alternative materials. Indeed as most channel runs would be relatively short, adjustable stands need not be employed at all but substituted by columns of blocks, bricks etc. or wooden trestles. Fine adjustments of height being effected by slithers of plastic sheet, slate etc. The distance apart of the 'stands' would depend on the tray material. Trays manufactured in GRP are fairly readily available and have the advantage of being long lived and lightweight as well as being generally less expensive than galvanised steel. Support for GRP trays is required at about 1 metre intervals. Alternative materials are polystrene board in 75mm section - very successfully used by at least one large commercial grower for lettuce production at waist height, other insulation boards, a range of scrap materials including doors and of course the ubiquitous plywood from which multiduct trays can be home fabricated in association with wooden battens. Be careful to cost out plywood. Suitable exterior grade is not cheap, it is surprising how often the DIY enthusiast entertains plywood construction without giving a thought to alternatives. Ordinary wood, preferably well weathered, may also be used.

The profile of the tray has attracted considerable attention. Whatever is the shape of the tray so will be the channel. The flow must not be interrupted so smooth surfaces are required. Thus the basic tray is a flat sheet with sides. The sides being present to prevent slippage of channelling and, as will be demonstrated later, to enable fixing of covering materials. A minimum side of about 2.5cm is required though up to 6 cm has been used.

An alternative tray base is slightly concave. Here the nutrient stream is contained initially in the centre of the channel. In these channels plants are placed to the outside with the spreader mat (page 57) ensuring initial wetting at each plant. Provided the tray is of good size for the plant being grown, concave trays are quite successful. Note also that in practice the flat base tray usually forms a slight concave shape as the sides are held rigid by the edge strengthening whilst the centre tends to depress.

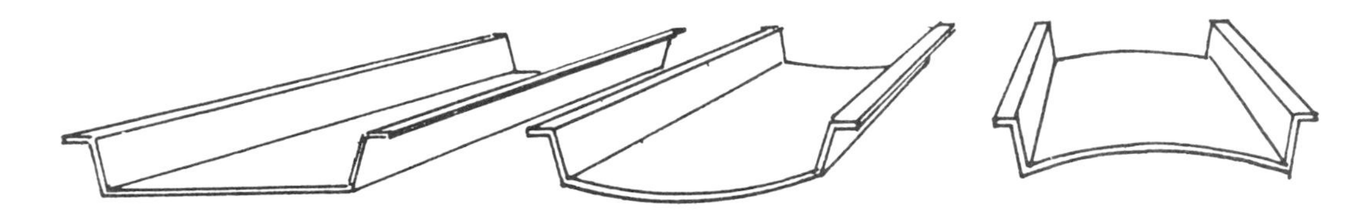

Fig. 3/8 Tray profiles

Convex tray bases allow plants to be set out on the raised mid-section, again initial dampening is by spreader mat from the solution flow passing on either side. It is claimed that this channel shape reduces the risk of excessive wetting of the propagation block when the plant is first introduced to the solution. There is indeed some evidence to support this claim but the disadvantage of the trays is that it allows only central planting which makes individual trays suitable for only a number of similar plants, ideal for the monocrop commercial grower but less so for the private gardener. Figure 3/8 illustrates alternative tray profiles.

The idea embodied in the convex tray has been developed one stage further. The use of multiduct trays has already been mentioned. It is possible to so construct the multiduct that the raised inter-channel spaces can be employed for setting out plants, their roots eventually intercepting the solution flowing in the channels on either side. At the same time, or subsequently, plants may be placed conventionally in the smaller channels. This arrangement is shown in figure 3/9.

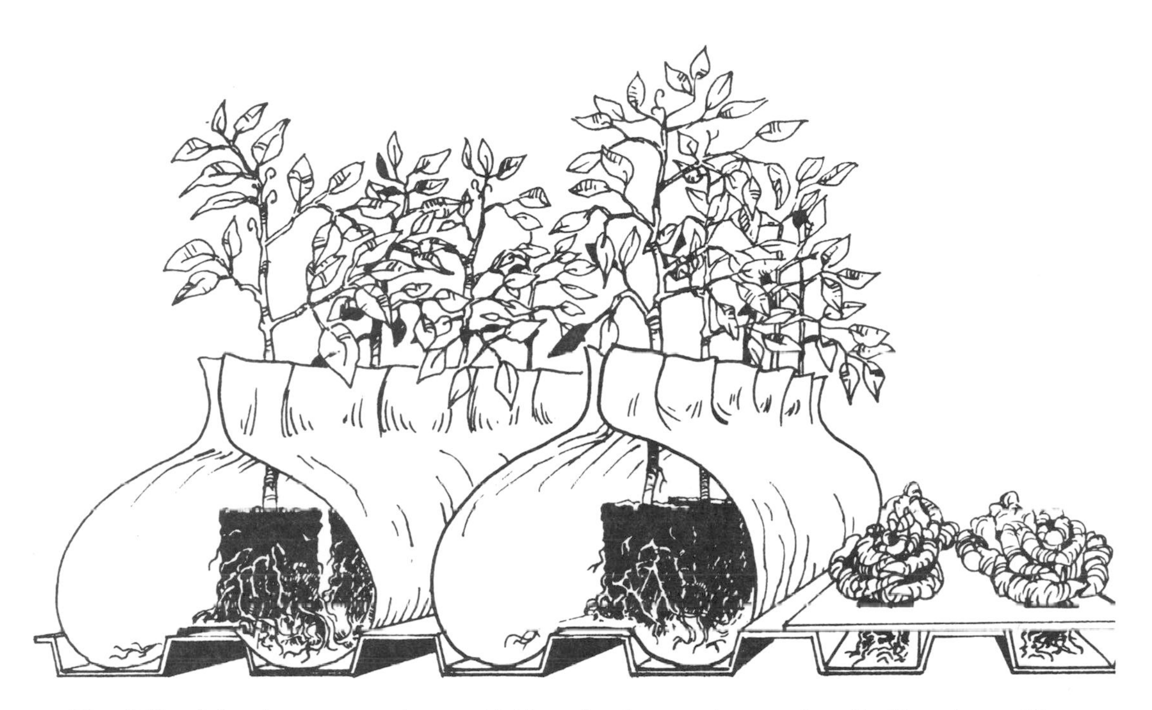

Fig. 3/9 Adapting narrow base multiduct for larger plants using flexible channelling

This idea has enabled multiducts originally designed for small plant production to be rapidly converted to accommodate large plants. Recent trends tend to obviate this arrangement by providing wider bases in two or three channel multiducts as shown in figure 3/10, thereby accepting in each channel, either one row of larger plants or two rows of smaller ones.

The question is asked; why not use a flat tray, say 1 metre wide? The problem is that this shape is inherantly weaker than a tray with edges or multiples of edges and therefore a disproportionate amount of raw material is required if sufficient strength is to be achieved. However sometimes such materials can be available quite cheaply such as secondhand plywood or blockboard or old doors. Solid slopes of this construction provide excellent surfaces for laying channels of any type.

Trays of any profile can of course be laid on ground slopes to complete rigidity and to provide holding positions for flexible sheets. In these cases it is normal practice to insulate between tray and ground with 2.5cm of insulation.

TANKS

Tanks suitable for use in NFT are normally manufactured in plastic. Commonly GRP in the larger sizes i.e. above 450 litres or polypropylene in smaller sizes. The most popular range are those manufactured for domestic cold water systems and central heating

Fig. 3/10 Adapting wide based multiduct for mixed planting using a combination of channel types

"expansion" tanks. A great advantage of these tanks is the wide variety of dimensions available. The importance of choosing a tank with adequate volume has already been stressed. Dimensions too are of serious practical significance. If a tank is deep, say 50cm or more, it makes for very considerable work on placement. What is more the excavation may be into hard clay or rock sub-soil which means that cold ground water will lie around the tank for the bulk of the year. In this situation it is essential to fit at least 2.5 cm of insulation, suitably waterproofed, and this requirement adds to the work of excavation. As an alternative a larger second tank of any material may first be inserted into the excavation, and the circulation tank placed within, but on a layer of insulation. Finally the gap between the walls of the two tanks is packed with insulation. This ideal arrangement is illustrated in Figure 3/11.

Sufficient capacity may be achieved using a shallow tank but if this is both wide and long it may be an awkward fit. Long narrow shallow tanks can be highly advantageous as they may do away with the need for a collecting duct or return pipework as the channel outflows can run directly into the tank. Such tanks are manufactured especially for NFT and indeed for other purposes. Further advantages of this type of tank are; much less contact with cold ground water, making it easier to install and insulate, and a lower pump size is required to empty the tank. This latter may be quite important since it is often possible to so design the NFT system that a very low wattage pump will provide adequate flow into the channels only to find that the pump will not empty the circulation tank as its lift capacity is insufficient.

Tanks should be fitted with lids or covers. Lids may be more or less of any material rigid enough to do the job. Most domestic cold water tanks are available with lids but sometimes the lid is as expensive as the tank. A home built cover would be just as useful. Perhaps the best type of tanks are known as "semi-closed" types which feature a small top opening for access the rest of the top is covered in manufacture.

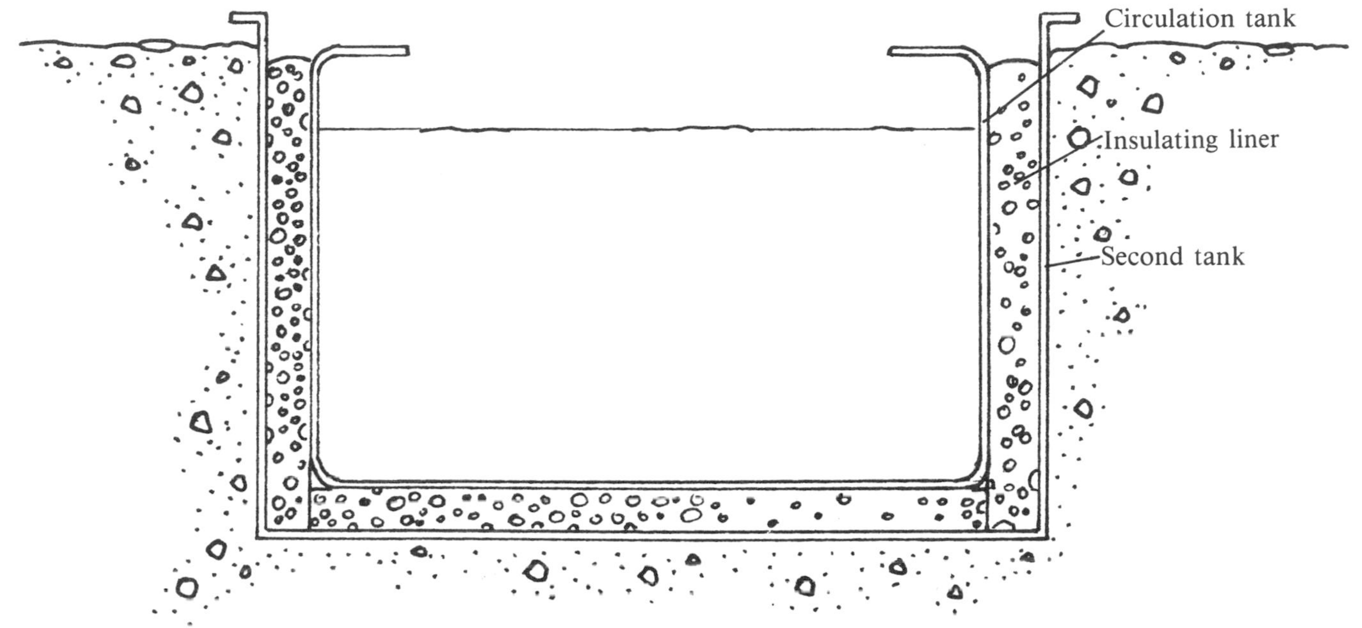

Fig. 3/11 A method of using two tanks to prevent ground water breaching insulation

It is surprising how many tanks and containers we use in our daily lives. Some may be adapted as circulation tanks for NFT systems. One such would be plastic dustbins. Brittleness can be a problem in the cheaper types whilst polypropylene ones may be expensive. Also they tend to have too great a depth but it may be possible to cut them down to useful size. Other sources include tanks used to transport foodstuffs, e.g. fruit juice.

Galvanised tanks can be converted to NFT use by lining with polythene sheet. Normally polythene of at least 500g would be required for this job. So that the risk of holing the sheet is reduced, and to provide essential insulation, it is good practice if the tank is first lined with at least 2.5cm of polystyrene panels. The same technique can equally be applied to wooden troughs of home construction, and indeed to trenches dug into the ground where pond lining material might be a better choice than polythene.

The problem of ground water in terms of heat loss has been dealt with, but rising ground water brings another great danger. If the water level inside the tanks is lower than the maximum level of the ground water then the tank will lift out of the excavation by displacement. Figure 3/12 shows the dramatic result of this happening.

The problem is exacerbated because it is usual to run NFT systems with the tank filled to less than maximum volume and because the use of insulation lowers the specific gravity of the tank unit. On certain sites the problems of ground water encourage the use of alternative flow systems whereby the main circulation tank is set above ground level. In these cases ensure that the tank is sufficiently strong to hold the solution without the aid of ground support. On other sites it is sufficient to add weight to the top of the tank. A lot of weight may be needed, to take this weight a good strong lid is required and again this might be best facilitated by using a tank of the "semi-closed" type.

Fig. 3/12 Effect of rising ground water

PUMPS

The total delivery required of the pump is easily calculated by multiplying the number of channels with the desired flow rate per channel. How do we choose the correct size of pump? The nominal output of the pump is of little use because this is a figure of output at no lift but it is certain some lift is required with commensurate loss of output by the pump. The lift is the height the pump has to raise the solution and it is the height difference from the surface of the solution in the tank to the highest point reached by the solution. A practical example is shown in Figure 3/13.

Sometimes it is possible to obtain a complete graph of the pumps performance known as its "performance curve" but usually only the shut-off point i.e. the least height at which no solution would be discharged, and the nominal output are available. From these calculate performance at the height desired by constructing a graph as shown in Figure 3/14.

Since the figure arrived at is unlikely to be dead accurate and since allowance might have to be made for pipe friction losses (see page 31) and because it is useful to provide capacity for greater output at the channels than the minimum, it is always advised to obtain a little extra performance when choosing a pump. What type of pump should be choosen? We are concerned here only with pumps used to circulate the nutrient solution and so from the great variety of pump types we can immediately dismiss metering and injection pumps which are generally unsuitable. Also generally unsuitable for small scale use are petrol (or gas) driven motors.

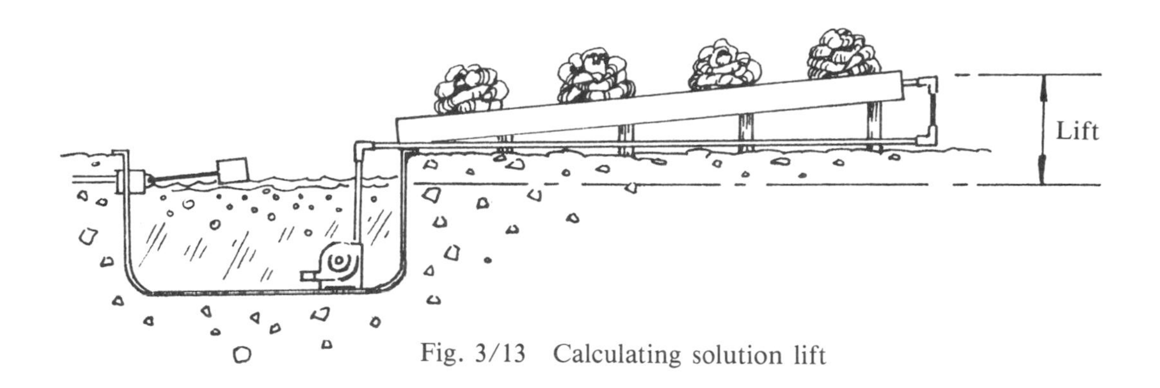

Fig. 3/13 Calculating solution lift

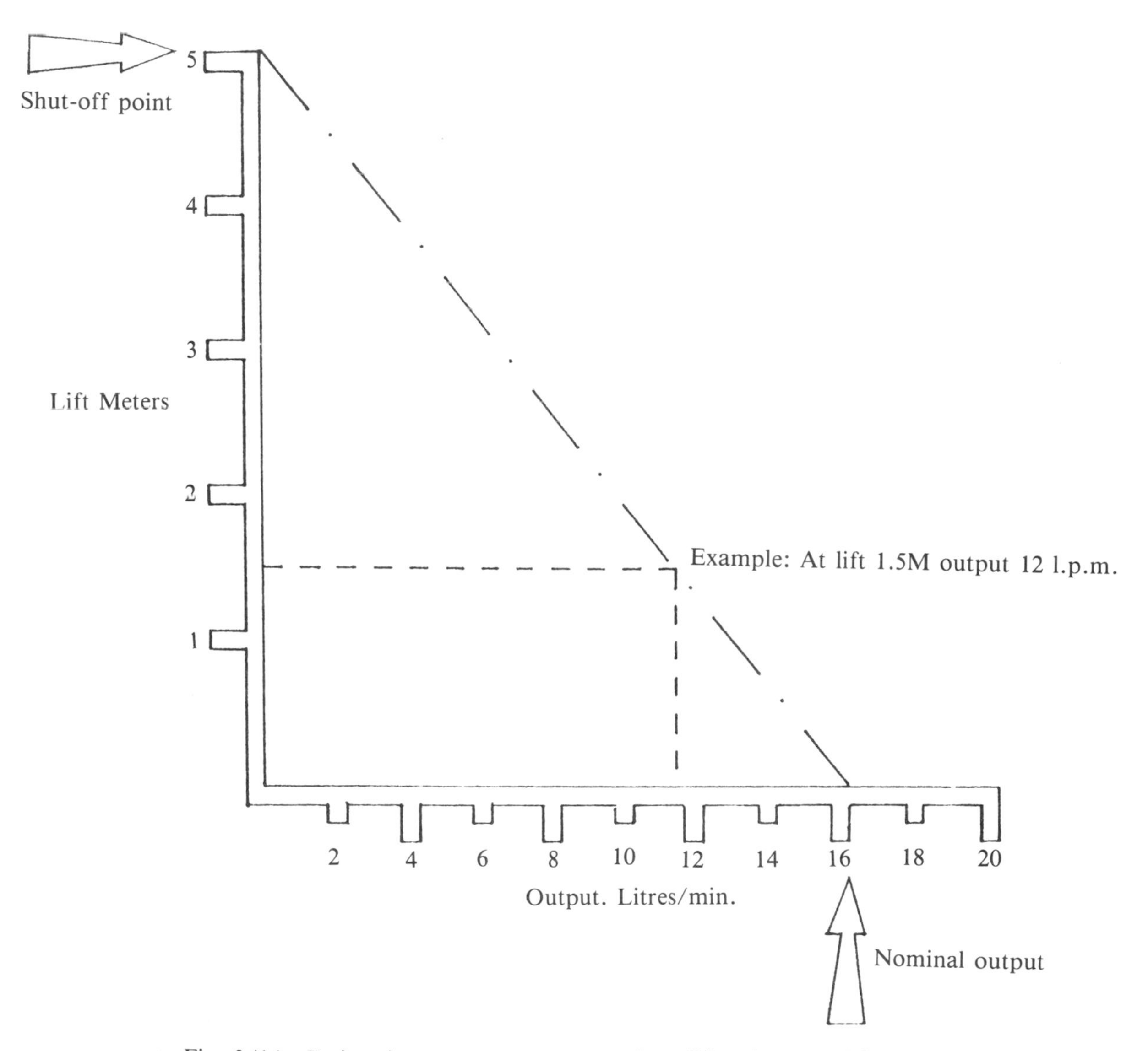

Fig. 3/14 Estimating pump output at a given lift using a graph

Electrical Pumps

Electrically powered pumps are almost universally employed. This is not surprising because of the dual advantage of being particularly convenient and not ruinously expensive. The electrically driven pumps most commonly used are centrifugal pumps. They consist of two principal components, the pump head and the electric motor. The pump head is that area where the work of moving the nutrient solution occurs. This is done by an impellor which beats the solution in the desired direction. Because of this action the centrifugal pump is most efficient when pumping relatively large volumes with relatively low lifts. This is precisely the requirements of most NFT system designs. Further, the impellor is simply an extension of the pump motor rotor. The rate at which the impellor turns is proportional to the output of the pump, accordingly simple control of output is afforded by restricting the orifice of the pump output side. In turn this is a simple control of channel flow rate. No harm to the motor will ensue if the output side of a centrifugal pump is restricted but it is essential that the input side is unrestricted.

Centrifugal pump electric motors are of one or other of two basic types. First is the series wound motor. This is the most efficient motor type but it is unsuitable for use where continuous operation is required because the motor contains contact bushes which require regular adjustment or replacement. These motors have a very high torque (or twist) which gives them greater output at given power consumption but they should, in general, be avoided for application in NFT systems. Second is the induction motor, a little less efficient but, especially at small outputs, not significantly so. These motors are noted for their reliability and are ideal for use in NFT. One possible problem is that they display a phenomenon, known as starting surge, whereby the current consumption on starting is much greater than in the running phase. Accordingly a power supply capable of accepting the heavier starting load is necessary. This is of practical significance only on large sites. Of more importance is that allowance should be made for the starting surge when designing or procurring pump control equipment. Often there is no need for such equipment, but note that one advantage of NFT is the easy application of such controls.

The most common choice facing a prospective pump purchaser is between submersible and open-air types. Submersible pumps are easy to install, quiet in operation, very efficient and require the minimum of fitments. They are therefore generally preferred in small and medium size units. The disadvantage of the submersible pump is clearly the proximity of the motor and nutrient solution. The motor must be sealed both in its casing and its shaft from ingress of solution. It is relatively easy to seal the case but not so easy to seal the shaft. Also, the nutrient solution is slightly aggressive and may reduce seal life. For this reason a range of fountain and pond pumps together with some sump and industrial pumps are unsuitable for use in NFT systems. This may be no bad thing because many of these pumps are quite high users of electricity relative to output. Suitable pumps are fitted with chemically resistant seals. There is another type of operation which has much to recommend it, this is magnetic drive. Here the motor and the impellor are entirely separated, movement of the impellor is effected by magnetic attraction. Magnetic drive pumps are widely used in the chemical industries and have found great favour in small and medium scale NFT work. Submersible pump casings must not be toxic. The vast majority are manufactured in corrosion resistant plastic, often the polymer ABS. Non-plastic cased submersible pumps should be used with caution. One advantage of submersible pumps, namely quietness of operation, is achieved because no fan is required to cool the motor. Cooling is effected by the solution which necessarily gains a small amount of useful heat.

Non-submersible pumps generally need more precise and expensive fitments and this is particularly true at the small end of outputs. The reason is simple enough. Most small non-submersible centrifugal pumps require that the inlet to the pump head be flooded. Naturally this is easy enough done while the pump is running but it is at starting that problems occur. One way of achieving a flooded inlet is to install the pump in a position lower than the solution level in the reservoir. This arrangement is shown in Figure 3/15.

Fig. 3/15 The use of a small non-submersible pump ensuring a flooded inlet

This position is usually totally impracticable in NFT work because the circulation tank is so often fitted in an excavation. Alternatively the pump must be primed, but this requires constant attention on starting and is a chore which should be avoided. A one-way valve can be fitted but many small pumps will have reduced performance with this fitting. With larger non-submersible pumps there is generally much less trouble in fitting and they may be specified with confidence.

A major factor in choosing a pump should be the running costs. Most NFT systems are run more or less continuously so that even small differences in consumption add up to a significant difference in running cost. Very often is the case where in a single season the savings on running costs more than offsets a purchase price difference.

Alternatives to electrical centrifugal pumps

There are two disadvantages associated with centrifugal pumps. Firstly, possible high purchase cost and secondly, poor efficiency at pumping low volumes to heights. As a cost saving alternative the air lift system of pumping has been developed for use in NFT. The basic scheme of things is illustrated in Figure 3/16.

The air lift works by the displacement of water by air and uses an air pump. Such pumps are particularly inexpensive and usually very reliable. The telling disadvantage of the air lift is that the solution is not moved under pressure and therefore cannot easily be distributed e.g. to two or more channels. Accordingly it is often necessary to provide an air lift to each channel, thus multiplying cost and complexity. Additionally the air lift cannot normally be used to empty the tank and unless drainage by gravity can be arranged this can be a serious drawback. Similarly the air lift is susceptible to falling solution level in the tank. A slight advantage of the air lift system is the introduction of air into the solution thereby adding oxygen. The most common uses of air lifts are in single channel set-ups especially NFT kits such as GRO-TANK units.

Normally it is not necessary to pump the nutrient solution in small volume to any significant height. Even very large commercial projects may have a maximum lift of

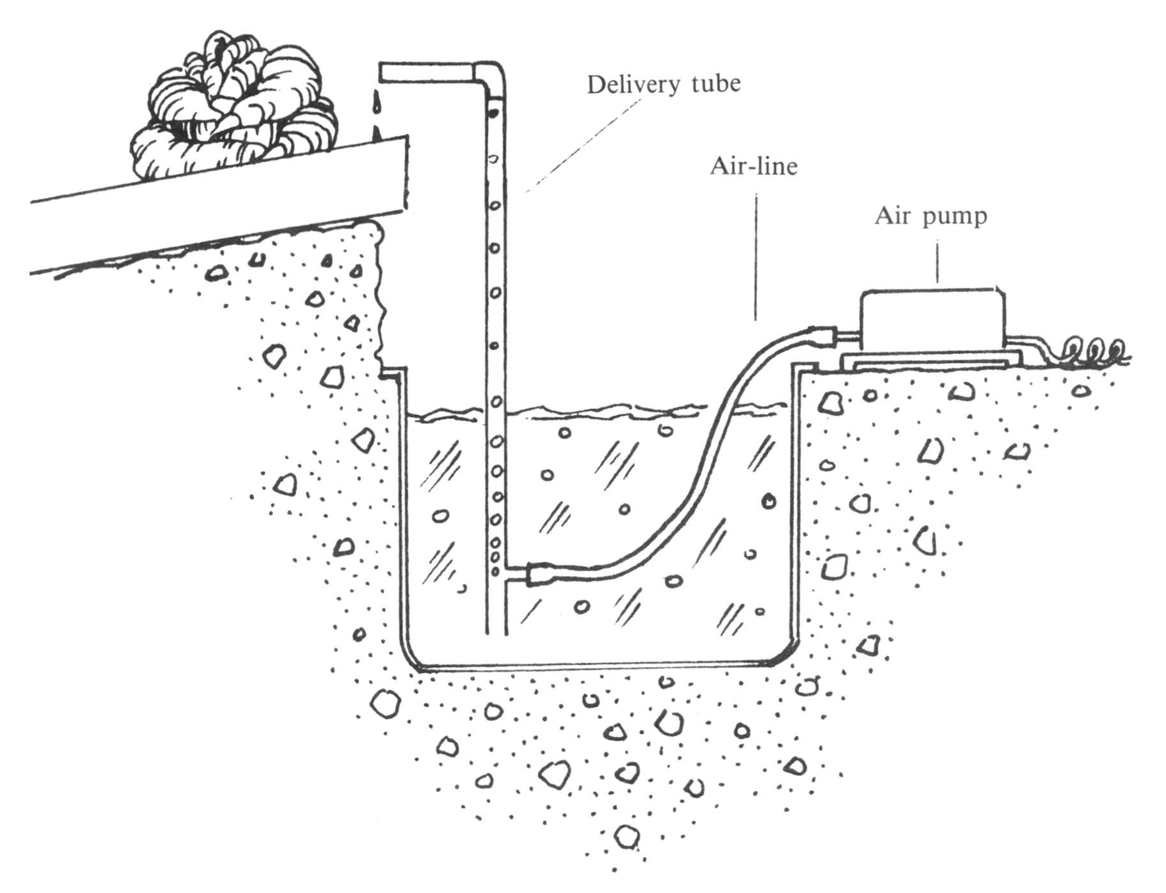

Fig. 3/16 The air-lift pumping system

as little as one metre, but there are occasions when greater lift performance is required. Pumps known generally as positive displacement pumps will do the job but they are usually very expensive. An alternative displacement system using air has been developed and proved extremely reliable. Such an arrangement is especially useful in supplying solution to tiered wall mounted systems, where a lift of 2 metres or more may be achieved for perhaps as little as 4 or 6 watts power. For comparison if the same lift was achieved by a centrifugal pump upwards of 40 watts might be consumed. Figure 3/17 shows the components and arrangement of a air pressure pumping system suitable for use in a NFT system.

Note, some specialist equipment is required to construct the air pressure lift system. Materials may not be readily available on the 'high street' but fortunately there are specialist suppliers.

Alternatives at sites not supplied with mains electricity

The first option is to supply mains electricity either as a permanent installation or as a temporary extension from the nearest permanent supply. Do not hesitate to consult a qualified person. The power requirements are small, indeed for many small greenhouses they may be just 7-10 watts for the pump and 100 watts for a heater, if opted. Alternatives to fitting a mains supply are inherantly less reliable and this is good reason why it is advised to fully consider possible electricity supply options.

The air lift pumping system can be used by siting the pump at the nearest electrical supply, e.g. outhouse or garage and running the air line to the air lift. Distances well in excess of 30 metres can be serviced this way. If the air line crosses an area where it may be crushed or damaged, e.g. a pathway it may be buried or sheathed in a protective pipe.

Direct current (DC) systems i.e. electricity supplied by batteries have been developed. These use either 12V or 24V DC pumps. Suitable pumps may be found in the automotive

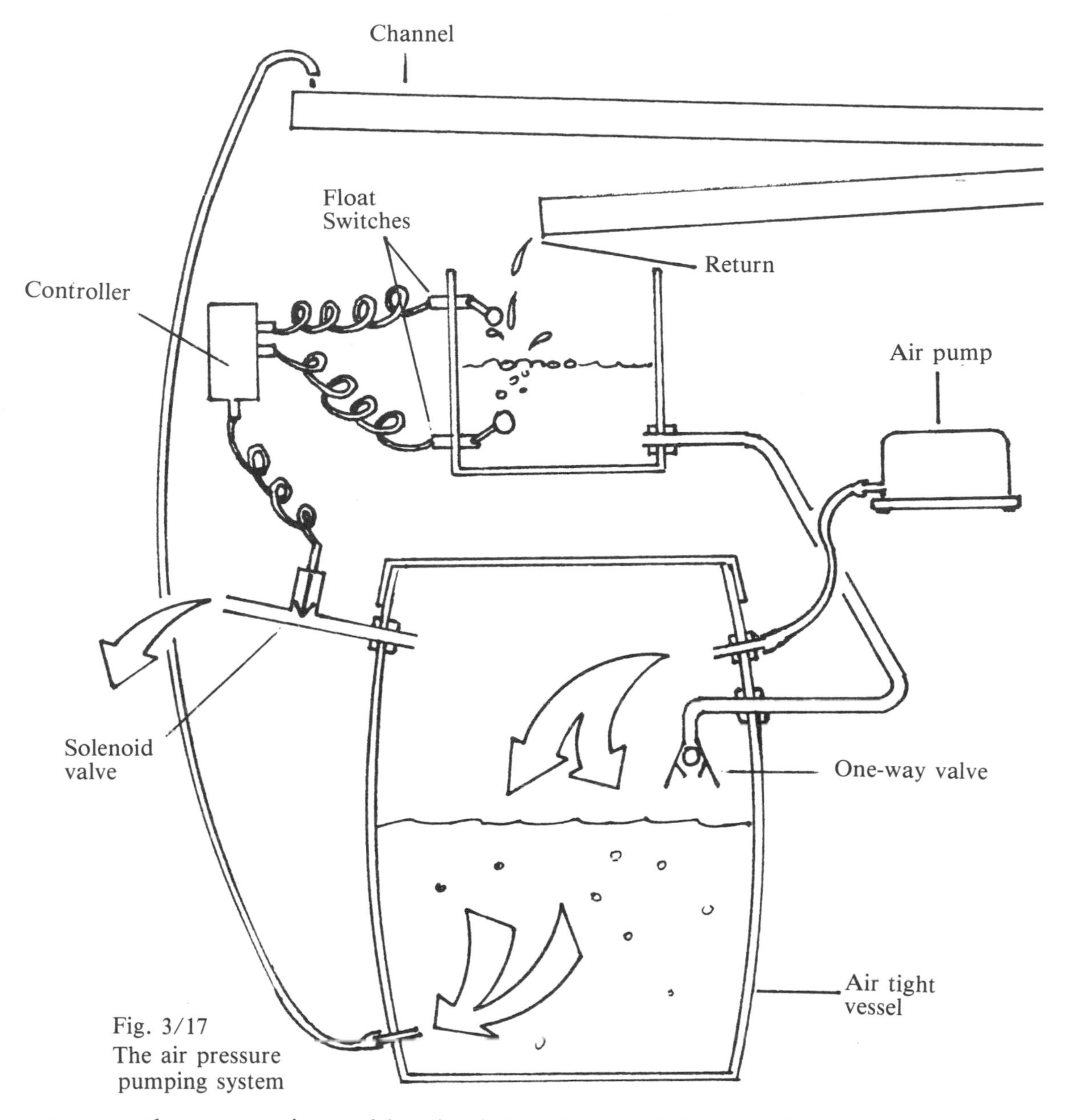

Fig. 3/17
The air pressure
pumping system

parts or the caravanning and boating industries, but their operation in NFT systems is not usually straight forward. The problem is to conserve battery life so that the recharging of batteries does not become an impossible chore and to do this intermittent pumping is desired. There are two common arrangements of using DC pumps, namely; the two tank method and the timed pumping method.

The two tank method using DC power.

This method, shown in Figure 3/18, attempts to use to advantage the good output to power consumption ratio which is a common feature of DC pumps. It does so by instituting a short pump on-time whereby sufficient solution is raised to a header tank to enable a relatively long pump off-time to follow as this solution is fed to the channels by gravity.

The sequence of operation is:—

1. Bottom float switch off. Top float switch on. Pump runs.
   Header tank fills. PUMP ON-TIME.
2. Bottom float switch on. Top float switch off. Pump off.
   Header tank empties. PUMP OFF-TIME.
3. Repeat from 1.

To calculate the ratio of pump on to off-times and hence battery life, obtain the following information. a. Pump output at header tank inlet height. b. Capacity of header tank between float switches. c. Rate of out-flow from the header tank. A realistic example is:

Pump output at 1.5 meters	45 litre/min.
Volume between float switches	90 litres.
Channel flow, 8 at 275ml/min.	2.25 litres/min.

Therefore pump on-time 90/45 = 2 mins.
pump off-time 90/2.25 = 40 mins.

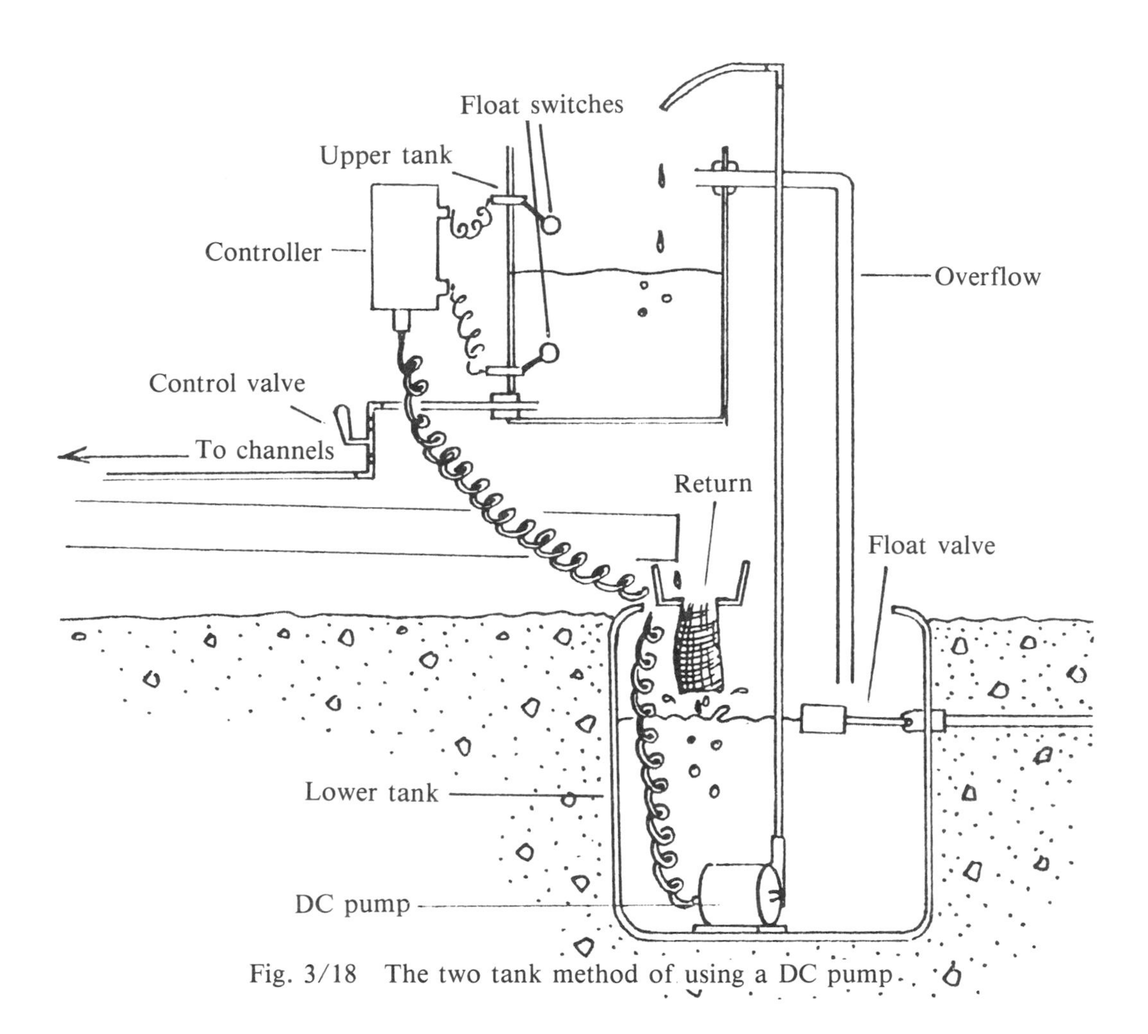

Fig. 3/18 The two tank method of using a DC pump.

Therefore the pump runs for 2 mins. in each period of 42 mins. This is approximately 3 mins/hour. Now, if the pump was rated at 4 amp/hour (running continuously) it would therefore use only 4 amp x 3 mins/60 (mins. in hour) = 0.2 amp/hour when the system is operating. If a 30 amp car battery was used, the battery would continue to operate the system for 30 amps/0.2 amps = 150 hours i.e. around 6 days. Allowing for the battery not being 100% exhausted and allowing also for loss of pump performance as the battery approaches no charge, then the example would run on a 4 day battery recharging cycle.

A complication of the two tank method is the requirement for automatic top-up facilities. A float valve should be fitted to the lower tank at a point such that at least the between float switch volume (of the header tank) is available at the float valve off position. Further, the above float valve volume should be at least equal to the between float switch volume. Only when these conditions are satisfed can the system operate, a. without overflowing of the lower tank during the pump off period and, b. without over-running the pump due to insufficient solution in the lower tank. It greatly assists the smooth running of the method if the float valve delivers make-up water fairly rapidly, i.e. not less than half of the pump delivery rate to the header tank, and for this reason mains supply is preferred though if the below float valve volume is considerably increased this preference can be ignored.

The two tank method is a proven arrangement for using DC power. It is especially useful for medium sized units when the cost and work of installation can be best justified. Of costs all the specialist materials are not inexpensive though DC pumps tend to be reasonably priced. Although differential distance float switch and controller assemblies are manufactured for special purposes e.g. automatic cellar drainage, such units are not always readily adapted to NFT installations. It may be necessary to have at least the float switch controller specially manufactured and for this reason it is probably best to consult a specialist NFT supplier.

Timed pumping method using DC power

This is a much simpler installation. Here the DC pump is fitted into the NFT unit in exactly the same way as an AC mains pump. It may be submersible or open air and indeed the possibilities of the latter are improved by the use of DC supply because such pumps often incorporate effective suction lift. The pump does not run continuously, instead a controller is fitted by which intermittent pumping is programmed. During summer growing conditions, and with hydrophillic plants, it is considered unwise if the flow is run for less than half of the time so that the saving in current used is about 50%, but of course this doubles the battery life. It is also recommended that the off flow period is never more than 10 minutes so as to avoid stress on plants during hot weather. Accordingly a regime of 5 minutes on-flow and 5 minutes off is considered close to ideal, but to accomplish this, simple inexpensive time switches are unsuitable so necessitating additional expense on a more sophisticated model.

The timed pumping method is most suited to small scale NFT systems where DC pumps consuming as little as 0.3 amps at 12V may be used, thereby giving an interchange period of up to 200 hours using a 30 amp battery and 50% on-time. Under these circumstances the method has the advantage over the two tank method because of the simpler installation and reduced costs. However, if even a moderate sized pump is required the timed control method quickly becomes unworkable because the pump on-time is too large a proportion of total time.

Features of DC pumping systems

Certain features of DC systems are common to either pump control method. Firstly, it is much preferred if two batteries are available so that whilst one is running the NFT system the other is recharging. Secondly, extension to the life of each battery change may be had by reducing the pump on-time in particular circumstances. This may be achieved either by switching off the system completely or reducing the channel flow rate with the two tank method, or increasing the pump off-time with the timed pumping method. Circumstances where these practices are either beneficial to the plants or else occasion no harm are detailed in the subsequent text where flow is considered, but two common occasions are; during unfavourable conditions and when growing hydrophobic plants. Thirdly, DC pumps are constructed with motor bushes which have a limited life span and require periodic changing or adjustment. Generally the operation is not required so frequently that the system becomes unworkable but some advice on the matter should be sought at the time of pump purchase.

Alternative energy

Regarding alternative energy supplies. Certainly windpower may be readily adapted for supplying an NFT system either with a trickle charge for a battery or directly lifting the solution. A suitable device is shown in Figure 3/19. Note that the power requirements are very small so inexpensive apparatus may suffice.

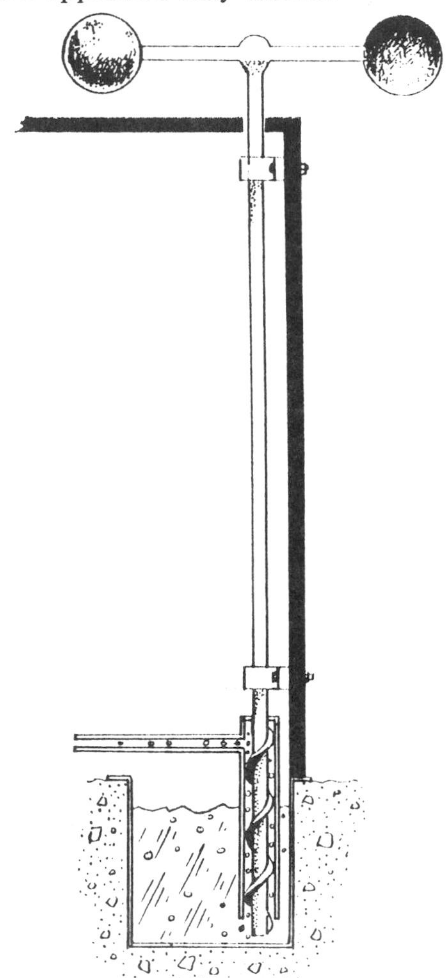

Fig. 3/19 A wind powered pumping system

A common feature to all alternatives to mains electricity is their inability to supply heat. This may limit either the range of crops or the time of the year when they can be successfully grown. However space heating alternatives may be employed for a particular crop and it is as well not to underestimate what can be grown without solution heating.

PIPES AND FITTINGS

Except in the case of some single channel designs such as 'GRO-TANK' kits, all NFT systems require pump and channel to be connected by pipework and, more often than not, the outflow of the channels is also connected to the circulation tank by more pipework. It is essential to use good quality non-phytotoxic materials and in practice this means plastic pipework. There are two plastic pipe systems, flexible and rigid.

Suitable flexible pipe is normally manufactured in polypropylene. There are many manufacturers and much is imported. Various gauges are available, some is to relevant British standards which apply a pressure rating quality to the pipe, but normally for NFT purposes only thin walled non-pressure pipe is employed and therefore it is often unnecessarily expensive if pipe from the plumbing and construction industry is used. Instead irrigation suppliers are more likely sources. The main advantage of flexible over rigid is simplicity of fitment since flexible pipe will readily bend into position and assume awkward shapes. Care should be taken to avoid kinking. Occasionally a flexible pipe may kink, often having remained as a smooth bend for a long period, with obviously disruptive consequences. This is probably a result of temperature change affecting the qualities of the pipe. To avoid this possibility use elbows in potentially troublesome areas.

A further advantage of flexible pipe is that, especially in small diameters, inexpensive 'push-fit' friction fittings are available. Such joints are best made by immersing the end of the pipe in hot water to expand it before pushing onto the fitting. On cooling the pipe grips fast to the fitting ensuring watertightness. Friction joins of this type are difficult to disconnect, though they may possibly be moved if hot water is poured onto the joint. Accordingly use friction joints only where breaking of the joint will not normally occur, and it is prudent also to allow a short length of extra pipe in any pipe run so that the pipe can be reconnected if the original joint has to be cut free with the loss of a short length of material. Push fit joins normally used with flexible pipe are available for pipes of 20mm internal diameter and less, but this range covers most small scale NFT work.

With larger flexible pipes fittings tend to be of the "compression" type where a sealing ring is squeezed tight onto the pipe by a threaded locknut. Such fittings are relatively expensive. There are however a number of manufacturers who produce fittings of this type for small diameter flexible pipe and, though more expensive than friction fittings, they are not outlandish. They have the advantage of being releasable so they should be used at any point where disconnection is likely.

Many flexible pipes and fittings from different manufacturers are interchangeable so obtaining items to extend or modify existing pipework should be easy. To be sure, check that threaded fittings are made with B.S. threads as this will ensure the availability of conversion fittings to other pipes.

Rigid pipework is normally manufactured in polypropylene or uPVC. In the case of the former cemented joins cannot be made and sealing ring connections such as are commonly used in domestic waste water disposal are usual. These joins are disconnectable but are reliable only when not under pressure. Accordingly they are suitable for return pipework but not supply from the pump. In the case of uPVC, cemented joins are quick, easy and very permanent, making uPVC pipework well suited to the supply side. For use on the return side, uPVC joins can normally be left uncemented as they are made to very close tolerances making a non-pressure watertight join when properly located. uPVC pipes are available from very small to large diameters but it is usually only in sizes of 25mm and above that they are used as alternatives to flexible tube.

What size of pipework is required? On the supply side the orifice of the pump will give a good guide. If the pump outlet accepts 12.5mm tube then use 12.5mm for the main supply tube. It is quite in order to use a tube of larger diameter than the pump orifice but do not use smaller diameter as this could seriously affect the output of the pump. The reason for this is the accumulation of friction losses, that is, the action of the solution against the walls of the pipe induces friction which must be overcome if the pump is to move the solution. The larger the volume of solution to be moved and the smaller the pipe diameter the greater is the friction. Also it follows, the longer the pipe the greater the total friction. As it is important to use pumps with as low power consumption as possible it is obvious that friction in the pipework should be reduced where possible. Accordingly, when long lengths of pipework are employed friction losses should be calculated with a view to using pipework of such a diameter as to make them insignificant. Most pump suppliers will give ready advice on this aspect but it is useful here to illustrate the point with facts. Over 30 metres of 12.5mm I.D. pipe, 4.55 litres/min. accumulates a friction loss equivalent to 60 cm of extra lift at the pump, whilst at 18 litres/min. the friction losses increase to 6 metres of lift.

A further consideration is evenness of input. Normally one pump feeds several, perhaps many, channels and the channels are usually fed with solution at approximately the same rate. In a poorly designed system the entire output of the pump may be discharged into one channel the others being more or less dry. Evenness of input is achieved by applying a small back pressure (friction) to the supply tube system thereby equalising pressure over the entire pipework. This is done by using small diameter inlet tubes at the channel head. Thus the situation exists where friction losses affecting pump output are avoided by using wide diameter pipe for the bulk of the supply tube, whilst at the inlet end friction is applied to effect the even distribution of the solution.

Where changes in flow rate are desired the simplest method is to vary the output of the pump by using a restrictor or valve on the main supply tube. Some pumps have the restrictor built into the pump head which is very useful. Where different flow rates are required in different channels it is often possible to fit smaller diameter inlet tubes to those channels requiring the least flow and wider diameter tubes to those requiring greater flow, e.g. narrow base and wide base channels. Figure 3/20 shows how flow may be controlled at the channel inlet using a small diameter insert. Occasionally it is desired to vary the flow at each channel and in this case the simplest method is to fit flow control valves to the inlet tube. If this is done it would not be appropriate to use, at the same time, small diameter inlet tubes because this combination is prone to blockage by particles in the solution. Inlet tube flow valves are also necessary to control flow where channels are sited at greatly differing heights e.g. tiered systems as it can be somewhat tiresome effecting even flow with various sizes of inlet tube. Finally, to close off inlet tubes not fitted with a flow valve simply bend up to kink pipe and hold fast with an elastic band.

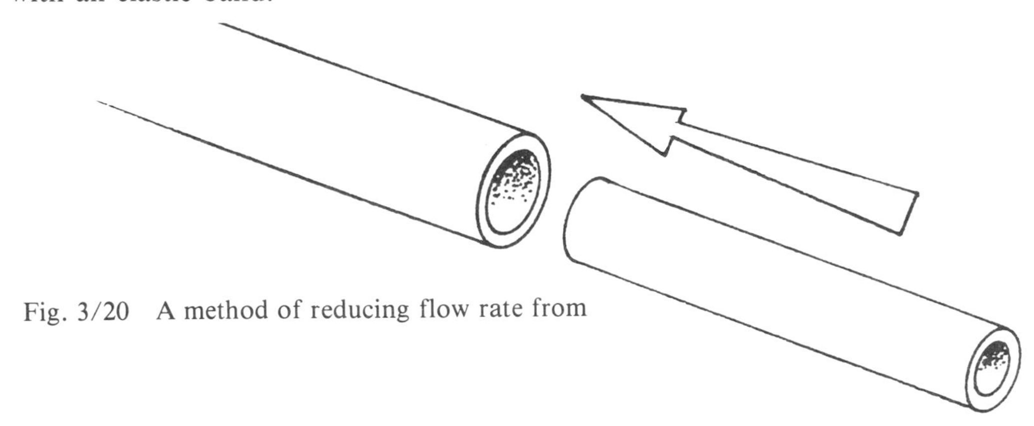

Fig. 3/20 A method of reducing flow rate from

The fitment of small bore inlet tubes onto larger diameter supply tubes could present an unwarranted expense on larger NFT systems if at each take-off point a reducing tee junction was necessary. In fact a neat joint, known as a friction joint, overcomes this hazard. Here, small bore tube sharpened in a pencil sharpener is inserted into a tight hole drilled into a larger tube. The sequence of the operation is shown in Figure 3/21.

This technique can be further adapted for making airtight joints for air pressure supply systems. In this case once the small diameter tube is through into the pressure vessel a flexible plastic insert, usually a tight fitting small diameter tube off-cut about 3cm long, is placed inside the tube and the tube then pulled back so it fastens tightly onto the walls of the predrilled hole. Here, subsequent application of pressure within the container only serves to tighten the joint making it entirely effective.

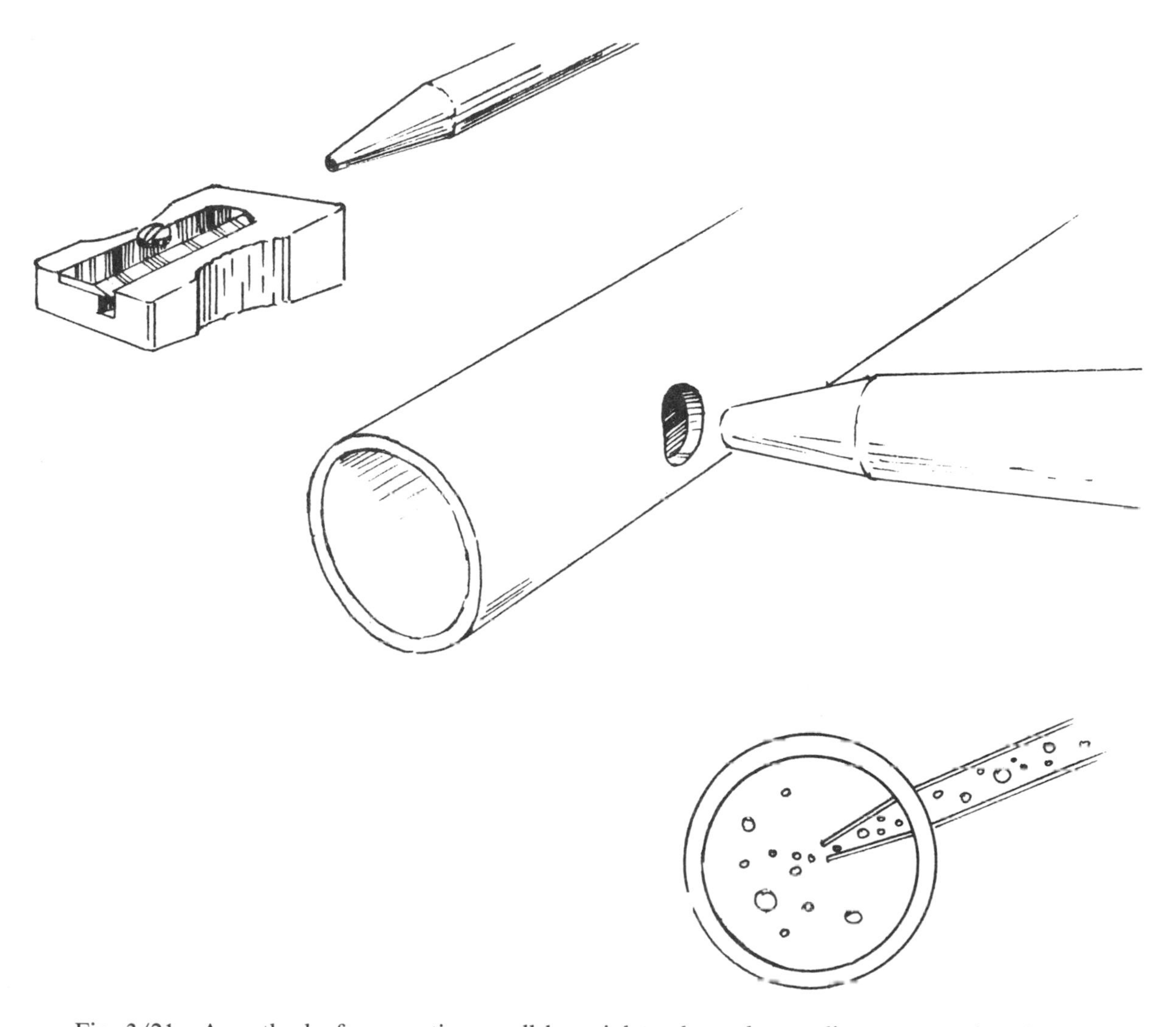

Fig. 3/21 A method of connecting small bore inlet tube to larger diameter supply tube

Return pipework is normally not less than twice the diameter of the supply pipework because it takes the solution by the pressure of gravity alone. Therefore movement of the solution is slower in return pipework than in the pumped supply pipes and a greater diameter of pipe is required to accommodate the same volume of flow. Solution return may also be effected by utilising open ducting of which the best known type is guttering. The great advantage of open ducting is the ease with which the solution passes from the channel to the return without the need of connection fittings. A disadvantage is that algae will grow in open ducting unless a loose cover is fitted.

Although small section guttering is available it is prudent, even on a small installation, to use standard 110mm house gutter because there is otherwise a danger of blockage with material overhanging from the channels. Also, because there may be some disturbance to the line of the return duct caused by the weight of the channel if, as is often the case, the channel is allowed to rest on the rim of the gutter. On larger sites where the returning solution must cross pathways, open returns are not commonly employed because of the obstacle they present. Instead it is preferred to use underground pipework which enables pathways to be kept clear. Open returns are particularly handy in collecting the solution from raised benches. In this case they can be fixed to the final bench support. Where a series of benches are separated by pathways downspout and fittings are used to pass the solution from open duct to an underground return pipe. This arrangement is illustrated in Figure 3/22.

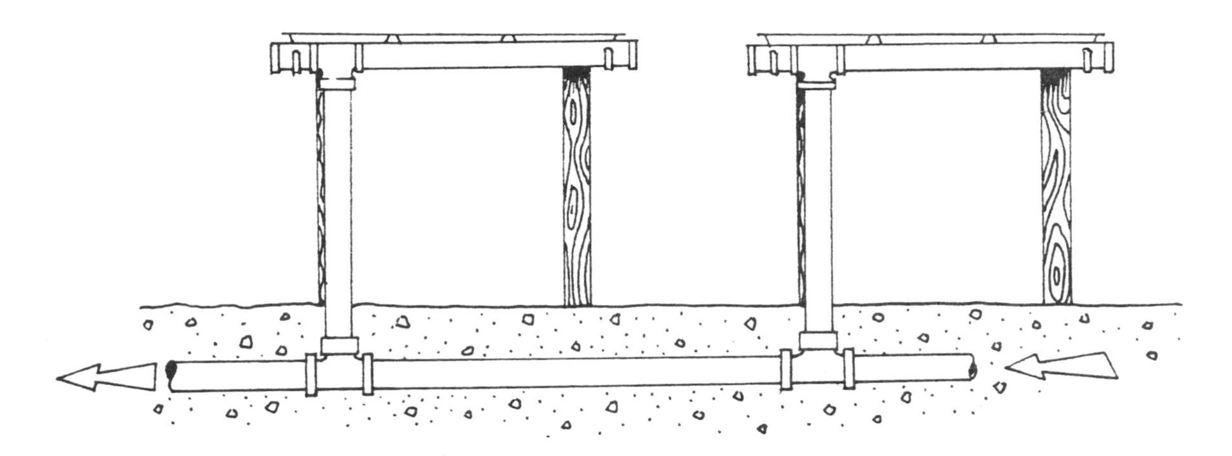

Fig. 3/22 Open return ducting with underground return pipe

In addition to control valves, other major fittings attached to pipework include filters and non-return valves. If the main purpose of the filter is to protect the pump then the filter should be fitted to the pump inlet or to the outflow of the return pipework. The latter case is easily achieved by the use of a bag type filter attached by means of a clamp to the outflow. Although nylon stockings have been used it is better to use a good quality filter bag specially manufactured for the purpose. In larger NFT systems the purpose of the filter is to prevent blockage of the inlet tubes. In these cases an in-line strainer on the supply tube should be fitted, perhaps with the added benefit of a pump inlet filter.

CHANNELLING

NFT channelling is strictly that container or bag which accommodates the circulating nutrient solution and into which the plants are placed. There are said to be two basic types, flexible and rigid, but in reality these are only the two ends of a spectrum of rigidity. The choice of channelling is probably the most difficult material choice facing the inexperienced NFT grower, though his choice may often have been dictated by his previous choice of slope formation.

The greatest influences on channelling are the characteristics of the slope and the plant types which are to be grown. What is the simplest case? There are many large commercial sites in the U.K. where NFT is used to grow monocrop tomatoes. The majority of these sites have the slope constructed in stands and trays, much of the remainder grading a slope from the earth. On these slopes black on white co-extruded polythene channelling is almost universally employed. This polythene, white on one side black on the reverse, is manufactured in a range of gauges; 400, 600, 800 and 1,000 and range of widths; 61cm, 69cm and 76cm. The preferred combination is 69cm x 600 or 800g. In use polythene channelling of this and similar type forms a flat based tunnel through which the nutrient solution is passed. A use and the form of polythene channelling is shown in Figure 3/23.

The plant roots develop within the channel and the plant shoots are free to develop at the top. At the end of the season, which may be as much as 11 months or a year, the top is cut from the root conveniently above the channel and the entire channel and root mass is disposed of, normally by burning. The major advantages of this chanelling are that it is inexpensive, easy and clean. The crucial disadvantage is that it cannot be used satisfactorily for plants which do not have extended stems. Accordingly tomatoes, cucumbers, melons, peppers, aubergines, chrysanthemums and some bulbs are grown commercially in just such channelling. As it is easy to vary the channel size in base width and in other dimensions by using narrower sheet and by varying the position of the fastening, the various row space requirements of plants can be allowed for.

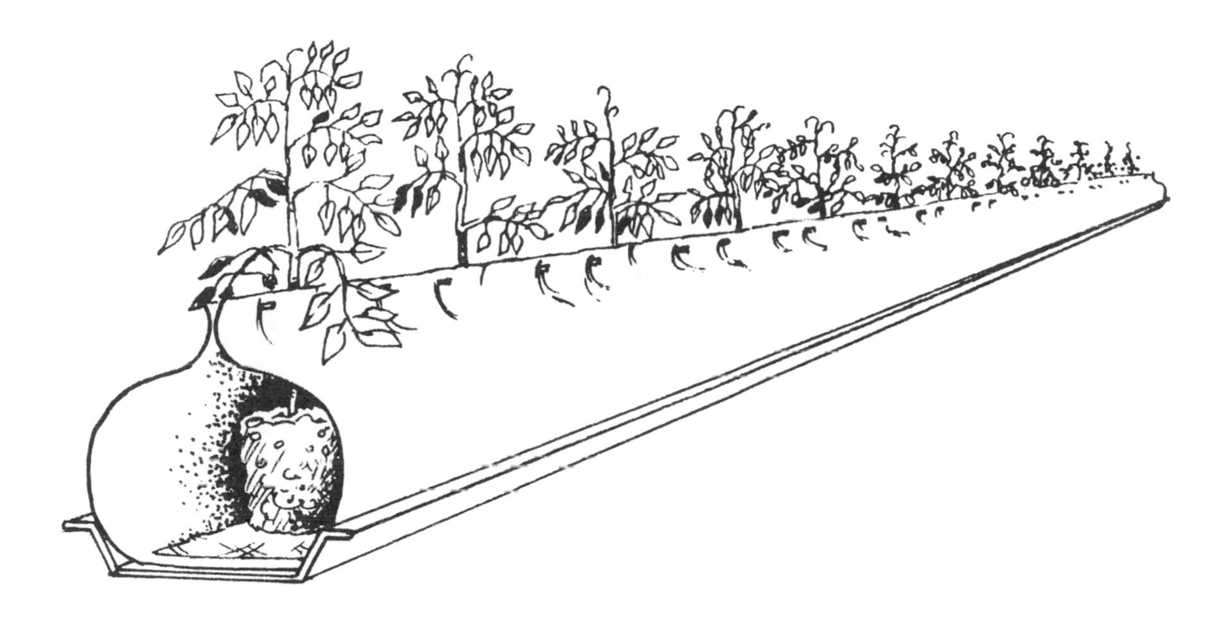

Fig. 3/23 Flexible polythene channel laid on a rigid support tray

There are a number of variations. Black polythene or indeed any other non-translucent mono-colour can replace black on white polythene. The advantage of this latter, it is claimed, is that the white outer surface reflects useful sunlight onto the foliage of the plants whilst this would otherwise be absorbed as heat and transferred to the nutrient solution. In the case of black polythene it is postulated that so much heat would be absorbed in fine summer conditions that the solution temperature would be raised to a point where harm to the plants could be caused. In practice, advantageous light reflection by white surfaced polythene can be vastly over-rated as far as the UK climate is concerned and the problem of potential solution overheating is completely alleviated if the ratio of plant capacity and solution volume is kept at or above the minimum figure recommended. In more generous climates it would clearly be risky to use black polythene, but elsewhere a strong case for the more widespread use of black polythene can be made on three counts. Firstly, because black polythene is cheaper than black on white. Secondly because it lasts longer so that it may be possible to retain the channel for a second year, perhaps using "inside out" the second time round. Thirdly, because the heat absorbed by black polythene is mostly useful heat, whereas light reflected by white surfaced polythene is often surplus to requirements anyway. Furthermore the amount of heat accumulated corresponds closely with the increase of air space temperature and light, and hence with shoot activity. It is in just these conditions that there is a good case for applying heat to the root zone. As far as small scale NFT work is concerned I am of the opinion that black polythene is advantageously employed.

As well as polythene there are some combination sheets, e.g. silver paper bonded to polythene and waterproofed paper sheets which have been used as NFT channelling, but their use is unlikely to be widespread. Materials which should be avoided include anything to which a finishing colour has been applied and polythene which has not been U.V. stabilised as this will break down well within one season. Clear polythene is not recommended. In spite of the general belief to the contrary plant roots show little antagonism to light, instead they are oblivious to it. Consequently it is theoretically possible to use clear polythene channels but their use should be avoided because light entry into the channel promotes the growth of algae which is both unsightly and restricting to the solution flow.

There are a number of alternative fasteners for polythene channels. Amongst them are various press studs, a proprietory fastener and clothes pegs, but much the best is the staple. Using a small pocket stapler the channel is easily fastened and surprisingly none or little damage is done if it is pulled open. Indeed unfastening and restapling many times is in order.

It is important to avoid tearing or puncturing the polythene sheet "below the waterline". Fortunately there are surprisingly few occasions when small stones or dust particles puncture the sheets. If a leak does occur it can be repaired using electricians tape on dried surfaces whilst there are also specifically manufactured tapes used for repairing polythene greenhouses.

After tomatoes and cucumbers the most popular crops grown in NFT are lettuce and strawberries. What channelling is employed for these crops? Again it is usual for rigid channel support trays to be employed, probably in multiduct form, and either raised to bench height on stands or laid on graded earth. All that is required to convert these trays to suitable channels is to lay a base sheet of polythene the entire length of the trays, thereby effecting a seal at the overlaps between trays. This base sheet is universally black polythene probably in 500 or 600g and it may be used in individual channel widths or as a sheet wide enough to seal all the channels in one multiduct width.

Planting is quick and easy, simply set out the plants at the preferred planting distance onto the base liner having first used spreader mat if appropriate. For the commercial UK lettuce grower no serious algal problems occur because the plants grow quickly to shade the solution surface and thus inhibit algal growth. Additionally it will be readily appreciated that speed of planting, harvesting and subsequent replanting will be extremely rapid in these open channels. In hotter climates it would certainly be necessary to protect the solution by closing the channel, firstly, to prevent too much heat accumulating in the solution and secondly, to prevent rapid algal blockage of the channel. For strawberry growers the open channel is less than satisfactory because the rate of growth of this plant is relatively slow and because strawberries occupy the channel much longer than lettuce. Accordingly algal growth is a problem. More importantly the development of the flowers and fruit increases the top weight of the plant such that it becomes unstable in the solution, perhaps even toppling out. For these reasons a channel cover is employed.

The channel cover may be a further polythene sheet stretching across the channel. Planting being carried out through holes or slits made in the polythene. In practice the lightweight and flexible properties of polythene make it somewhat unsatisfactory as a channel cover, though there will always be a use for this inexpensive option. Instead more rigid tops known as top plates are preferred. These can be made from a variety of materials including insulation board, wooden boards and even glassfibre, but all are out-classed by extruded polypropylene fluted board. This material is available in a range of weights, widths and colours. For most NFT purposes black is best, but U.V.I. white is preferred in hot climates. This material as well as being clean and easy to use will last almost indefinitely though it is not especially expensive to replace should this prove necessary.

Fastening is normally by clips or studs to the top edges of the rigid support tray.

Figure 3/24 illustrates a channel of this type.

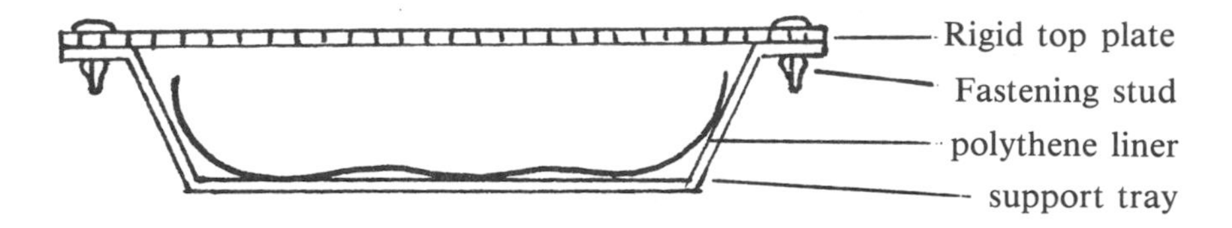

Fig. 3/24 Section showing components of multipurpose channel

There is a great deal to be said for the use of this arrangement for the majority of NFT applications in the private greenhouse. If used in conjunction with a suitable base width channel support tray the entire range of plant types can be successfully accommodated in the one channel type. It only requires that the top plate be modified to suit the different spacings which are desired. In the case of narrow width multiduct tray bases large plants and small may still be accommodated in the same multiduct at the same time, Figure 3/25a, but it is generally easier to work with wider bases, as shown in Figure 3/25b

It is clear then that the two basic approaches of the commercial NFT grower are easily and suitably adapted for use in the small NFT unit, but there are of course some modifications and variations which might only be of use in the small system. If a very short channel is proposed and the rigid channel support tray is in one piece then the base liner could be dispensed with. Similarly, if the tray is of a material suitable for contact with the solution e.g. uPVC, this could be waterproofed at the joins and again the base liner dispensed with. In practice this is not a recommended approach not least because the liner is useful to waterproof the ends of the channel and because its rapid disposal effectively cleans the system. Furthermore, on-site joining of trays is never quite as easy or effective as envisaged. Rigid PVC guttering for which special joining pieces are available can certainly be used but it is very expensive for all but widths suitable for the smallest plants

More rigid channelling suitable for use on graded slopes has been in use for some years but has never become popular. The problem is that for the additional rigidity to make any significant difference to the stability of the slope the cost of the extra material becomes prohibitive, whilst semi-flexibility offers no advantage at all to the slope but does lend itself to keeping the channel open which is theoretically desirable. Figure 3/26 shows a common style of semi-rigid channel. A disadvantage of semi-rigid channelling is that its inherent stiffness makes it very difficult to lay particularly with longer lengths. Semi-rigid channelling is available in polythene of 2000g+ and polypropylene.

The tendency for flexible channelling to collapse on top of the root system has not proved a hazard probably because the coverage of the root is incomplete, whilst there is some evidence suggesting increased growth probably due to higher moisture content of the air trapped above the root mat. If collapse of flexible channelling is a problem on any site it can be avoided by tying the top of the channel to an over channel wire. This idea has been developed so that the wire runs inside the channel, fastening of the two edges of the sheet being above the wire.

CHANNEL ENDS

Very often when leaks occur in an NFT system, they occur at the channel ends. Consequently it is important to design channel ends which ensure a good degree of reliability.

Fig. 3/25a Adapting narrow base multiduct for mixed plantings using rigid top plates

Fig. 3/25b Mixed plantings are more easily facilitated in wide base multiduct

The simplest ends are open ends, i.e., the solution drains from the channel directly into an open collecting duct or tank, whilst at the inlet end of the channel the essential slope prevents back-up and loss of solution. In fact, open channel outlets are very acceptable provided that there is good contact between the actual material of the channel and the duct or tank. This is because solution left to drop between the two may display an unwanted surface tension characteristic whereby the solution will actually run up the underside of channel before being lost outside the collection vessel, as shown in Figure 3/27. This phenomenon is best illustrated by the well known action of tap water in running up ones sleeve if, inadvertently, contact is made with a drip from the tap.

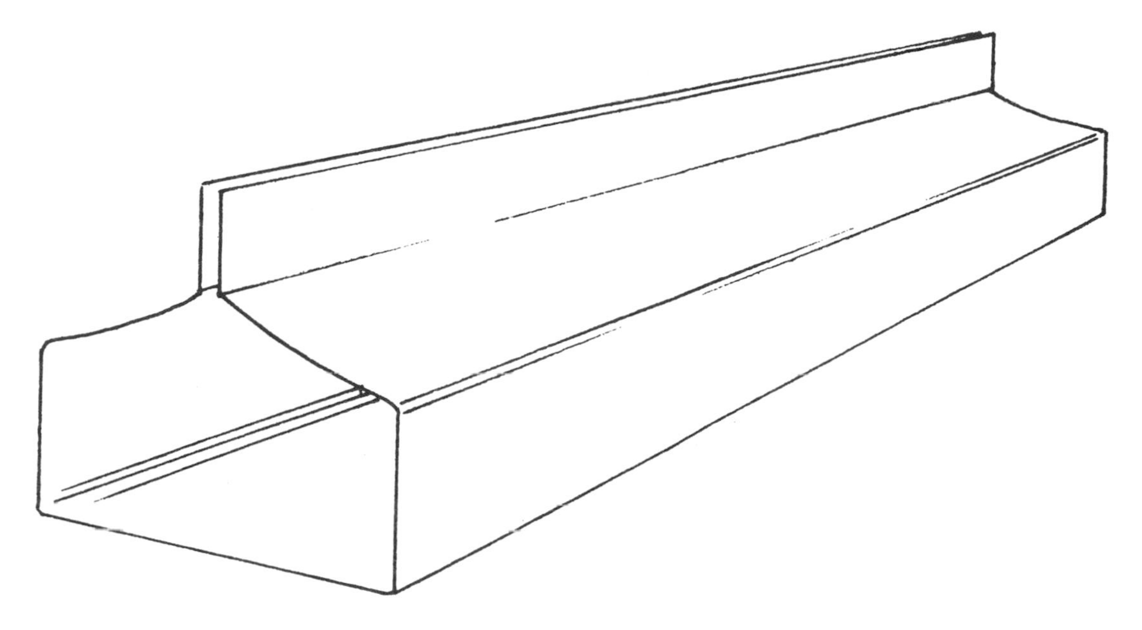

Fig. 3/26 Semi-rigid channel

This type of leak is extremely difficult to detect not least because of the inaccessibility of the underside of the channel once the system is laid out and operating. To improve open ended channel outlets, spreader mat used in the channel should extend from the channel and into the collection duct/tank, thereby providing a surface to which the solution can 'adhere' by the very surface tension which might otherwise be so troublesome. This arrangement is shown in Figure 3/28.

Fig. 3/27 Solution might be lost at open channel ends

Of course only non-degradable spreader mat should be used for joining channel and return otherwise the benefit would soon be lost. Open channel outlets are not normally recommended for outside use except in docile climates.

At the inlet end a simple improvement to the open system is to raise the end of the channelling to form a barrier by resting it against a solid object such as a house brick or wooden block.

Fig. 3/28 The use of a spreader mat overhang prevents solution loss at an open channel end

Closed channel outlets are good alternatives. They involve a connection piece fitted between the channel and the return tube. In this way light is excluded and algal growth prevented. The most effective connection fittings are waste outlets which are primarily manufactured to take the discharge from sinks and baths. Fitment is achieved by cutting an accurate accommodation hole in the channel a short distance from the end, make a mark by pressing the outlet on the channel polythene. Pass the shank of the waste through the hole and secure with the nut and gasket. It is usual for the gasket to be placed on the underside of the channel to prevent undue raising of the lip of the outlet within the channel causing a pool of solution to form, but this is unimportant on sites with an adequate slope. A common problem with waste outlet fittings is to achieve a perfectly watertight junction. The best remedy is to smear the flange of the outlet and possiby the surface of the polythene surrounding the accommodation hole with silicone sealer. This is sometimes known as "bathroom sealer" when it is available in small tubes at most D.I.Y. stores and indeed in larger tubes at builders and plumbers merchants, or as "instant gasket" when it is found in the motor repair trade. Figure 3/29 illustrates the fitting of a waste outlet.

Waste outlets are manufactured in a variety of sizes, commonly 25mm, 40mm and 50mm. Generally 25mm is considered a little on the small side with the danger of becoming blocked with loose debris found in the solution. The size 50mm would be somewhat oversize especially if the return pipework was of smaller diameter than this. Size 40mm is very useful and may fit neatly into the commonly used 40mm return pipe, whilst 32mm outlets which are made are probably ideal but are not widely distributed. Try to fit the outlet to the return pipework before purchasing large quantities of materials as adaptor fittings, especially in larger sizes, are expensive. Waste outlets are manufactured in polypropylene but many are supplied fitted with chromium top which should be removed. Others are made in stainless steel which of course is entirely acceptable.

To prevent the nutrient solution flow overshooting the outlet, the channel material should be drawn up behind the outlet and fixed in this position using blocks or very probably by fixing a vertical member to the channel support tray. Such members can be fabricated from many materials, including plywood. Commercially available channel support trays may be supplied with ends of fluted plastic sheet into which the base polythene can be fixed with stud fastners.

SOLUTION HEAT AND INSULATION

Heaters

We have already looked at the arguments for and against the use of black

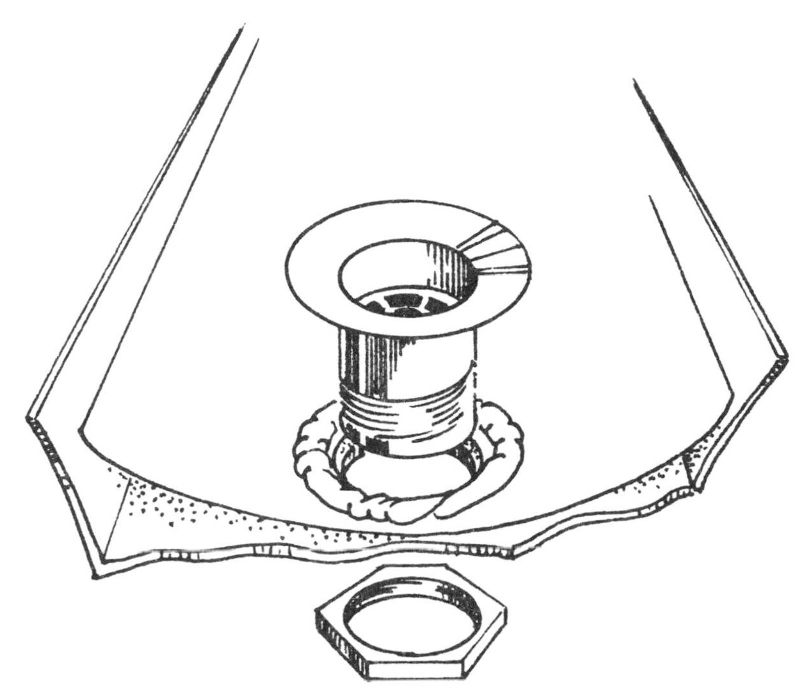

Fig. 3/29 Fitting a waste outlet to channelling

channelling material and noted the benefit of heat accummulated from this source. Similarly, the other items used to construct the NFT system which come into contact with the nutrient solution should, as far as is reasonably possible, be black. In mid-summer under U.K. conditions this "free" heat may be all that is required to keep the nutrient solution at an ideal temperature, but depending on the plants to be grown and the season some external source of heat may be required. By far the most commonly used heat source is electricity which whilst having the disadvantage of high unit heat cost has the major advantages of inexpensive installation, effective operation and ready availability of equipment. Two types of electrical solution heating units are available. They are aquarium immersion heaters and cable heaters. Millions of aquarium immersion heaters are used in the U.K. and elsewhere and they have an excellent record of safety and reliability. They are available in outputs of 50 to 300 watts and may be combined with an integral thermostat or used in conjunction with a separate thermostat. This equipment is normally sited in the circulation tank and, especially with higher wattage equipment, it is important to keep the element enclosure from direct contact with the tank wall/base material because the high heat intensity which characterises these heaters may damage the tank. Usually a special clip is provided whereby the heater may be secured 'spaced' from the bottom. Alternatively the heater may be suspended in the tank well below the water line. This arrangement has the danger of exposing the element to air if the solution level in the tank drops, if this occurs the heater would probably be destroyed. Accordingly this method is only suitable for use in tanks automatically topped up to level. Another alternative is to place a layer of stones, perhaps contained in a flatish dish, on the base of the tank upon which the heater may safely be laid.

Should combined heater/thermostats or separate heater and thermostat be used? Combined equipment is usually a little less expensive to purchase but this could easily be offset if, as is often the case, two or even three heaters could be run from one thermostat. Certainly there is more wiring for the latter alternative and this may be a crucial point. Finally, and again in favour of separate units, is that failure of one item of equipment would be less expensive to replace than combined equipment.

Aquarium heaters, especially in larger wattages, have the disadvantage of high heat intensity which precipitates salts, including nutrient salts, dissolved in the solution causing a coating of precipitate to form on the heater element enclosure. The risk is loss of efficiency of heat transfer to the solution, raising the temperature in the heater, and threatening damage to the heater. This scale is fairly easy to remove, but do so only when the heater has cooled. The problem can be much reduced by employing low wattage heaters and by careful siting of the heaters under the solution return from the return pipe/duct.

Another alternative is to site the heater in an enclosure of tap or, in hardwater areas, distilled water. The enclosure may be quite large, e.g. a small aquarium or a demijohn or as small as a milk bottle. The arrangement is shown in Figure 3/30.

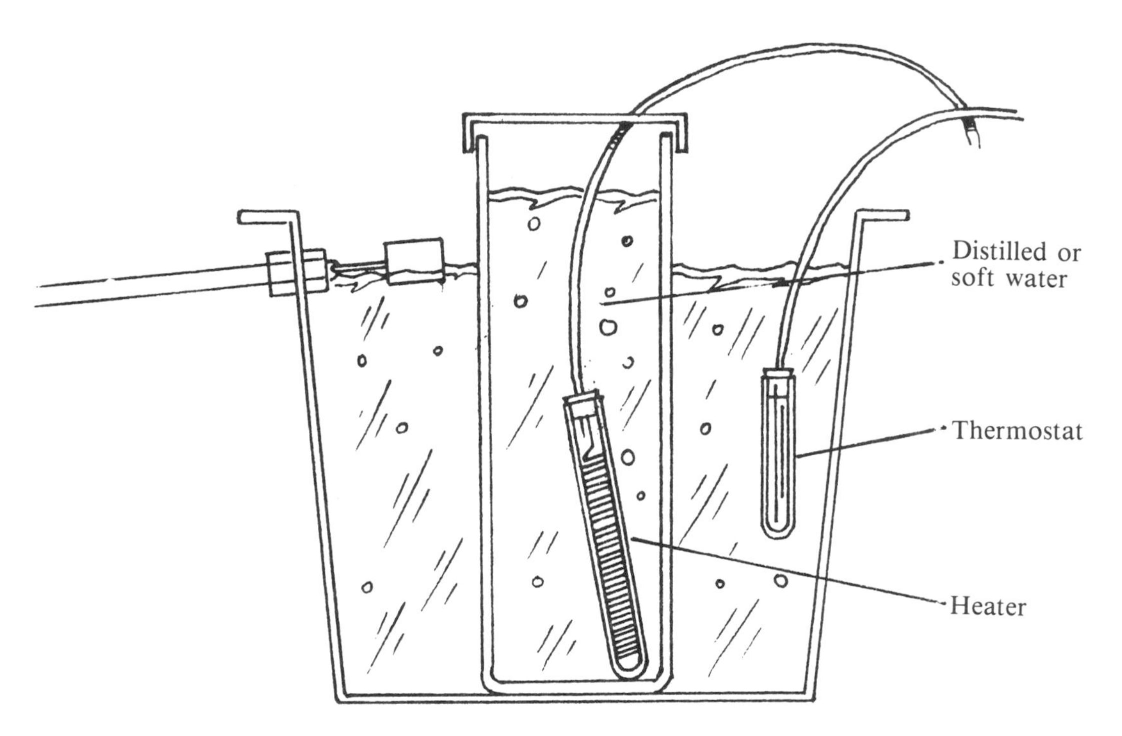

Fig. 3/30 An arrangement for preventing scaling on heater elements

Whatever size of enclosure is used, this system is only appropriate if separate heater and thermostat is employed and the thermostat must of course be sited in the nutrient solution.

The cable heater is familiar to gardeners as soil heating equipment, but this equipment is generally, check with the supplier before use, equally suited to solution heating. The main site of use is the circulation tank but, because it is considered important to ensure separation of the cables, it is necessary to wind the cable onto a frame which is then immersed in the tank or, alternatively, the cable may be laid in a channel where the length of run makes for easy fitting. These cables have a low intensity of heat at any point on the cable so no damage to an adjacent plant will occur. Cable heaters are generally more expensive than aquarium heaters but they have a longer lifespan than the higher wattage aquarium heaters. However to obtain high wattage in cable may involve so much length of cable that real difficulty occurs on fitting.

Heater Control

It is possible to run small NFT systems without a thermostat. For instance a 50 watt heater in a 50 to 100 litre unit would never overheat the solution, whilst all the heat gained would probably be useful. Additionally it is entirely reasonable to effect control by switching the heater on and off as required, e.g. two days on, two days off during the early season, which provides a useful boost to growth but limits electricity consumption. However, the more usual approach is to provide a heater capable of significantly increasing solution temperature above the ambient air temperature and to effect control of possible excess heating by thermostat. Submersible thermostats are most widely used. They are sited in the circulation tank. Non-submersible thermostats may be attached to the sides of the circulation tank when they respond to the heat received through the walls of the tank. Sometimes a thermostat consists of separate receptor and control, the receptor being placed in a pocket which in turn is placed in the solution. Suitable pockets are adapted from sealed-off lengths of plastic pipe, naturally the pipe must be a close fit on the receptor. Thermostats of this latter type are generally of very good quality. The main problem with fully submersible thermostats has been difficulty in adjusting the temperature setting since, necessarily, the controls must be sealed. Recent improvements in design have somewhat alleviated the problem. Wherever the site of the thermostat, check the temperature achieved in the channel and adjust the thermostat accordingly.

Another recent introduction has been that of the electronic thermostat. These units are very accurate and particularly reliable because they have so few parts. An advantageous feature is that they can easily be manufactured to accept larger electrical currents than their mechanical predecessors. This may save considerable installation costs on larger sites as specialist help and switches may not be required. Electronic thermostats are generally about twice the price of conventional models but it is envisaged that this price differential will be rapidly reduced.

An alternative method of heater control is provided by the use of time switches. Here the heater is set to come on for a predetermined period(s) each day. Time switch heater control has several advantages. Firstly, the method provides a strict limit to the amount of heat which is applied thereby providing fine control of the costs of heating. Secondly, alterations to the time switch are usually more simply and exactly accomplished than are alterations to thermostat settings. Finally, there appears to be some growth advantage in time controlled solution heating. This arises because limited heat may be applied strictly at the time(s) when it is most effectively used by the plants. For example, increasing water uptake capability of the plants during the heat of the afternoon may be easily effected by setting the time switch to bring the heater on during the appropriate period. In the same way, offsetting evaporative heat losses from the solution may be most economically achieved by applying an hour or so of heating during the early morning. Additionally there is some evidence suggesting increased growth and performance of the aerial parts of plants if heat is applied intermittently rather than continuously. This improved growth probably results from the shoot benefitting from reduced environmental advantage of the root when the heating is off. When the heating is on the root it is advantageously placed to make satisfactory growth. It is probable that the same balanced growth may be had using thermostatic control but it is difficult to know exactly what solution temperature to set especially if the shoot environment is subject to great variation as is often the case in the smaller greenhouse.

Time controlled heaters may be run using a readily available controller without a thermostat provided that the heater capacity has a limited solution temperature lift. If there is any danger of overheating the solution during the heater on period, then clearly thermostatic back up is essential. Suitable time switches are reasonably priced and are widely available at electrical goods stores.

Alternatives to electrical solution heating

In commercial NFT units heat is normally applied to the nutrient solution from the boiler which also provides heat for the air space. The heat transfer is effected by a coil usually sited in the circulation tank whilst the supply of heat into the exchanger is controlled by thermostats operating a solenoid, or similar, valve. Can hot water supplies be adapted for similar purposes in smaller applications? In fact, there is no compelling reason why not since the heat exchanger need not be expensive, simply a coiled length of alkathene pipe. Supply to the coil would probably be by central heating pump which itself would be easy to control thermostatically. If this approach is chosen, clearly the most economical source of heat should be used so as to maximise running cost savings and to offset the slight complication and expense of the equipment. In most households the domestic hot water or central heating unit is the most economical heat source but of course external boilers using coal, gas, oil or waste oil might also be used. The problem with the separate boiler approach is that the heat requirements of solution heating alone are normally relatively small so that the boiler may run at an uneconomically low level. Of course a space heating system for the greenhouse could be provided at the sametime this being identical to the usual commercial operation but on a smaller scale.

Do not be afraid to add hot water to the NFT system but do so only when the pump is off. In this way a speedy rise of temperature in the morning can be effected, with beneficial results to either heated or non heated systems. Also this is the best method of raising the water temperature on refilling the tank. Generally tap water is very cold and the solution heater alone often takes a long time to raise this to the desired circulation temperature.

How much heat is required?

A most important point to make at the outset is that successful NFT does not require any solution heating or indeed any space heating. Many plants can be grown successfully without any heat application including many temperate plants, and excellent harvests of hot house plants such as tomatoes and cucumbers can be obtained. Solution heating should be installed where it is planned to have an extended growing season and where plants are being grown which respond to solution heating. Note also, that if an economic space heating system already exists in the greenhouse it may be entirely unnecessary to provide more heating in the form of solution heating.

As a guide derived from much commercial experience, it has been found appropriate under U.K. conditions to provide heat in the ratio of approximately 1 Kw to 200 tomato plants, equivalent to an area of approximately 100 square metres. On a smaller scale this boils down to, for example, a 4 metres × 3 metres greenhouse entirely converted to NFT requiring 120 watts of solution heat. In fact for the small greenhouse, application of the commercial ratio results in a figure which would, in practice, prove a little too low. There are several reasons for this. Firstly, because on a small scale space heat is usually less generously applied and secondly, because commercially the tank volume to plant capacity ratio is lower and therefore the solution heating is more responsive. To adjust for these factors allow about 30% extra for small to medium projects with a minimum heater size of 100 watts under normal conditions of use. On larger but still non-commercial sites an allowance of +10 to 20% is all that is required. If frost protection is provided by applying solution heat at least twice the normal heat requirement should be available.

The figures arrived at above assume a reasonable level of insulation if the site and circumstances demand it. In practice, where the circulation tank is sunk into the ground and comes into contact with ground water, insulation is essential. The loss of heat being in the order of 50% or more of heat applied, but even worse, cold ground water will cool the nutrient solution when the heater is switched off and this effect could seriously damage the plants.

Insulation

To insulate sunken tanks apply at least 2.5cm of water resistant rigid insulation board to the sides and base of the tank before it is placed in the excavation. Suitable boards are polystyrene, polyurethane and closed cell styrene. A temporary fixing with tape is sufficient. Next enclose the tank and insulation within a wrapping of polythene sheet preferably 1000g, but 800g would suffice. On the base of the excavation lay about 2.5cm of polystyrene boards to protect the polythene and unless a soft backfill around the sides is to be used, provision for more polystyrene protection around the sides should be made. It is not difficult to envisage that a considerable excavation is required for the proper fitment of even a fairly small circulation tank.

For tanks not sunk in the ground it is sufficient to apply one layer all round of 2.5cm of insulation. It is convenient to fit this with tape. For all tanks a top insulation is recommended. Channels are usually insulated between the ground and the channel base. Again 2.5cm of polystyrene board is sufficient. It is also appropriate to apply insulation to long lengths of supply tube, especially if it runs adjacent to the wall of the greenhouse or across an exposed area.

Channels themselves are not normally of insulating material, though fluted polypropylene sheet used as a top plate is a reasonable insulator. However the characteristics of the channel can greatly affect the efficiency of solution heating. Remember that only a film of solution flows in the channel therefore an ample surface exists from which heat can be lost. If the solution runs only slowly, considerable temperature difference between the inlet end and outlet end of the channel will ensue. The effects of this can often be seen on long channels say 20 metres + where a gradient of growth reflects the heat loss gradient along the channel. In the short channel run it is more likely that insufficient slope is the cause of the heat gradient. Open channels lose heat very rapidly.

AUTOMATIC TOP-UP FACILITIES

Even the smallest users of NFT will be surprised at the volume of water taken out of the circulating solution by growing plants. With small systems this water usage can be made up quite adequately by bucket or hose provided that at least the recommended circulation tank capacity has been provided and that the interval between topping-up is not too great, perhaps every two days in summer. With medium and larger size NFT units, manual top-up is still possible provided regular attention can be given, namely every day, and that large circulation tank capacity has been provided.

Sometimes manual topping-up can be difficult especially when illness, long weekends or holidays prevent the usual inspection of the unit. In these circumstances, auto. top-up is advantageously employed.

Auto. top-up is similarly advantageous when outside help is occasionally used, because it is simpler to have one's relative or friend fill the top-up tank during planned absences than to involve them in the responsibility of manual topping-up of the circulation tank. However, the popular reason for fitting auto. top-up is simply to reduce the chore of manual topping-up, this being a logical development of the adoption of NFT which is so often undertaken out of the desire to take the most tedious work out of growing good quality plants. A further benefit of automatic top-up is the possible reduction of the circulation tank capacity. This is possible because the tendency for the plants to concentrate the nutrient solution by preferential removal of water is offset by incoming make-up water. Accordingly, as little as 2.5 litres of circulation tank capacity may be provided together with auto. top-up for each tomato plant or equivalent growing area, but this is subject to a minimum figure of not less than 50 litres.

Two methods of topping-up automatically are available. These are, via a header tank or via the mains water supply. Dealing with a header tank supply first. The volume usefully available in the top-up tank is easily calculated from the approximate daily figures for water usage, e.g. 9 litres/day for a row of 10 tomato plants or the equivalent space occupied by other plants and the number of days of water provision required. In many cases just two days is sufficient as this would provide cover for usual absences, whilst the header tank can be topped-up by a friend when a longer absence occurs. In other cases much greater provision is required, perhaps for up to 14 days. A difficulty here is the siting of a large volume tank which may be required, but this is not impossible as it is quite in order to site the tank outside and adjacent to the greenhouse or indeed at any convenient point provided it can be connected by hose to the circulation tank. Small volume header tanks e.g. 40-50 litres, are conveniently sited close to the circulation tank often inside a greenhouse. For either small or large tanks it is important to ensure that access for topping-up is easy. Provided a low pressure valve system is used it is not normally necessary to raise the header tank base more than 15cm or so above the circulation tank solution level. Tanks used as header tanks will probably be plastic. Rusted and galvanised metal tanks are unsuitable. There are many economical water butts available which are entirely suitable as are many second-hand containers.

Connections to the circulation tank are as follows. Tank connector and hose adaptor; suitable flexible connecting tube and float valve. Additionally some form of tap either in-line or at the tank connector is very useful to isolate the header tank when emptying the circulation tank. Also useful is a mesh filter inside the header tank which will prevent small particles reaching and blocking the float valve. For the same reason it is usual to insert the tank connector 3.0cm. or so from the base of the header tank so that particles settling out are not drawn into the tube. The preferred arrangement is shown in Figure 3/31.

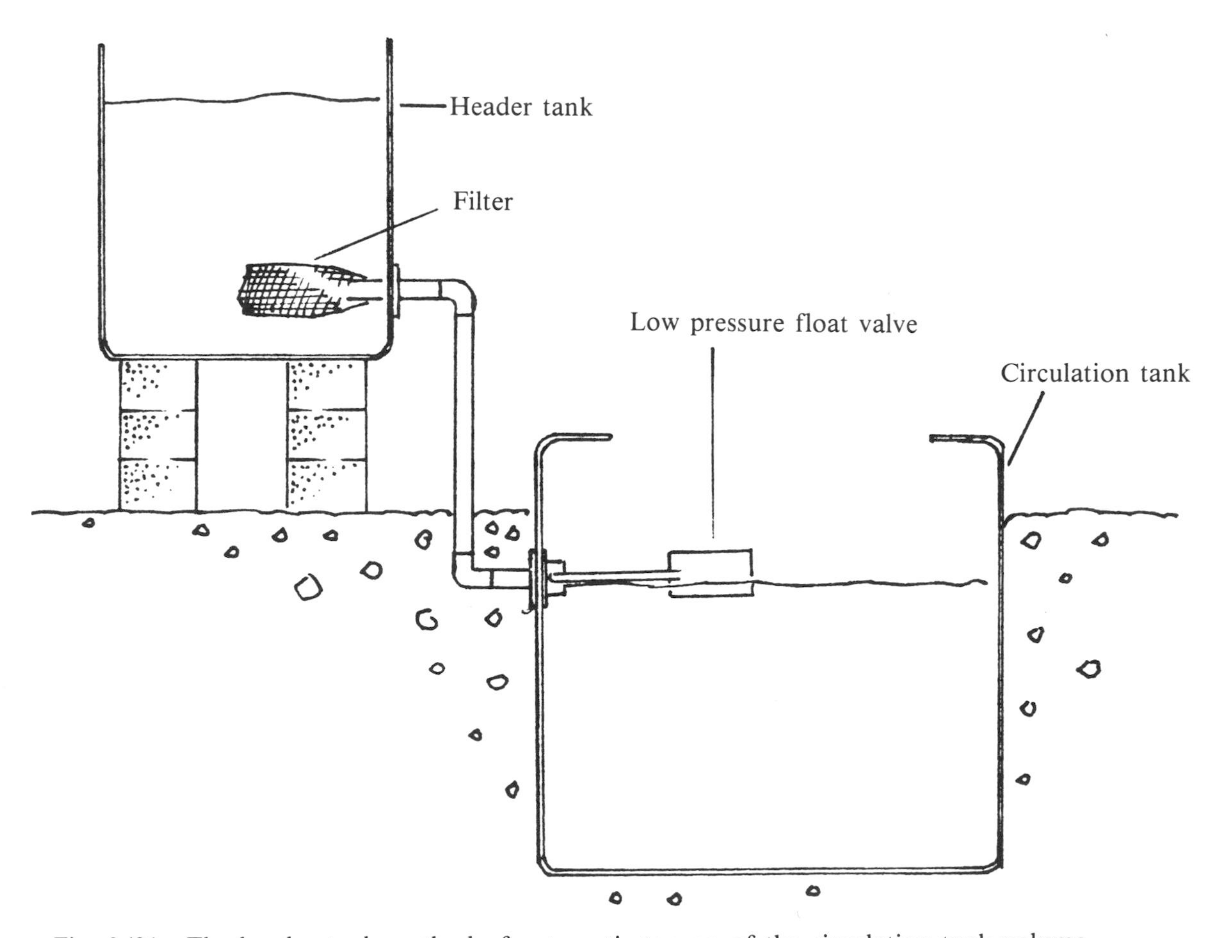

Fig. 3/31 The header tank method of automatic top-up of the circulation tank volume

Low pressure float valves are widely available. The principal features to look for are ease of connection to the supply tube and presence of plastic, not copper, float. Some float valves may be difficult to fit into the circulation tank where space is limited. This is especially true of long narrow tank/return ducts when a long arm float valve may be impossible to fit. Fortunately there are short arm valves available.

Any NFT system can be connected to the mains water supply but there are two good reasons why this should not be the first option for small and medium units. Firstly, because easy nutrition programmes using header tanks have been developed for small and medium scale use and secondly, because it is sometimes expensive to fit a mains supply. In the U.K., mains water supplies to NFT systems must be fitted such that they satisfy the standards of the local water authority. This means that only specified materials may be used i.e. of suitable quality and pressure rating and that an isolating method (tap) is provided. Finally, the work must be carried out by a competent person. These regulations mean that it is not sufficient to attach garden hose to a stand tap and then to a float valve. Notwithstanding the expense, mains water auto. top-up facilities provide excellent service and are regarded as almost essential for the success of large scale NFT.

CONDUCTIVITY METERS

Who needs a conductivity meter?

The need for a conductivity meter in operating an NFT system arises when changes in the nutrient concentration of the solution are so rapid that they are unpredictable with reasonable accurracy by non-quantatitive assessment methods. This situation most usually occurs on larger installations, say of 40 tomato plants or equivalent growing area or more and accordingly a conductivity meter is ordinarily necessary to run these systems effectively. However on somewhat smaller sites, unless the system is designed with extra solution volume, the changes in solution concentration are still sufficiently rapid so as to present a significant work load if operated with one of the non-conductivity based nutrition programmes. Accordingly, there is a convenience advantage to be had in using a conductivity based nutrition programme on sites where strictly there is no necessity to do so. Furthermore a conductivity meter can be used to obtain a quantitative statement of the concentration status of the nutrient solution at anytime and this is reassuring to a large number of NFT users, especially newcomers to the technique. With small scale NFT there is normally no growth advantage in using a conductivity based nutrition programme and purchase of a conductivity meter would generally be an unwarranted expense except perhaps where specialist plants are grown when a conductivity meter might be a prudent investment.

There are sites where using a conductivity meter is not just uneconomic but positively detrimental. These are few in number, but if the NFT system is serviced with very hard water the massive influence of dissolved ions contributing to water hardness make conductivity monitoring of the nutrient status of the solution much more problematic. On small sites these problems add appreciable complication to conductivity based nutrition programmes so that the choice of an alternative programme is much more attractive. Similarly if NFT is set up where the operators are unfamiliar with the use of the meter or where there are serious doubts as to the maintenance of accuracy of the meter because, for example, of difficulty in obtaining battery replacements or excessive wetness in the atmosphere, then alternative non-conductivity nutrition programmes should be employed. If the scale of operations is large, alterations to the design may need to be made to promote the smooth running of these programmes.

Electrical conductivity and the nutrient solution

The electrical conductivity of water varies, amongst other things, with the concentration of dissolved mineral ions. So for example, sea water conducts electricity rather better than rain water because sea water has a high level of dissolved ions whilst rain water has very few. This feature is used to effect monitoring of the total nutrient solution concentration in NFT systems. As nutrients are added to the circulating water, the electrical conductivity of the solution rises. As the plants remove nutrients the electrical conductivity of the solution decreases. Note that electrical conductivity does not vary with, nor can it be used for monitoring, the concentration of individual nutrient ions, but serves only to gauge the total concentration of the solution. Furthermore, both nutrient and non-nutrient ions contribute to the electrical conductivity of the solution.

The electrical conductivity (EC) of a solution is scientifically reported as microsiemens/centimeter (uScm^{-1} or uS). There are other expressions in occasional use, these are:— millisiemens (MS) and millimho (mmho) but for NFT purposes a very practical expression known as the conductivity factor (CF) is in everyday use. Accordingly conductivity meters manufactured specifically for NFT, and indeed some for other purposes, are often calibrated and read in CF units and throughout this text reference to solution conductivity will always be made in terms of CF. Because other meters with alternative scales are available, it is prudent now to present the conversion of one expression to another. It is:— 1 millisiemen (MS) = 1 millimho (mmho) = 1000 microsiemens (uS) = 10 CF units.

Choosing a conductivity meter

Apart from price there are certain important features of conductivity meters. It is prudent to assess a conductivity meter in terms of these features before making a purchase.

Scale. The relevant scale is CF 0-50. Preferred meters show equal increments of conductivity in equal gradation on the scale. This encourages easy and accurate reading. Some meters show increments of CF logarithmically so that at high CF values the scale gradations are very much closer than at low CF values. Generally meters with this type of scale are less preferred particularly in hard water areas where work at higher CF values is common and of course where the user may be experiencing sight difficulty which would be exacerbated by the scale. As a general point the larger the scale the easier it is to read so that all other considerations being equal the larger scale meter would be choosen.

Temperature Compensation. Electrical conductivity varies with temperature. The nominal rate of variation is 2%/°C. Accordingly it is highly desirable that a conductivity meter should incorporate temperature compensation to increase accuracy.

Temperature compensation mechanisms may be manual or automatic. In the case of the former the on/off switch normally includes a temperature scale. Set the meter to read at the temperature of the solution to be tested. Automatic temperature compensation is integral to the meter. Meters incorporating this feature tend to be somewhat more expensive than their manual counterparts. However there is little advantage in automatic temperature compensation because it is generally desirable if a temperature reading is taken at the time of monitoring the solution concentration as a check on solution heating, artificial or natural. Certain conductivity meters display both conductivity and temperature value and these instruments are ideal where the scale of the enterprise justifies the cost.

Non-temperature compensated meters should not be dismissed as useless, because in practice solution temperature does not vary wildly in normal conditions so that working accuracy will be obtained when using such a meter. This is especially true of soft water areas where accuracy in measuring solution concentration is much less important than in hard water areas. Non-compensated meters should of course be offered at a good price advantage.

Digital Display. The rapid advance of modern electronics enables even mundane instruments to be fitted with digital display. Whilst there is no doubt as to the pleasing elegance of digital display there is no practical advantage in the facility which can justify much greater cost. It is often stated that digital display gives a more accurate readout usually displaying to more than one decimal point. However, such fine accuracy is inappropriate to NFT work and can lead to serious numbers confusion.

Portability. It is generally much preferred if the conductivity meter can be used at the NFT site instead of necessitating a sample of solution being brought to the meter for testing. Such portability is facilitated by battery as opposed to mains operation, though some meters incorporate both. Portability is improved by robustness of construction and possibly by the provision of a carrying case or strap. As a rule electronic instruments in the moderate price range (and many high priced models also) do not store well in damp atmospheres and it is considered unwise to keep a conductivity meter in a greenhouse environment.

Two important considerations arise from the feature of portability. First, battery type. It is lamentable that developments of battery operation, be it in watches, regalia of modern life, or practical instrumentation, have not coincidentally improved the interchangeability of batteries between competitive models. Indeed the situation has worsened. Accordingly choose a conductivity meter which uses a readily available battery. This will save immense frustration later on. Second, choose an instrument with a robust cell. Some conductivity meters are provided with glass cells which have a good reputation for accuracy but these are wholly inappropriate for NFT work as they are inevitably easily broken. Instead look for plastic construction.

In-line or Dip Operation. Conductivity cells may be fitted "in-line" that is within pipework so that the solution flows continuously past the electrode or they may be dipped into the nutrient solution, usually at the circulation tank, at the time of testing. In-line cells should be detachable from the instrument so that they can be left in place between uses when the instrument is stored in a drier atmosphere. Usually in-line cells may also be used in the dip mode. There is no compelling advantage of one mode of operation over the other. However, in-line operation is considered slightly more accurate because interfering air bubbles are removed from the surface of the electrodes by the flow. This same action also encourages cleanliness of the electrodes. Dip operation is nearly essential when a multiplicity of NFT systems is monitored with the one meter.

Possible Alternatives to Manufactured Conductivity Meters

Conductivity meters meeting the desired standards can be a significant additional expense with a small NFT installation. It is possible to rig up a usable instrument less expensively. The chief area of adaptation centres around the use of electricians multimeters which, considering their apparent complexity, are amazingly inexpensive. It should prove possible to obtain a reading on the resistance scale of the meter which relates to the solution strength. Of course, now, higher readings (of resistance) denote lower solution concentration. The main problems of adaptation appear to arise at the cell. It is essential that the contacts are fixed at a permanent distance apart, derived by experimentation and that the concentration of charged ions around one pole (akin to electro-plating) is prevented. To assist this latter only momentary operation is desired, scrupulous cleanliness should be instituted and stainless steel or platignum contacts employed. It greatly assists the would-be innovator if a range of solutions of known conductivity are available for check purposes. A solution of known conductivity may be accurately made up if a saturated solution of calcium sulphate dihydrate is prepared. This gives CF20 at 20°C. However a more practical approach is probably to prepare a full strength nutrient solution from NFT nutrient instructions and calibrate the home produced meter from this and dilutions of the same.

OTHER INSTRUMENTATION

pH (Acidity) Meter

Portable pH meters are found in two forms. Firstly the electronic type, the pH companion of the portable conductivity meter. Secondly, the "manual" type typified by probe style soil pH testers. There is nothing to recommend either type of instrument for use with NFT. The reasons for the unreliability of the instruments are complex, but the decisive argument against the meters is that as far as NFT is concerned an unreliable reading is far more a danger to successful cropping than is no reading at all. Of course it is always possible that in the future, reliable pH meters will become available but it is unlikely that such meters would be so competitively priced as to give them a practical and economical advantage over a good colorimeter test.

Automatic Nutrient and Acid Dosing

Very large scale commercial horticulture uses a variety of very complex instruments to control the environment of the plants. Amongst the range of devices used is automatic nutrient and acid dosing equipment. Is there any advantage in using this equipment in small scale growing? The answer is decisively no, because reliable automatic equipment as well as being a hopelessly uneconomic investment also requires time and skill in operation. The fact is, it takes less time to manage a small NFT system using manual dosing than using automatic equipment. Furthermore, the level of management can be more accurate and more productive than can be achieved by using ordinary automatic equipment. As a matter of interest the scale of NFT enterprise required to give practical and economic advantage in using automatic equipment is in the region of one acre of cropping in average UK conditions, whilst in isolated overseas localities it is difficult to envisage any advantage whatever the scale of enterprise.

Other Instruments

Other instruments used in NFT include accumulation water meters and electronic time controllers. It should be noted that the vast majority of small scale NFT installations require no such instrumentation at all, their use being mainly of interest to specialist set-ups. As regards purchase, industrial models tend to be expensive and it is usually advantageous to see if domestic apparatus can be utilised.

CHAPTER FOUR

CONSUMABLES USED IN NFT

NUTRIENTS

The recirculating nutrient solution used in NFT must contain all the elements essential to plant growth. Although plants grown in experiments have been found to take up, and apparently to use, a great number of elements including some quite rare metals, it is generally agreed that the elements required in a nutrient solution are:— Nitrogen (N), potassium (K), phosphorus (P), calcium (Ca), magnesium (Mg), iron (Fe), manganese (Mn), copper (Cu), boron (B), molybdenum (Mo) and zinc (Zn). Two other elements are generally understood to be essential: these are sulphur (S) and chlorine (Cl) but these are always present in the water supply or are added coincidentally with the salts used to provide the eleven essentials listed above. Note that the list of essential elements comprising the ingredients of an NFT nutrient solution is entirely mundane. Contrary to widespread belief there is no secret growth stimulating ingredient.

Concentration of Essential Elements in Nutrient Solutions:

It is a feature of successful NFT that the nutrient solution contains an excess of all essential elements and yet the total solution concentration remains below the level at which unacceptable interference with water uptake occurs. In this state, what is a desirable composition of the solution? Fortunately the composition of the nutrient solution need not be at all exact. Table 1 gives the suggested range of values for individual nutrients, together with two common contaminents.

Table 1. Nutrient concentrations for tomatoes in nutrient film culture.

©Crown Copyright 1987

Element	*Concentration (mg/litre)*		
	Minimum	*Optimum*	*Maximum*
NO_3-N	50	150-200	300
P	20	50	200
K	50	300-500	800
Ca	125	150-300	400
Mg	25	50	100
Fe	3	6	12
Mn	0.5	1	2.5
Cu	0.05	0.1	1
Zn	0.05	0.1	2.5
B	0.1	0.3-0.5	1.5
Mo	0.01	0.05	0.1
Na	—	—	250
Cl	—	—	400

The figures demonstrate the remarkable flexibility of NFT nutrition and should allay all fears of experiencing on-site difficulty in producing and maintaining a vital solution. Incidentally if nutrient solutions using soft water were made up exactly as listed in the three columns the resulting solutions would have conductivity values of approximately 6, 20 and 50 respectively.

Features of NFT Nutrients

In producing nutrient solutions many chemical compounds have been used. Experience has elucidated some areas of special interest in nutrient formulation.

Source of nitrogen

Nitrogen may be supplied in two forms, ammoniacal nitrogen (NH4) nitrogen or nitrate nitrogen (NO_3 nitrogen). It is recommended that NH4 nitrogen should not supply in excess of 15% of the total nitrogen because higher levels have been implicated in a number of disorders including stem base rot and blossom end rot of tomatoes. It is unfortunate that this is the case because NH4 nitrogen is particularly inexpensive and because it has a useful capacity to neutralise hard water.

NO_3 nitrogen is commonly supplied in two compounds namely calcium nitrate and potassium nitrate. Calcium nitrate is particularly useful in soft water areas supplying as it does both calcium and nitrogen in approximately equal ratio. Potassium nitrate supplies both potassium and nitrogen but it is heavily loaded in supply of the former and therefore in practice convenient formulations, both for hard and soft water, generally use calcium nitrate to supply a sizeable proportion of total nitrogen. Calcium nitrate is available in a range of grades. Originally technical grade calcium nitrate was specified. This is more or less free of ammonium nitrate impurity. Agricultural grade calcium nitrate contains quite significant amounts of ammonium nitrate, together with other impurities and is generally regarded as unsuitable for NFT work. Nowadays hydroponic or "glasshouse" grade calcium nitrate is specially manufactured. It contains up to 2% ammonium nitrate and is considered ideal for all NFT work except in extremely soft water areas where one option to counterbalance acidity is to use only technical grade calcium nitrate.

Source of phosphorus

Phosphorus may be supplied from phosphate rich inorganic components of the nutrient mix or it may be supplied directly to the circulating nutrient solution in the form of phosphoric acid when it is used to adjust the solution pH. Of course, phosphorus may also be supplied concurrently from both sources.

Clearly the extent to which phosphorus can be supplied from acid additions alone depends on the volume of acid used in pH adjustment. In soft water areas insufficient acid is used to satisfy the phosphorus needs of plants growing in the resulting solution, but in hardwater areas there is no doubt that phosphoric acid addition alone is a reliable source of all phosphorus requirements. Accordingly it is appropriate to use nutrient formulations not containing inorganic phosphate when using also hardwater supplies and in conjunction with using phosphoric acid for pH adjustment. The advantage of doing so is largely one of economics since inorganic phosphate sources may cost up to one third of the total nutrient mix costs. However, there is also some evidence suggesting that continually rising levels of phosphate in the nutrient solution deleteriously affect the growth of plants. This situation might occur when phosphate rich nutrients and phosphoric acid are being used in a hardwater area. Of more importance is the influence of the excess phosphorus on the solution conductivity which could lead to low nutrient levels being masked by satisfactory conductivity readings. These matters should not unduly concern the small scale user of NFT since both influences are corrected by changing the nutrient solution as suggested in the later text. Incidentally, the rate of 70% phosphoric acid usage for pH adjustment which coincidentally provides all phosphorus requirements is generally put at around 175 ml/1000 litres of water.

Source of iron (Fe)

A number of inorganic sources of iron are available including ferrous sulphate and ferric ammonium citrate, but these are not recommended because the iron they contain may be converted in the solution to a form which cannot be taken up by plants. Instead chelated iron, usually in the form of EDTA iron, is almost universally used. Chelation is the binding of the metal to an organic compound. The rusty nail technique of providing iron, apparently so primitive, has in fact more to recommend it than using other non-organic sources. This is because inorganic iron is continually being released from the nail, consequently some is always available to the plants before it becomes bound.

Two component formulation

In theory it is perfectly possible for the required weight of each of the individual chemical components to be added directly to the circulating water in order to make up the complete nutrient solution. This approach, however, is entirely impractical. Instead the dry chemical compounds of the nutrient formulation are usually mixed together in the correct ratio to produce a concentrated dry powder mix. All that is required to charge any NFT system with nutrients is simply to add an appropriate weight of the concentrated dry powder mix. In practice even this weighing may be avoided if the dry powder mix is made up into a concentrated stock solution so that dosing becomes a matter of adding a small volume from the stock solution to the circulating water. If the nutrient mix is made up "on-site" i.e. D.I.Y. then the individual dry chemical components may of course be added directly to the stock solution water.

The use of stock solutions introduces the potential problem of components of the nutrient mix reacting one with another to form insoluble precipitates which are useless to plants. The main potential culprits are calcium nitrate and magnesium sulphate which readily react together, but phosphates too are in danger of being precipitated as calcium phosphate and there are other possible reactions. To prevent this risk NFT nutrients are mixed in two components normally described as nutrient 'A' and nutrient 'B'. Nutrient A contains only calcium nitrate and possibly also EDTA Fe. Nutrient B contains the remaining ingredients including the EDTA Fe if this is not included in A. This two component formulation, as well as preventing precipitation problems, has the major attraction of separating a large proportion of the nitrogen (N) from the whole of the potassium (K) thereby facilitating the easy adjustment of the K/N ratio in the nutrient solution. This facility is used to great advantage in advanced NFT to improve flavour and control foliage growth.

Common Compounds Used in Formulating NFT Nutrient Mixes

From the large number of possible compounds used to formulate NFT solutions some are in widespread use. These are shown in Table 2.

Table 2. The nutrient content (%) of some salts used in hydroponic systems, together with the weight of each salt required to supply unit weight of nutrient*.

©The Institute of Horticultural Research

Salt	*Element*	*% nutrient*	*Weight of salt per unit weight of nutrient*
Calcium nitrate	Ca	17.0	5.89
Calcium nitrate	N	11.9	8.44
Ammonium nitrate	N	35.0	2.86
Potassium nitrate	K	38.7	2.59
Potassium nitrate	N	13.8	7.22
Potassium sulphate	K	44.9	2.23
Potassium sulphate	S	18.4	5.43
Potassium dihydrogen phosphate	K	28.7	3.45

Table 2. *(Continued).*

Salt	*Element*	*% nutrient*	*Weight of salt per unit weight of nutrient*
Potassium dihydrogen phosphate	P	22.8	4.39
Ammonium dihydrogen phosphate	N	12.2	8.21
Ammonium dihydrogen phosphate	P	27.0	3.71
Magnesium sulphate	Mg	9.9	10.14
Magnesium sulphate	S	13.0	7.68
Manganese sulphate	Mn	24.6	4.06
Boric acid	B	17.5	5.72
Copper sulphate	Cu	25.5	3.93
Zinc sulphate	Zn	22.7	4.40
Ammonium molybdate	Mo	54.4	1.84
IronEDTA	Fe	15.2	6.58

*i.e., g salt required to supply 1 g nutrient or lb salt required to supply 1 lb nutrient.

The values listed are for the pure compound. Corrections should be applied where the declared analysis of a commercial fertiliser differs appreciably from that of the pure salt. This particularly applies to certain commercial samples of 'calcium nitrate', which contain a proportion of ammonium nitrate and may have up to 15.5% N. Chelated iron compounds generally contain less than the theoretical content of iron, and the relevant content should be ascertained from the supplier.

The column ''weight of salt per unit weight of nutrient'' provides useful information for D.I.Y. nutrient formulation since figures from this column can be used directly to calculate the required amount of compound to provide a particular quantity of nutrient. For example:—

1g calcium (Ca) is provided by 5.89g of calcium nitrate. Therefore to provide 200 mg/litre Ca in 1000 litres of water the following calculation is used:—

200mg × 1000 = 200,000mg or 200g = total amount of Ca required.

200g × 5.89 = 1178g = total weight of compound required.

Note: This quantity of calcium nitrate will also provide nitrogen (N). How much N can also be calculated from the table. viz:—

1178g ÷ 8.44 = 139.6gN

139.6gN in 1000 litres = 139600mg in 1000 litres = 139.6 (say 140) mg. per litre.

Obtaining NFT Nutrients

It is clear that whilst there is nothing complicated or secret about NFT nutrient mixes it is essential that they are formulated correctly. Accordingly, in most circumstances it would be foolhardy to use in NFT any nutrient mix not specifically formulated for NFT and not declared as such. In practice obtaining NFT nutrient mixes boils down to a simple choice between using a properly formulated manufactured product or making up the nutrient mixes oneself. There are compelling reasons why using manufacturers mixes is the obvious choice, the chief of these being large savings in cost coupled with greater convenience.

Manufactured mixes

Manufactured mixes may vary somewhat in nutrient content on account of the formulation. For example, mixes may be tailored for hardwater use only. Such specificity should be indicated on the declaration. It is most important to ascertain the type of acid for which the nutrient is formulated. Other points of interest include the sources of trace elements. Some or all of these, like the iron, may be supplied in organic chelated form.

D.I.Y. nutrient mixes

It is perfectly possible for anyone with none but the least knowledge of chemistry to make up perfectly acceptable NFT nutrient mixes. What is required is a good level of methodology, some patience and normally access to fine scales. Nutrient mixes may be made up in accordance with published formulations or they may be calculated to satisfy particular requirements. Two commonly used formulations adapted from information produced by the U.K. Ministry of Agriculture are:—

1. For soft water use.

Stock Solution A.	To 25 litres water add:—	
	Calcium nitrate	2.42kg
Stock Solution B.	To 25 litres water add:—	
	Potassium nitrate	1.53kg
	Potassium dihydrogen phosphate	0.55kg
	Magnesium sulphate	1.27kg
	EDTA iron	75g
	Manganese sulphate	10g
	Boric acid	6g
	Copper sulphate	2g
	Zinc sulphate	1g
	Ammonium molybdate	0.25g

Use in conjunction with phosphoric acid for pH adjustment (if necessary).

2. For hardwater use.

Stock Solution A.	To 25 litres water add:—	
	Calcium nitrate	1.20kg
	Ammonium nitrate	60g
	(or 80g if chemically pure calcium nitrate is used)	
Stock Solution B.	To 25 litres water add:—	
	Potassium nitrate	2.59kg
	Magnesium sulphate	1.27kg
	EDTA iron	75g
	Manganese sulphate	10g
	Boric acid	6g
	Copper sulphate	2g
	Zinc sulphate	1g
	Ammonium molybdate	0.25g

Use in conjunction with phosphoric acid for pH adjustment.

Supplies of individual nutrient compounds may be had from a variety of sources. The main problem is scale of purchase. Several components including calcium nitrate, potassium nitrate and magnesium sulphate are fairly widely used as agricultural/horticultural fertilizers but the available bag sizes, reflecting this usage, are usually too large for the small scale NFT user to contemplate. Instead most chemists will be able to supply reasonably small quantities of all the compounds required though the unit cost is likely to be high. EDTA iron may be obtained as iron sequestrene when some declaration as to the quantity of iron it contains should be sought as this is extremely variable. Alternative sources of iron and other trace elements are mixes of chelated compounds which are used in agriculture and horticulture. Specialist fertilizer suppliers may be able to assist, as indeed may specialist NFT suppliers.

Organic Alternatives

The possibility of using organic sources of nutrients in NFT has been examined. There appears to be two basic concepts. Firstly, using a raw abundant organic material, suitably diluted, as the nutrient solution. An example of such a material is pig slurry. Secondly, "manufacturing" a nutrient mix from organic material. There is no overriding reason why either of these options should not work even if the results in terms of yield are likely to be lower than might reasonably be obtained using inorganic nutrient mixes.

In the case of using diluted raw organic material, it is probable that the most satisfactory results may be obtained only if the solution is fortified with elements missing or deficient. There is also a danger of contamination especially with heavy metals but conceivable also with known pathogenic organisms. For these reasons this approach is likely to be appropriate only to large scale enterprises where analysis facilities can be justified.

"Manufactured" organic nutrient mixes may be made up entirely from locally obtainable organic matter or instead a proprietory concentrated product may be used. In the latter case it may be desirable to reinforce the nutrients, particularly the trace elements, from a good organic source, one such being the leaves of the comfrey plant. The method by which organic matter is converted into a nutrient mix is rather imprecise, which may not be a bad thing. Ordinarily this would involve steeping organic material in water for several weeks. Certainly this is the technique used by the leading practitioners of the use of such nutrient mixes, namely the Small Farms Association at their Home Farm headquarters.

Regarding the method by which the "manufactured" nutrient mix is added to the circulating water. Here again practice has been rather hit and miss but I am confident that because of the variable strength of such mixes the conductivity based method of nutrition, i.e. using a conductivity meter, is the obvious approach irrespective of the scale of enterprise.

ACID

Two acids have been used in NFT systems. One, nitric acid, whilst quite suitable for use with certain nutrient formulations, is quite unsuitable for home and garden use. Nitric acid is a fuming, noxious and highly inflammable liquid the least spillage being capable of causing grievous injury.

The second, phosphoric acid, is relatively innocuous, but like all acids it should be handled with caution. All spillages should be washed down with large volumes of water. All contact with the skin should be avoided. Contact with the eyes is dangerous, wash copiously with water and seek medical attention as soon as possible. Keep phosphoric acid out of the reach of children and store in suitable, marked containers. Note that this advice is very similar to that offered with many household cleaning and sterilising chemicals. Sometimes it is desirable to use diluted acid solutions. Here take concentrated acid and add to the water. Never add water to acid.

Supplies of phosphoric acid can be had from chemists, where it may be necessary to order in advance, and from specialist NFT suppliers. Be careful when comparing prices that concentrations are comparable. Clearly 70% phosphoric acid is better value than 50% if the price is the same. In fact the concentration is sometimes given as the specific gravity (s.g.). As a guide 70% phosphoric acid has a s.g. of 1.7 whilst 50% has a s.g. of 1.5. Incidentally these figures show that concentrated phosphoric acid is nearly twice as heavy as the same volume of water. If the supply you obtain does not seem much heavier than the equivalent container of water you can assume it is quite dilute.

How much phosphoric acid is required? Well, an accurate figure can be found if a sample of the water to be used in the NFT system is taken for laboratory test to determine the amount of acid required to neutralise the alkalinity. Fortunately this trouble and expense is unnecessary, useful guide figures are:— Soft water or rainwater, less than 125 ml 70% phosphoric acid per 15 tomato plants or equivalent growing area, per season. Hard water areas about 250 ml 70% phosphoric acid for the same area. The figures given will be subject to variation on account of differences in water quality and the neutralising value, if any, of the nutrients added. However the amount of acid used is normally sufficiently low so as not to add appreciably to running costs.

TESTING pH OF THE SOLUTION

Acid is added to the nutrient solution to make the solution more acidic. To do this job accurately we require a method of testing the pH of the solution. First, what is pH and how does it relate to acidity? The pH scale is from 1-14, pH 7 is neutral, i.e. neither acid nor alkaline, values progressively higher than 7 are more and more alkaline and those progressively lower than 7 are more and more acid. Most soils are in the range 5.5 to 7.5 and for NFT purposes the best pH is generally agreed to be between 6 and 6.5 and this means that it is usual to add acid to the nutrient solution because most water supplies are a little higher value, usually in the range 6.5-7.5

The pH scale 1-14 represents a range of acidity and alkalinity which is really quite enormous. From the figures above it is clear we are primarily concerned with the area about the middle of the range i.e. from mildly acid through neutral to mildly alkaline. Accordingly whatever means is used to check pH it should be active and accurate in this area. Fortunately this around neutral area is also the most important to a variety of everyday activities and it is not surprising then that there are available quite a number of pH test kits. Sources include aquarium and brewing stores, together with school and laboratory suppliers. These kits work on the colour comparison method whereby a test solution is made up according to instructions and the resultant colour is compared with a standard colour chart provided to indicate pH value.

Suitable test kits should show a decisive colour change at or around the pH which the NFT system will be operated. They should also be quick, easy and inexpensive as they will be used regularly.

The most common alternative to liquid colour comparison tests are colour test strips which only need to be immersed briefly in the solution. The strip colour indicates pH. Experience suggests these are more suited to laboratory work in good dry conditions than to damp greenhouse conditions which tends to partly activate the strip before immersion.

SPREADER MAT

Spreader mat is a thin material placed in the base of the NFT channel and its sole function is to spread the nutrient solution over the base of the channel. This ensures that all plants on being placed in the channel receive the nutrient stream. This problem of solution interception arises only with young transplants into NFT. If spreader mat is not used the nutrient solution tends to form narrow rivulets when flowing over clean plastic surfaces and these rivulets may well pass by the transplants. Although mat placed in the channel may indeed spread the nutrient solution by capillary action there is a need to avoid confusion with capillary mat used for bench watering systems and therefore from an early stage in NFT development the term "spreader mat" has been used.

The best spreader mats are made of non-bonded fibres. If a bonded fibre mat is used it is possible the glue may be phytotoxic. Instead the fibres may be woven or heat bonded. The most widely used materials are man made fibres especially polyester, nylon, polypropylene and glassfibre. Not all formulations of these materials are hydrophillic. Accordingly it is wise to check before purchase that the material will accept water when placed on a flat surface. Only very lightweight fabrics are required, usually about 50 grams/sq. meter. If heavier gauge material is used, such as conventional capillary mat, two problems are possible. Firstly, the plant root axes develop under the mat and subsequently become oxygen starved when the mat becomes impenetrable to air as a result of waterlogging or the deposit of particles from the solution. Secondly, the mat may act as a surface upon which nutrient and other salts in the solution may precipitate i.e. form solids. This often occurs in hardwater areas. The deposits impede air penetration. Of course light-weight mats are much less expensive than heavier mats and this is most important in keeping NFT running costs as low as possible.

Spreader mats are most often used in widths approaching the base dimensions of the channel. If wide channels are employed parallel strips of mat may be required. The most common width available is 200 mm and this is ideal for single rows of larger plants whilst it will also fit, but less comfortably, in narrower base channels. Narrower and wider spreader mats are produced but do not seem to be so widely distributed. As an alternative to running spreader mat along the length of the channel, sometimes short lengths of mat are placed across the channel effecting complete interception but using rather less material.

Where there is a raised centre section to a channel on which the propagation block is placed, and to which it is necessary to draw up the solution from streams passing on either side, a heavier gauge of mat is required which has greater capillary action. There is no need to purchase a special mat for this purpose, simply use several thicknesses of lightweight mat.

Spreader mats of the type described are not broken down during the growth of the plants though they are usually fully penetrated by the root system and are definitely not recoverable. However the mats are not so strong that they cannot be broken away when a plant is removed. This is a good feature because it allows successive plantings into small vacant areas, often of just one plant space. Sometimes a small piece of spreader mat is placed in the position before a new transplant is set out. In other cases there is no need to place spreader mat prior to setting out either, because the site into which the plant is to go is moist, or because the root mat of an adjacent plant acts as a spreader mat upon which it is quite in order to set out a new plant. Occasionally a short lived spreader mat may be prefered. One circumstance is in the production of grass from cereal grains when the entire mass, roots and all, is fed to animals. Here it may be possible to proceed without any mat but otherwise a digestible mat of cellulosic fibre would be employed. A possible problem with degradable mats is blockage of channels, pipework and pump with debris. Finally, a heart-felt word of caution; under no circumstances feed animals with feedstuff containing indigestible spreader mat. This is likely to cause dreadful pain and agonising death.

CHAPTER FIVE

DESIGNING SYSTEMS

Once it has been decided to institute a venture into NFT, certain practical questions relating to the proposed system design and fitment constantly arise. It is useful to deal with these matters directly.

ELECTRICAL SAFETY

The majority of NFT units consume mains voltage electricity. The electrical supply to the site and the electrical appliances used, such as pumps and heaters, should be safe and competently fitted. This is clearly true of any situation where mains electricity is used. The question which needs posing is:— are there any special electrical safety risks associated with using NFT? Strictly the answer is no because NFT does not constitute a unique or peculiar use electricity. However, the reality is that NFT is often associated with, and may contribute to, an environment of increased risk of electrical shock from a faulty supply or appliance. This is because in plant growing areas thc atmosphere tends to have a high humidity, because floor surfaces may be damp and because materials used in the construction and processes within may be highly conductive to electricity, for example, aluminium and water.

In the U.K. there are electrical safety regulations which specify that when a new electrical supply is connected to an area of increased risk, such as the greenhouse, then additional safety must be provided by the fitment of an automatic circuit breaker. Where an electrical supply is proposed or where it has recently been connected to a plant growing area, then it is probable that the appropriate safety provision has been made. If this information is not known for certain it can do no harm to check that this is so.

In the case of older installations, there is much to recommend that when new equipment, such as an NFT system, is installed then at the same time the electrical supply may be improved to comply with modern standards. Generally the cost of doing this is not out of proportion to the cost of installing a properly designed NFT system.

Where a very small NFT system is proposed, it may be that improving the safety standard of the electrical supply would incur costs out of proportion to all possible gain and mitigate against the project. In this case an automatic circuit breaker can be purchased for use between the socket of the mains supply, and the plug, of the NFT equipment. This device is very inexpensive and widely available. It is most usually advertised as suitable for making safe the electrical supply to lawn mowers, cement mixers and the like. Alternatively, small scale NFT systems lend themselves to designs which do not require on-site mains electricity such as the use of the air-lift pumping system.

Finally if there is any doubt about the safety of an electrical supply or appliance do not use the equipment until a qualified person has been consulted.

TRIAL SYSTEMS

Is it useful to set up a trial system? By no means is a trial a pre-requisite of a successful unit, but there are good reasons why a trial makes sense. Firstly, because one cannot be sure, certainly from reading but also from observing the experiences of others that the possible benefits of NFT would be realised under a particular set of conditions. Secondly, because some work and expense is necessarily involved and it is prudent to examine opportunities by which this may be reduced or scheduled. Finally, because it might be convenient and easy to set up a trial NFT system on a small site when the ultimate planned point of use would be on a different site where the expense and work of introducing a trial would be out of proportion. Examples of this last situation include, where mains electricity is unavailable at the preferred site so a trial is set up elsewhere to ascertain whether it would be worthwhile introducing electricity, or if a new greenhouse was being planned when it is useful to evaluate NFT in the old greenhouse so as to simplify and quantify future requirements.

Whatever the reasons for introducing a trial the practicalities of installation allow for a convenient division. On the one hand are trial systems so large as to make design decisions entirely synonymous with those for any NFT system whatever its purpose. On the other hand, and of immediate interest, are those trials where materials, equipment and design, are influenced by the fact that it is a trial.

Purpose constructed NFT kits supplied from specialist manufacturers provide one easy method of introduction to NFT. The advantages for the trialist include convenience and some degree of confidence in the materials and construction together with the help and assistance of instructional literature. The alternative is to construct an NFT trial system from component materials, but is it worthwhile considering a subsequent possible expansion when choosing equipment for the trial? Except in the case where the expansion would merely be a small extension to the trial the answer is generally no. Here is why.

The circulation tank used for the trial system may be equally useful in a limited expansion because volume can be added to the system by siting a second tank at any convenient place (see page 68) but if the expansion was large then there would be no or minimal cost savings in trying to employ the original tank in the same job, though it may well be put to good use elsewhere, e.g: for holding a nutrient stock solution.

In the case of the pump it is possible that a slightly larger than adequate model for the trial would also suffice for an extension. More likely the pump would not give adequate output and to purchase the larger unit for the trial would involve considerable expense. Additionally the original pump may serve as a back-up pump in the larger unit, providing cover against failure of the main pump.

Pipework, fittings and channel supports are likely to be of use in an expansion even should it be necessary to re-arrange them. Essential work which clearly should not be underspecified on setting up a trial, includes such as pipework under permanent pathways and, in most cases, any electrical or water supply installation.

D.I.Y. OR 'OFF THE SHELF'

Many of the various materials and items of equipment which comprise a complete NFT system have been described in detail but they must be purchased economically and fitted competently. Are NFT kits a sensible option? They certainly are on some sites and circumstances.

A compelling reason for considering an NFT kit is convenience. It is simply a lot less trouble to purchase one lot of goods and it is doubly convenient if the kit is itself semi-assembled or easy to install. Kits may be the only method by which the elderly and infirm, the busy housewife, or persons with so many other things to do, can effectively introduce NFT.

Then there is the question of handiness. Clearly a certain level of constructive ability is necessary to be successful in using brought in materials. Often they need to be cut to size, or joined, or fixed either level, or on a slope. Some tools may be required such as an electric drill, a saw or spade. To some people the work is easy and enjoyable, to others quite out of the question. It is probably much more preferable to buy in an NFT kit than either do the work of construction and installation poorly or bring in a handyman to do the job.

Size of proposed installation is important. Clearly if a large area is to be converted to NFT a kit will not be available whilst if it is only a small area a kit may be ideal having advantages in ease of installation, economy of running and probably price economy too. What of the middle ground? At what size do kits become uneconomic. Notwithstanding considerations of handiness and convenience, the middle ground is probably between 3 metres and 5 metres of channel. If a single channel can grow a double row of plants this is a space equivalent to 3 to 5 square metres. Below this size NFT kits will probably be advantageously employed, except where some on-hand materials are available or can be obtained at highly competitive cost. Sometimes a site on which it is proposed to install NFT has awkward characteristics, being perhaps doglegged or right angled in shape. These may best be considered as two or more rectangular areas each quite small and accordingly very suitable for the introduction of a kit. The same applies to split level NFT. Here a single pump servicing the whole unit may be inordinately expensive and incur high running costs. If the levels are converted separately each may conveniently take an NFT kit.

Aesthetic appeal may be an important consideration especially in home or near home use, e.g., porches, conservatories and on window ledges. In offices and shops too, it is often not good enough to construct a NFT growing unit of bits and pieces. In these cases a well designed, nicely presented NFT system sold as a kit would have distinct advantages. On some other sites it may be physically impossible to fit an NFT system with the usual layout, that is, with a sunken circulation tank, an alternative method of accommodating the solution which may be an embodiment of an NFT kit, would be necessary.

The case for the use of "off the shelf" kits as trial units is very sound, often enabling a prospective NFT grower to introduce NFT rapidly, perhaps even saving a season. Subsequently it may be possible to utilise some kit components in a larger unit, but alternatively the kit may be kept on for further trials. In fact a large application of NFT kits is in trial and research work. Here, the manufacturers special skills would be undoubted benefits, saving the time of specialist staff and very likely considerable expense. Note also that some experimental work may be very much easier to perform in an NFT system than using conventional equipment or growing methods. For educational use and for temporary site use NFT kits would appear to have large advantages.

Where an NFT kit may be considered it is essential to ensure that the proposed kit meets all the basic requirements of a successful NFT unit. It should have at least the minimum tank capacity to plant capacity ratio. Some kits are not supplied with a pump whilst others may require work on constructing a slope, others may be complete in all respects.

SINGLE OR MULTIPLE NFT UNITS

Commercially large areas of NFT cultivation are serviced from a single circulation tank, but it does not follow that this should be the case for smaller areas. In fact, even the large grower generally breaks his holding into a number of convenient to manage units each a maximum of 0.25 hectares (½ acre) or thereabouts. Clearly small commercial growers, semi-commercial growers and private gardener growers of monocrops would be generally advised to introduce a single NFT unit provided that the proposed unit was conveniently sited and shaped. In many other circumstances there is a strong case for introducing multiples of units. Since there is no doubt that a wide range of diverse plants can be grown successfully in the same nutrient solution this advice may appear rather surprising. What factors support the argument for multiple units?

Practical considerations are utmost, of these running costs are often paramount. Accordingly where an area to be devoted to NFT involves two or more levels, then savings in pump running costs can be obtained by introducing two or more units each with a minimum of solution lift requirements, whereas a single unit would necessitate a pump with significantly added lift. A common example is ground bed and bench systems in the same greenhouse.

Another situation best served by two units would be when it is proposed to grow plants of differing root zone temperature requirements. Here it is generally uneconomic to heat the solution for heat responsive plants and supply the same heated solution to plants not requiring, or not economically responding, to the heat.

General cultural requirements of various plants do not usually influence the decision of number of units, but the advantage to be had from the ability to vary the concentration and composition of the nutrient solution certainly does. Details of relevant solution changes are given elsewhere (see Chapter 8) suffice it here to summarise with the general advice that if a wide range of plants is to be grown it may be advantageous to introduce two or more NFT units.

A key factor in any decision to employ more than one unit is the effect of scale. If the proposed NFT area was really quite small there is probably no economic advantage in multiplying self constructed systems, though it would certainly be possible to do so. In these cases manufactured kits might be advantageously deployed. Where a larger conversion to NFT is envisaged there is generally very little increase in total installation costs on dividing the area into more than one system. On certain sites there may even be cost savings, e.g. where intricate or long pipework would be necessary to connect up a single system. Additionally, as in the case of two small circulation tanks replacing one large one, there may be significant labour savings on installation.

Sometimes it is advantageous if a single unit is installed where two or more might at first sight be considered more appropriate. One example is outside (in the UK) NFT systems which are probably best constructed as summer appendages to permanent greenhouse installations. Another case involves DC pumping systems. These systems necessarily involve specialist control equipment but the pumps employed have excellent lift relative to output, a common feature of DC pumps. Therefore one circulation tank and pumping gear set-up may best supply as large an area as possible even to quite distant channels such as in two separate greenhouses.

NUMBERS OF CHANNELS

It is useful and convenient, once again, to examine practice on large commercial sites, this time for guidance as to the number of channels to be provided. Generally one channel of suitable base width for the crop is allowed for each row at normal row distances. Smaller users of NFT can confidently adopt the same practice which makes for easy design and reduces the work in training long stemmed plants. However there is no necessity to do so. An immediate exception is where the normal row is interrupted by stanchions or other obstructions, a fairly common situation in old style wider greenhouses. Here there is no necessity to provide a channel but instead the plants which are to occupy the interrupted row air space are set out in an adjacent channel and simply trained into the correct position. An illustration of this situation is shown in Figure 5/1. It is likely that the plants could be accommodated in the usual channel but it may be appropriate to increase the base width if there is any doubt e.g. from 225mm to 300mm. Clearly this technique applies only to long stemmed plants. With untrainable plants it is generally uneconomic to provide NFT channels between stanchions and this is certainly a possible objection to conversion to NFT, especially where the problem occurs several times in the same greenhouse, though the option to make pathways adjacent with the stanchions may be available.

The method by which two rows of plants can be accommodated in a single channel is equally well employed in the smaller NFT unit. It is a common feature of manufactured NFT kits. Also, remember that it is the air space illumination requirements of the plants which normally determine the row distances. Incidentally, little or no saving in pump capacity can be had by the widespread adoption of double planting on any site since it is usual to maintain flow rate commensurate with the "true" row number.

Fig. 5/1 Awkward spaces may be utilised by double planting in adjacent channels

Small plants are conveniently grown in multiduct channels which allow plantings at normal row distances. A multiduct of about 1 metre wide allows access from a side pathway since this width is around the maximum an ordinary person can reach over. On larger sites two rows of multiducts can be placed side by side forming a wide bed. Access being from pathways at each side. These beds can be multiplied up where space permits. Figure 5/2 shows this arrangement.

Note that at good working height (66-76cm) it is much easier to reach across channels than it is at ground level and therefore it is usual to allow for somewhat less reach over ground channels. Irrespective of bench or ground arrangement pathways of less than 37cm are not usually employed, though single harvest lettuce growers may make do with much less.

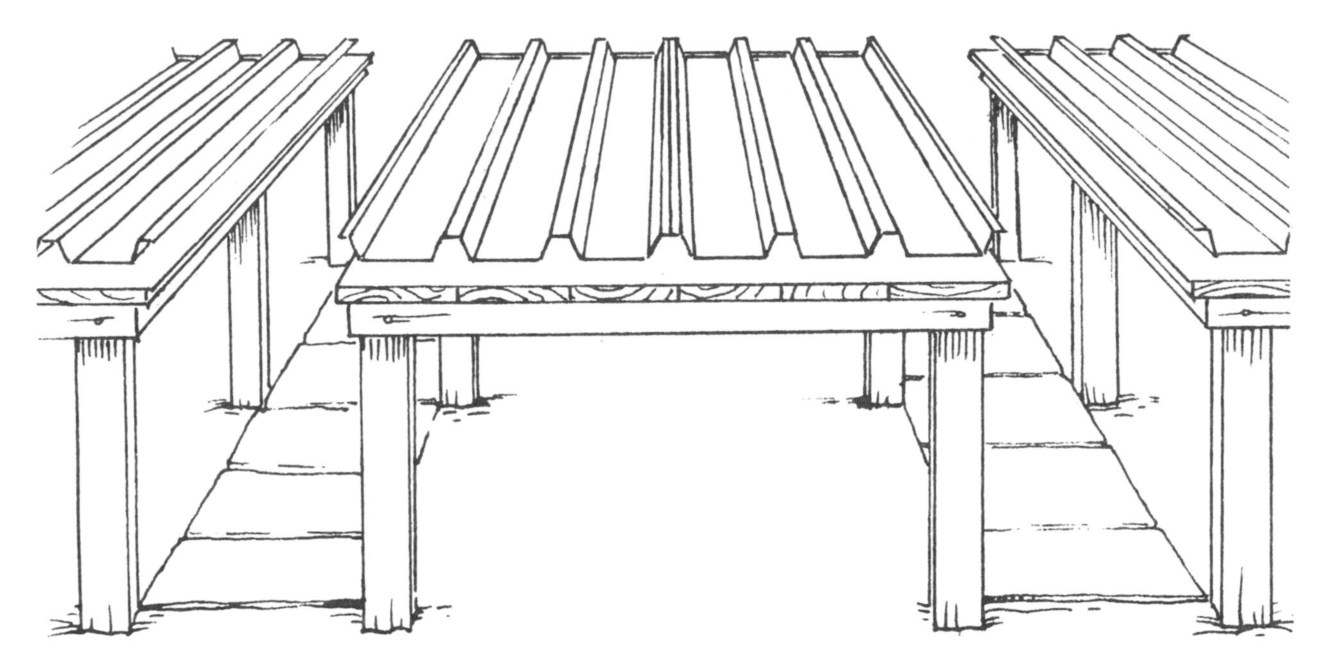

Fig. 5/2 Multiduct sheets placed side by side to form a wide bed

What of mixed plantings? How are these to be accommodated? Provided the channel base width is adequate for large plants, smaller plants can always be accommodated, if necessary in two or three staggered rows as illustrated in Figure 5/3.

Fig. 5/3 Mixed planting in a multiduct tray

To allow for this flexibility of planting, multiduct trays are popular with private gardeners, but note that in many cases there is no significant increase in plant capacity in fitting one 1 metre wide multiduct as opposed to 2 channels of base width 250mm or 300mm. In fact this latter has advantages, firstly, because on the ground, it provides good foot space between the channels and secondly, because any space not occupied by the foliage of plants growing in NFT can be used to place pot plants or seed trays etc., which might otherwise be difficult to accommodate. There is no doubt that for the general interest private gardener it rarely pays to cover the entire ground space with channels. The same arguments can be applied to bench systems but here the balance of advantage probably still lies with the complete covering multiduct.

Finally, on all but the smallest sites it is generally fairly straightforward to re-arrange channels from season to season to suit different plants and experience. Of course this does not apply to permanent channels such as those made in concrete and this indeed is one good reason why the technique is not popular with small scale users of NFT.

SITE OF CIRCULATION TANK

Whichever method of pumping is employed the circulation tank is the lowest placed component of any NFT system. As well as contributing to the smooth running of the circulating solution the site of the circulation tank often determines the direction of flow in the channels. It is usually important to have good access at all times to the circulation tank.

Often there is no difficulty in determining the correct site of the circulation tank. On most sites it will fit comfortably at the furthest end of the central pathway giving excellent access but yet not being a hazard. This arrangement normally ensures that only the solution supply tube would need to cross pathways and this is satisfactory because the supply tube, under pressure, can be taken in any direction e.g. under paving slabs. The return pipework flowing under gravity alone is restricted in direction. Also, the extra rigidity and size of the return pipework mitigates against complicating its route.

Small variations in the preferred placement are frequently adopted. A common case is where the central pathway may be a thoroughfare whence the tank would need to be sunk lower than absolutely necessary for NFT purposes in order that a bridge could be laid across. This arrangement is often unsatisfactory because deep sunken tanks are more difficult to access and because of the work and difficulty of the extra excavation. Instead, it is better to shift the site to the end of another pathway, or to one side and underneath a channel adjacent to the central pathway as shown in Figure 5/4. In this case the channel above the tank will most likely discharge directly into it.

Sometimes, to take advantage of a natural slope running towards the entrance of the unit the circulation tank should be situated at the entry end. In this case the tank would almost certainly be inconvenient if placed in the pathway but the arrangement above would be quite appropriate.

Very long runs of NFT channel are not encouraged. They generate heat gradients in the channel and they can slow down the speed of circulation. They also involve loss of headroom because the slope, at 1:50, becomes a significant height at the inlet end. To overcome these problems the circulation tank may be situated centrally thereby halving the channel length. In this case it is usual for the supply tube to branch to each end of the unit while the return pipework collects across the centre. Figure 5/5 illustrates this arrangement. Situations where this arrangement might be especially appropriate include all sites over 20 metres long and low greenhouses where loss of headroom should be avoided.

Combined tank/return ducts and trenches should be sited as far as possible distal to main entries and pathways. However should a natural slope dictate otherwise placement

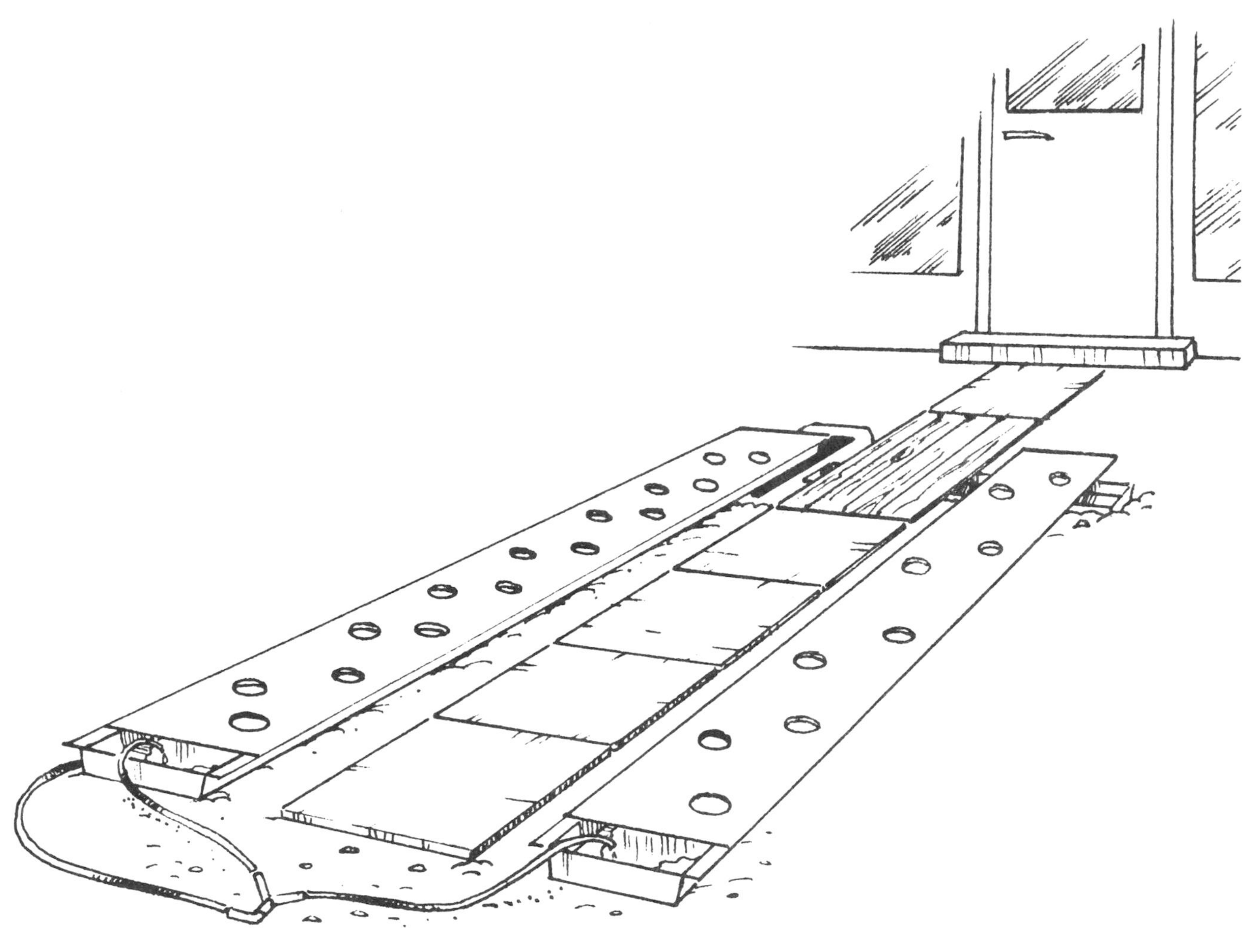

Fig. 5/4 Bridging a return duct as it intersects a pathway

at the inlet end should not prove a problem because these tanks are usually narrow and shallow making reliable bridges quite easy to construct.

Bench style NFT systems conveniently take the circulation tank under the bench, perhaps slightly protruding into the pathway so that good access is provided. Sometimes it will be necessary to make a limited excavation to accommodate the tank under the bench.

TANK PLACEMENT

It is generally preferred if the sides of circulation tanks sunk into excavations stand a little proud of the surrounding ground as this prevents much accidental ingress of dirt and debris. Normally the outlet end of the channels would be at, or a little above ground level and the return pipe or duct would be at, or a little below, ground level. Return entry to the circulation tank would be through the sides. This preferred arrangement is shown in Figure 5/6 but it is by no means universally adopted. Tanks placed under benches should be raised on blocks, where appropriate, so that the minimum of solution lift for the pump is contrived.

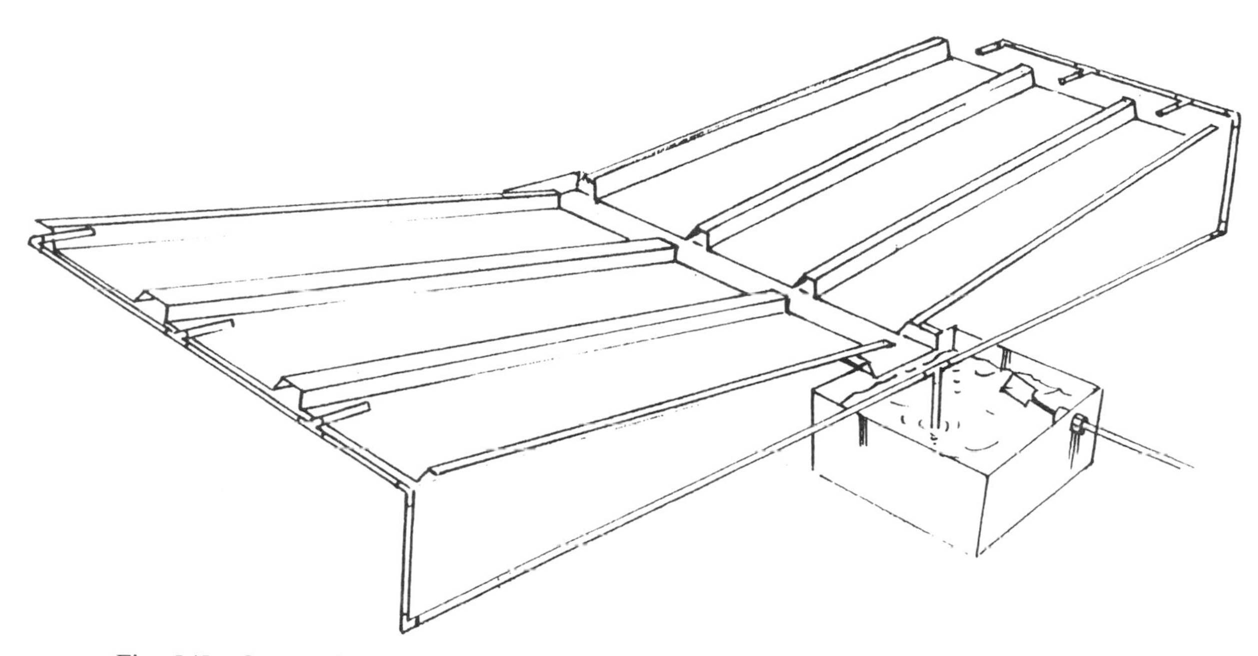

Fig. 5/5 One method of avoiding very long channels is to divide the unit into two slopes to the centre

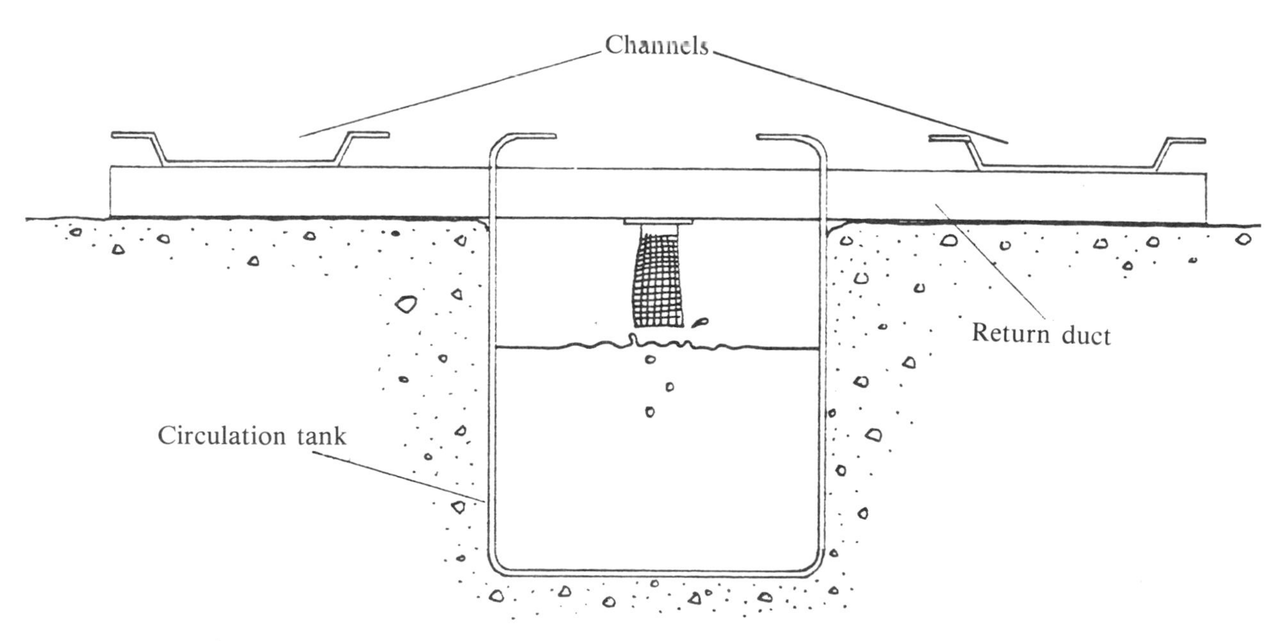

Fig. 5/6 An arrangement of channels, return duct and circulation tank

SOME SYSTEMS DESIGNED

Most sites to be converted to NFT are straightforward enough and it is therefore proper to examine in some detail typical conversions which might be useful as guidance for the conversion of similar sites to NFT. As, very often, there is more than one acceptable arrangement, alternatives are given as appropriate.

Proposal 1

A 3 metres × 2.4 metres greenhouse contains a bed 3 metres × 1 metre which is to be converted from border soil to NFT. Although mainly tomatoes and cucumbers have been grown in the past a multipurpose unit is required. Electricity is available and it is intended to fit auto top-up facilities.

The space 3 metres × 1 metre (3 square metres) would accommodate 13 tomato plants at a nominal but realistic 0.22 square metre per plant. Therefore a system capacity of 60 litres is required (see page 7). The plants would be grown in two rows. Certainly a manufactured kit might be an attractive proposition for the conversion of this small site to NFT, but alternatively it would be possible to construct and fit a two channel system from individual components. There are several satisfactory arrangements for this latter option.

Arrangement a

Figure 5/7 illustrates arrangement a. The use of a tank/return duct saves space and outlet fittings and should be easy to install. A tank of dimensions 1.1 metres × 225mm deep × 300mm wide holds around 60 litres and allows space to fit an automatic top-up valve. If a tank of a little under ideal capacity only was available this would be quite acceptable because of the beneficial effect of fitting automatic top-up. A small submersible pump is ideal, an output of about 1-1½ litres/min. at 0.3 metre head is all that is required. It is preferred if the pump intake is fitted with a filter. 12.5mm supply tube in black polypropylene should be used together with fittings to negotiate sharp corners and reducers to 4-5mm at the channel inlets. In this simple flow system no flow control valves are required.

Flat based rigid channel supports would be laid on a sloped earth base. Some earth may be beneficially removed when preparing the slope. Flat channel top plates over a base polythene channel would provide excellent multipurpose facilities, though at any time, when growing only larger plants, flexible chanelling could be employed.

Direct discharge into the circulation tank is provided. Channel ends and the circulation tank may be covered with a black polythene sheet, or similar, to exclude light.

This arrangement will be of use in many small and medium greenhouses and like situations elsewhere. The most usual difficulty especially as systems increase in size is to find a tank/return capable of holding sufficient volume.

Arrangement b

One method of increasing the volume of solution in an NFT system is to fit an auxiliary tank. This adaptation is shown in Figure 5/8. The auxiliary tank may be fitted at any convenient site, though between the channels, as shown, is likely to be ideal. It is essential to provide an overflow between auxiliary and circulation tank and this must be in tube at least one size larger than the supply tube from the pump. The discharges from the auxiliary tank to the channels should be fitted with flow control and the minimum inlet diameter should be 10mm because the feed to the channels is by gravity through the control valves. The adoption of this arrangement necessitates a slightly larger pump performance. Heating equipment may be sited in either tank but preferably the auxiliary tank which is least removed from the point of heat use.

Fig. 5/7 Proposal 1 arrangement a. A two channel system using a tank/return unit

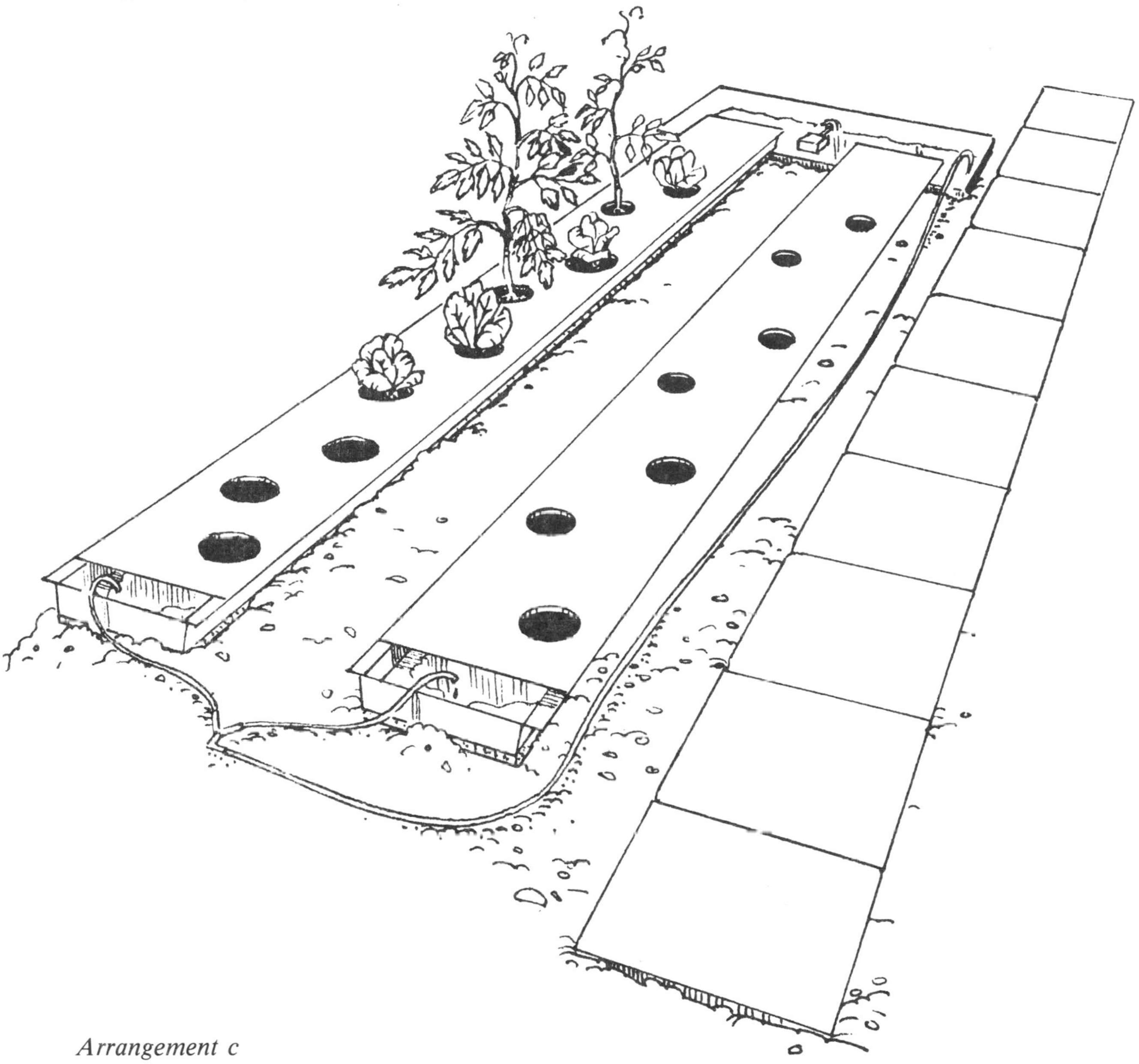

Arrangement c

Very often sufficient volume can be obtained by using a conventional circulation tank and connecting this to the channel outflow with a return duct. This arrangement is shown in Figure 5/9.

Probably the best site for the tank is at the end of the central pathway. The use of a return duct allows a filter to be fitted, which reduces the need for an inlet filter on the pump. When using this arrangement it is important to ensure that the pump has sufficient lift to empty the circulation tank.

Proposal 2

To convert a 5 metres × 3 metres polyhouse entirely to NFT. The principal plants grown are temperate and summer crops. A bench at good working height is preferred at one side, on the other ground channels for taller plants.

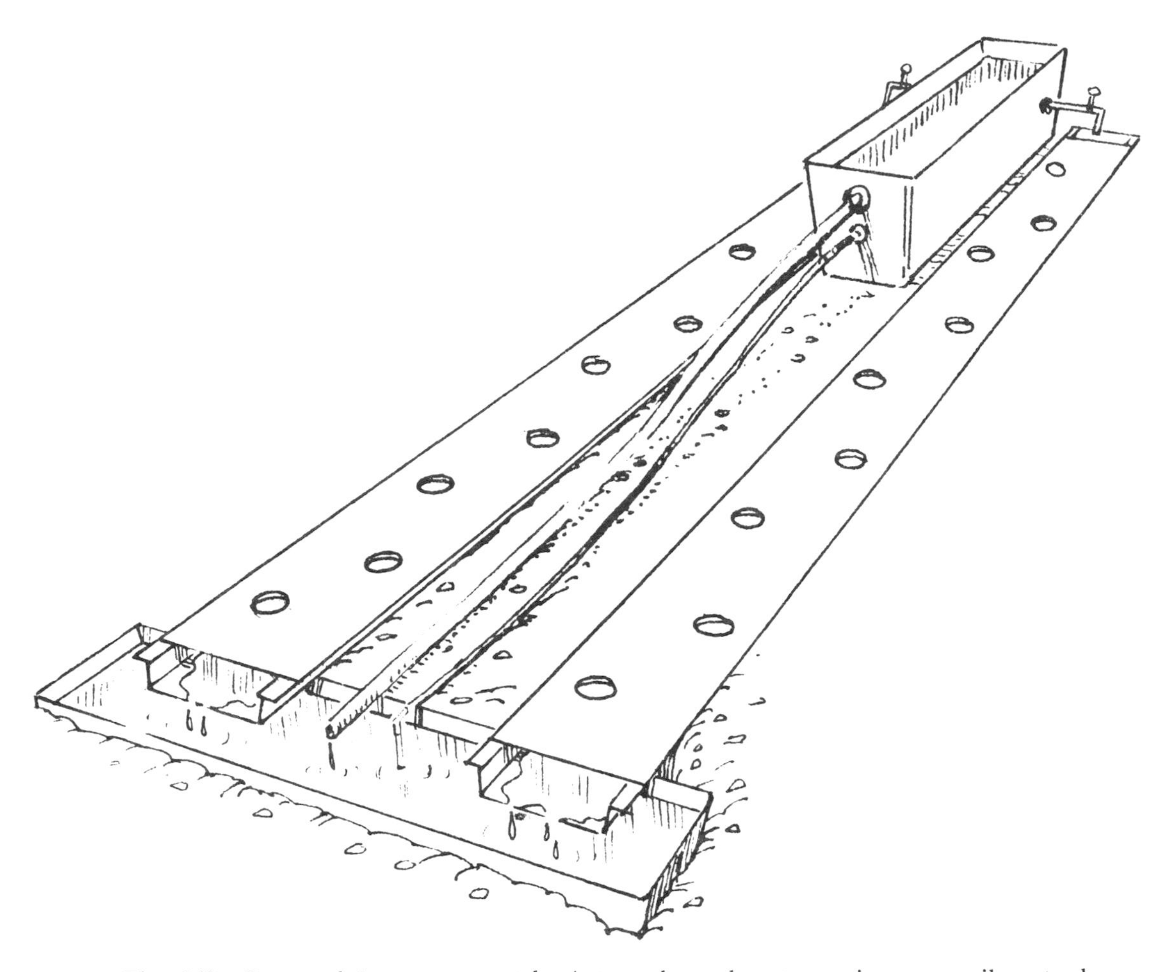

Fig. 5/8 Proposal 1 arrangement b. A two channel system using an auxilary tank

Arrangement a

This proposal neatly allows conversion by introducing two separate NFT systems. One for the bench and one for the ground. This arrangement, illustrated in Figures 5/10 and 5/11, minimises running costs and increases the flexibility of the system.

Allowing for the central pathway the ground bed is an area 5 metres × 1.2 metres but air space is lost by the sloping tunnel sides. Accordingly multiduct trays about 1 metre wide would provide more than adequate channels. Three channel multiduct is preferred as this will give flexibility to plant rows and spacings. It is probable that the slope could be constructed by shifting and grading the existing earth but it may also be necessary to bring in some ballast as care must be exercised not to loosen the structure. Insulation between multiduct and ground would be beneficial.

Where the use of a multiduct is thought inappropriate on account of awkward or limited access to the third channel, or because of loss of footspace, there would be very little reduction in plant capacity by siting just two wide based channels in the same space. Reduction of plant capacity would be noticeable only if smaller plants were regularly grown in this bed. If mainly taller plants occupy the bed then good training will ensure complete occupation of the bed from just two channels.

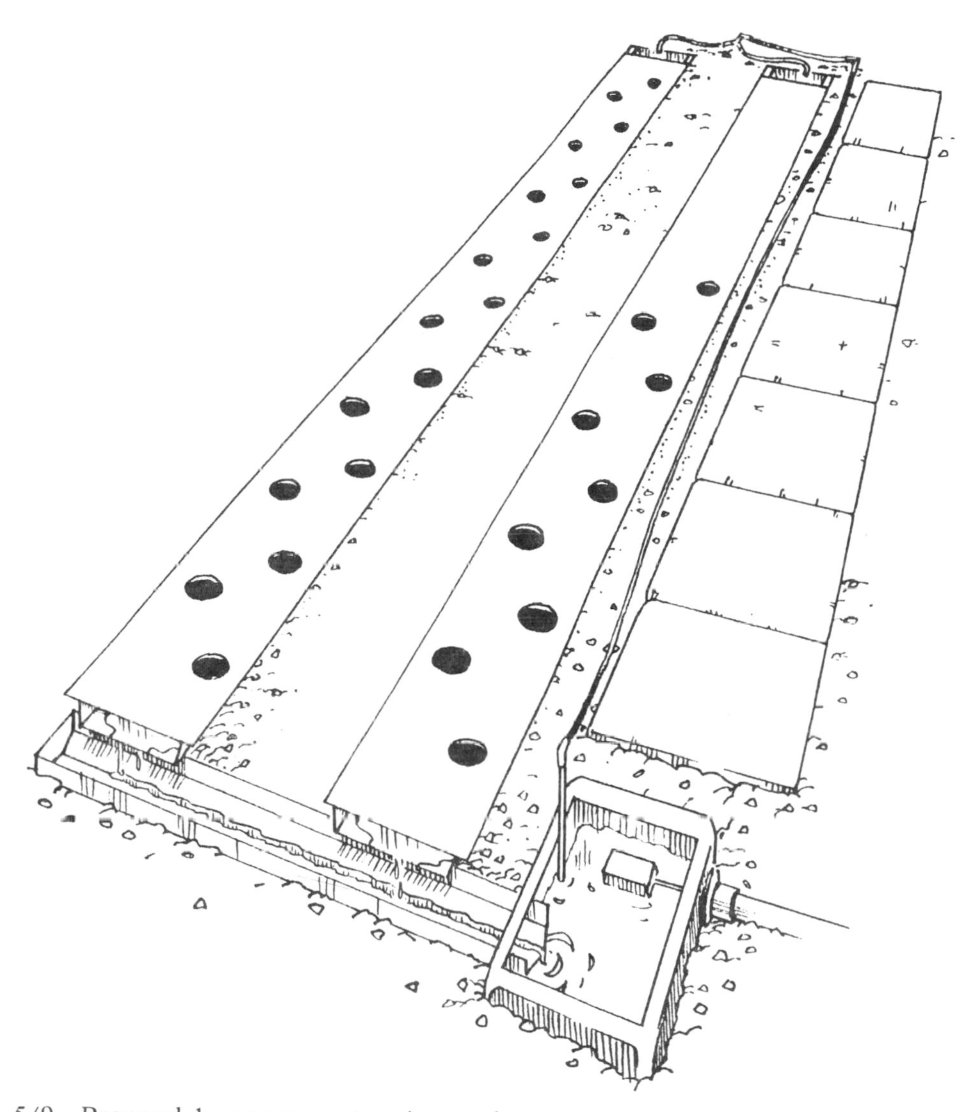

Fig. 5/9 Proposal 1 arrangement c. A two-channel system using a return duct

Assuming the system to be fitted with auto top-up, and the air space utilized to be 5 metres × 1 metre (5 square metres) a solution volume (page 7) of 90-110 litres is required. This capacity could be accommodated using any of the tank arrangements outlined in the first proposal.

A small submersible pump providing 1½/2 litres per minute at the channel head is all that would be necessary. This should prove most economical. It is unlikely that flow controls would be required.

The bench site is ideal for utilizing multiduct trays. If the bench is not already constructed it can be fashioned from simple trestle type supports of wood at each end and thereafter at 1 metre centres. Alternatively metal, probably galvanised steel, supports could be produced. Where there is an option, have the bench on the north side (in the northern hemisphere) so as not to shade plants in the ground channels. The best working height is about 75cm and with a slope over 5 metres being about 110mm this should pose no problem. A circulation tank of capacity 90-110 litres would be handily sited under the bench at the channel outfall end and will accept returning solution from an open return duct securely fitted to an end bench member.

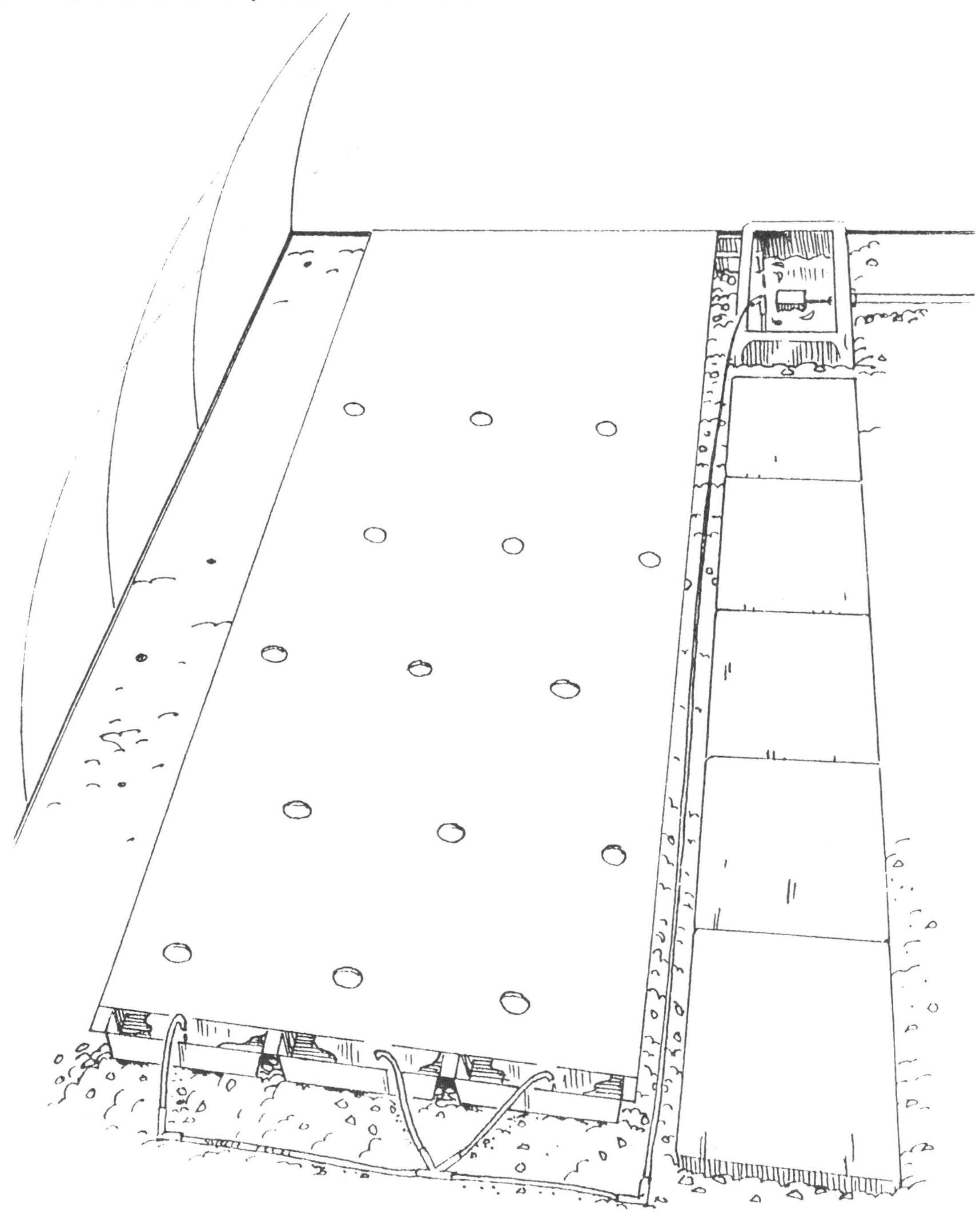

Fig. 5/10 Proposal 2, arrangement a. A ground bed system using multiduct trays

Providing the circulation tank is lifted as required the pump output required will be very similar to, or just a little greater than, the minimum specified for the ground channels.

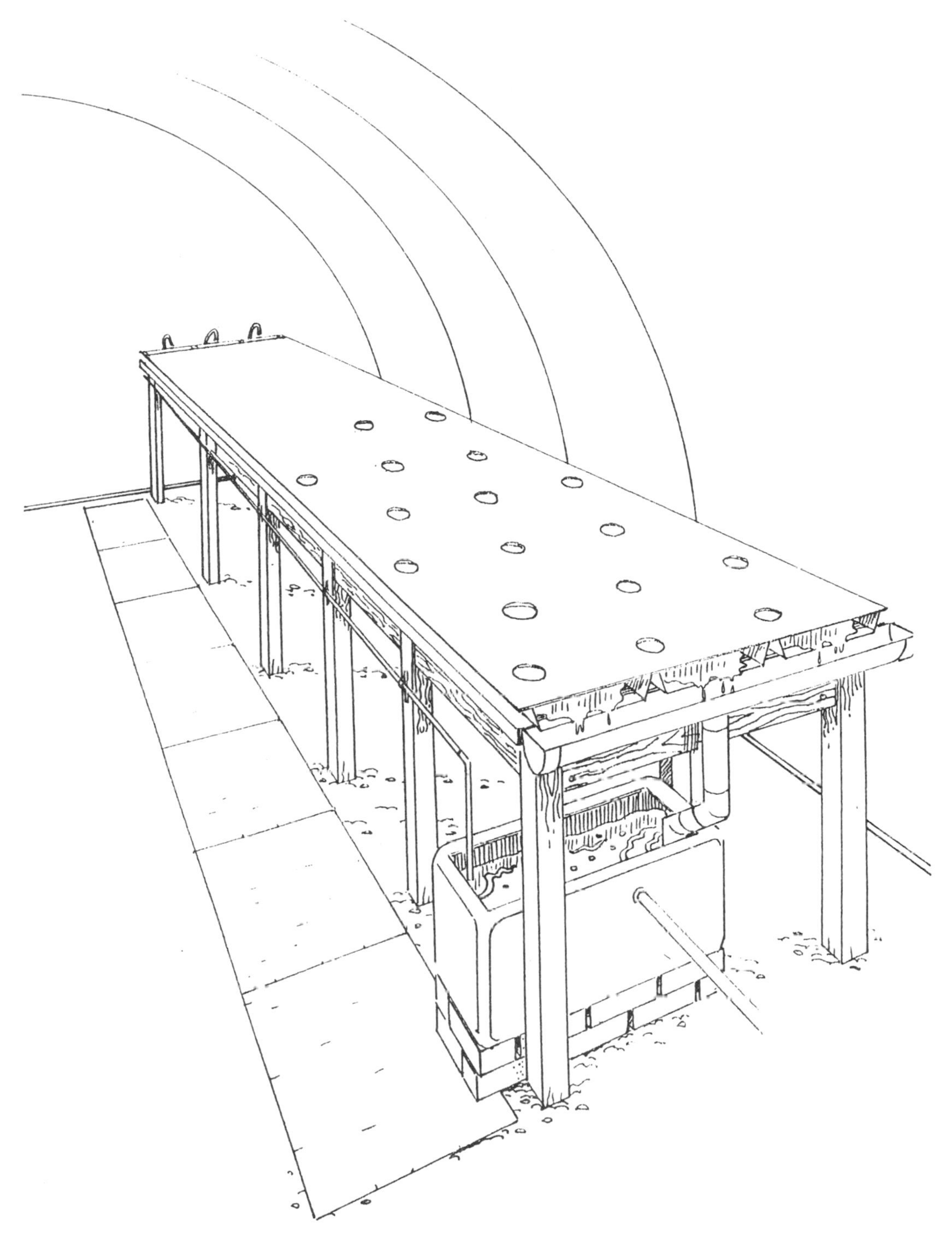

Fig. 5/11 Proposal 2, arrangement a. A bench system using multiduct trays

Supply pipework will be similar to the first example but should be secured by tying or saddle fastenings to bench members as there is a tendency for an unsecured supply tube to fall free.

Arrangement b

The entire house could be converted as one NFT system. A suitable arrangement is shown in Figure 5/12. In this case a circulation tank about 180 litres would be ideally placed in an excavation at the end of the central pathway or under the bench. Open return ducting, with downspout connector on bench side, would suffice to return the solution.

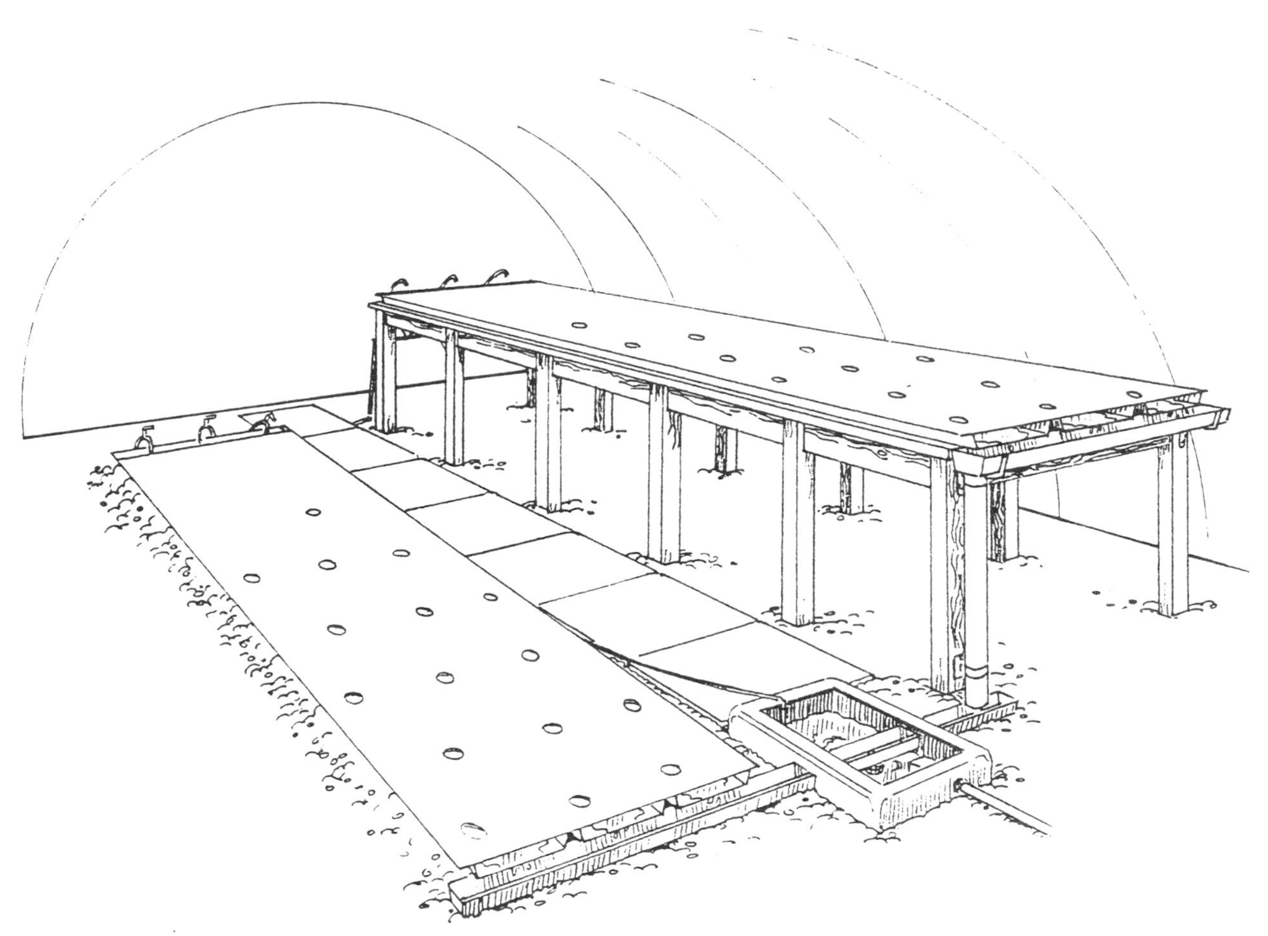

Fig. 5/12 Proposal 2, arrangement b. A combined bench and ground system

At 5 metres × 3 metres and similar sizes there are undoubtedly significant installation cost savings in installing a single NFT system as against two systems as preferred. However a larger pump with significantly increased purchase cost will partly offset savings made elsewhere. In addition there might be increased pump running costs, though the present example could be run with an efficient pump consuming under 40 watts.

A single supply tube should run to the top of the site and then a tee fitting branching the solution supply to bench and ground. Flow control is required as the ground channel would otherwise obtain preferential output. Control may be facilitated by a single flow valve in-line between the tee and ground channels which would restrict supply to the ground channels thus equalising the system. Alternatively fit flow controls at each inlet, but these may be only simple inlet tube inserts.

This single tank arrangement is highly suited to a large range of greenhouse and similar sites where a central pathway provides access to NFT beds on either side. No significant changes in design are required to convert areas as diverse as 2 metres × 2.4 metres and 9 metres × 3 metres.

Proposal 3

To convert an old 'Dutch Light' greenhouse 15 metres × 4 metres to NFT. Some multipurpose facilities are required but mainly tomatoes are grown for local sale.

Dutch Light greenhouses tend to have limited headroom so it is especially important not to compound this problem on converting to NFT. The area 15 metres × 4 metres is normally planted as 6 rows of 30 plants with two pathways. As the proposed NFT system will be fitted with auto top-up this plant capacity requires a solution volume of 325-450 litres. This may be contained in a single circulation tank about 90cm. dia. and 80 cm. deep.

The centre bed about 1 metre wide, is best fitted with a single three channel multiduct tray allowing multipurpose use. The shade side bed, or least well illuminated, may be converted to NFT using flexible channel thus saving installation costs. The light side bed is probably best fitted with two wide based channels on rigid trays. If this, or a similar layout, is adopted the option to grow smaller plants in a well illuminated sector always exists.

Arrangement a

Channels run the length of the greenhouse and the circulation tank is fitted at the top end of one of the pathways. All channels discharge to an open return duct. Figure 5/13 illustrates this arrangement.

Space is most severely limited above the two side beds. Here remove as much soil as practicable to form the base of the slope, which should be close to 30cm over the greenhouse length, and consolidate the slope with ballast. Lay 2.5cm polystyrene on the slope before laying the channels. In the centre bed limited headroom is less of a problem so raising multiducts on low stands and cross members or blocks is quite in order.

A pump output at the channel head of around 10-12 litres/min is necessary. This is most likely supplied by a good submersible using no more than 40 watts. Friction losses in the supply pipe are reduced by using 20mm tube the length of the house and reducing to 12.5mm at the tee junction. Flow control valves should prove unnecessary as control should be facilitated by the reduction in diameter of the inlet tubes. Filter the returning solution on discharge from the return duct.

Arrangement b

Loss of headroom may be too severe if the channels run the entire length of the greenhouse. Instead fit the circulation tank under one of the beds in the middle of the greenhouse. It is probably best if sited under the centre bed as this should have least contact with ground water. This arrangement shown in Figure 5/14 reduces the maximum fall to 15cm. Construction of the slope should be as described for arrangement a.

Pump output requirement is somewhat increased by adopting this arrangement. Now 15-20 litres/min are needed. This will probably still be achieved with a good quality submersible for less than 50 watts. The initial supply tube, again 20mm, tees immediately above the tank. Reducers to 4-5mm are again fitted at the channel heads and again flow control valves are likely to be unnecessary.

Returning solution crosses pathways and should be taken just below ground level in impact resistant plastic pipes. Note that it is quite possible to continue the run of flexible channel or channel base liner from one slope to the next so as to reduce the number of outlet fittings and length of return pipework. This innovation is shown in Figure 5/15. Of course it would be perfectly workable to use two sets of return fittings and pipework.

Arrangements a and b may be varied as appropriate, e.g. one or more beds being shortened to provide storage space. A commonly found variation involves the use of an over capacity pump, in this case a tee joint is fitted soon after the pump output.

One branch continues as usual to the channels the other is fitted with a flow valve and the tube directed back to the circulation tank. Control of the flow at the channel head is facilitated by operation of the flow valve. This arrangement, illustrated in Figure 5/16, causes turbulence and some aeration of the solution.

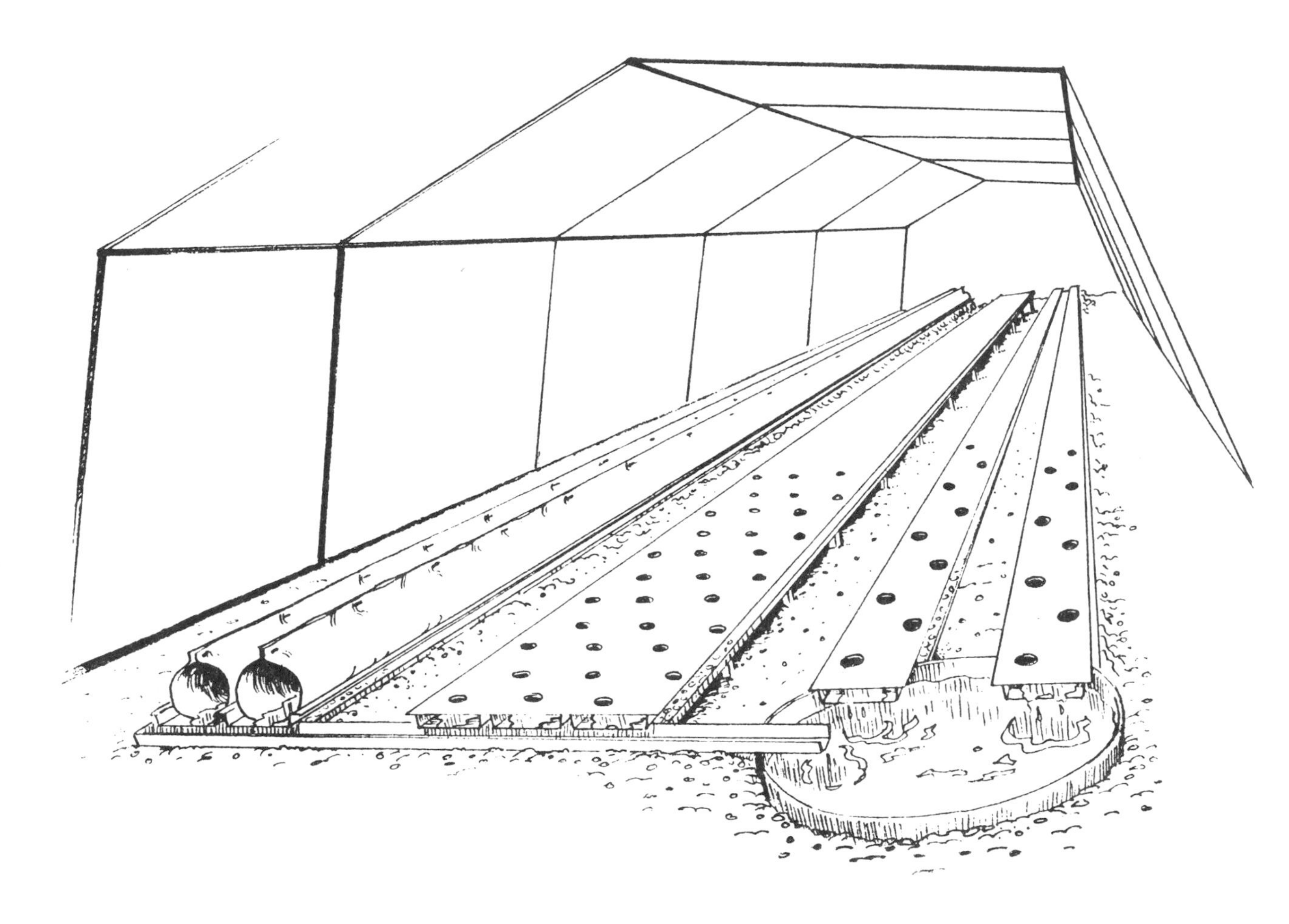

Fig. 5/13 Proposal 3 arrangement a. A larger site converted to NFT using full length channels

Another variation is to site the circulation tank at a convenient point outside the greenhouse. A possible scheme is illustrated in Figure 5/17. The motive for doing so is usually to improve access, but other factors such as the nature of the subsoil or the supply of power and top-up water may well be decisive.

It is clear that the general plans outlined for the particular house 15 metres × 4 metres are equally applicable to many multipathway sites so that in fact large areas may be converted to NFT using much the same flow arrangements.

Tiered Systems

There are two types of tiered NFT system. Firstly, where the channels are fixed to specially constructed supports known as 'A' frames or half 'A' frames. Secondly, where NFT channels are arranged in tiers on an existing wall or structure.

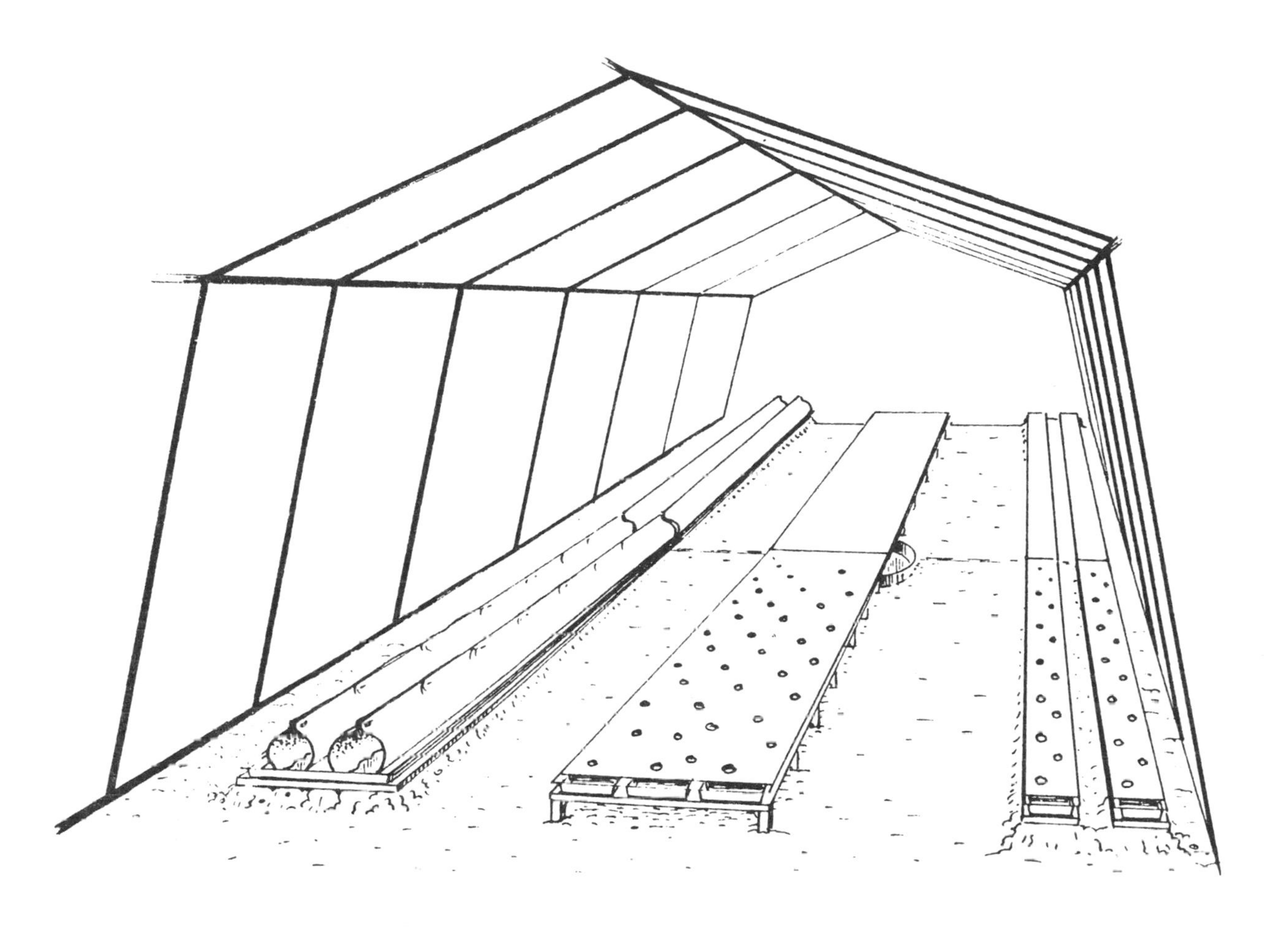

Fig. 5/14 Proposal 3, arrangement b. A larger site converted to NFT using channels sloping to the centre

'A' Frames

The 'A' frame system has received wide publicity because it has been seen as a method of increasing the number of plants which can be grown in a given area. Lettuce and strawberries are two crops which have been grown on the 'A' frame system. Commercial results in northern Europe have never been especially encouraging because the technique simply splits the limited sunlight amongst a greater number of plants. What is more, the split is never even due to inevitable increasing of shading of the lower plants by plants above. Results have been better with strawberries, which certainly tolerate some shading, than with lettuce which don't. In sunnier regions e.g. in Australia and South Africa, there have been generally better results.

For the private gardener a particular application of the 'A' frame system is for producing ornamental displays. Here the height difference of the channels allows the plants to be shown advantageously but the channels themselves may be largely hidden. The differential shading progressively lower down the 'A' frame provides an opportunity for placing plants with particular illumination requirements, as indeed do changes in the orientation of the system. To provide maximum light to all plants a N-S axis is required whereas on an E-W axis one side will be completely illuminated while the other is largely in the shade. Half 'A' frames are tiers with one aspect only. They may be set against a wall but if in the open they may cast a shadow.

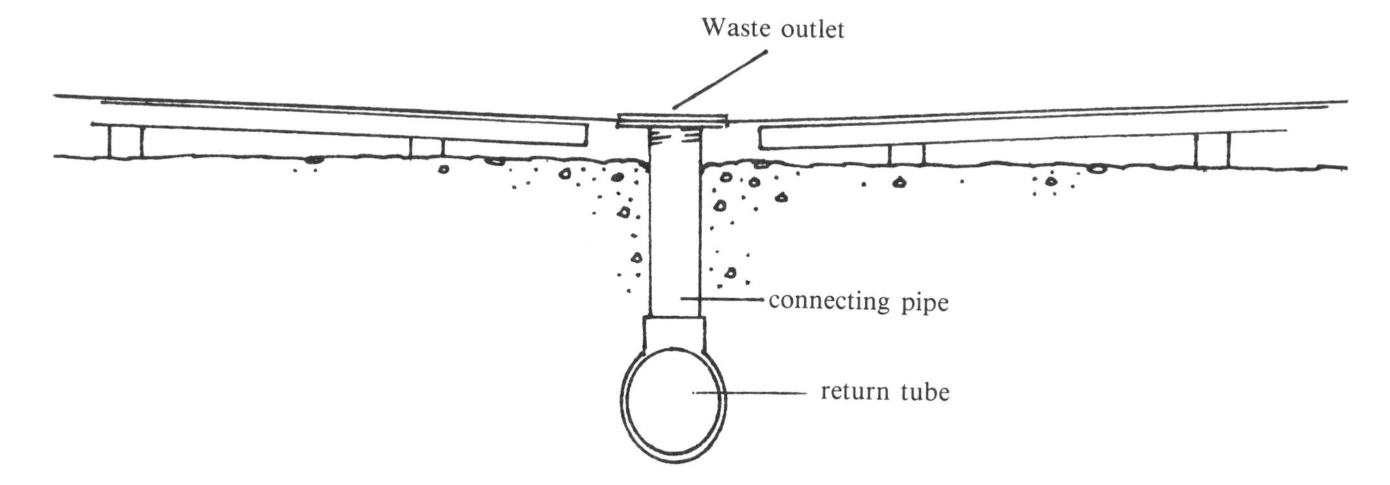

Fig. 5/15. Proposal 3 arrangement b. Side view section of the solution return from a continuous channel laid on two converging slopes

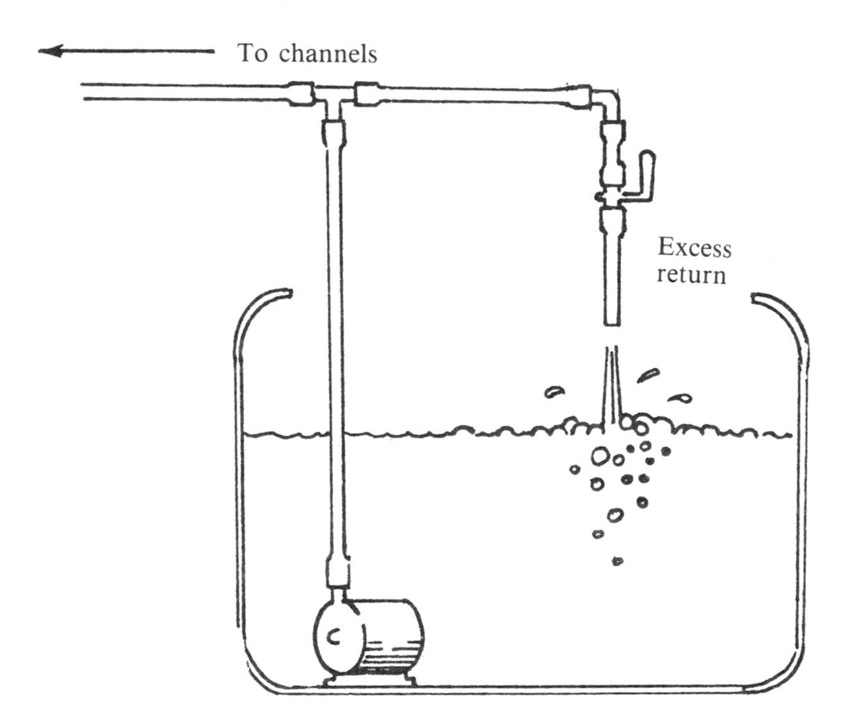

Fig. 5/16 The by-pass method of controlling flow in the solution supply tube

'A' Frames may be constructed from many rigid materials including metal, wood and plastic. Normally each channel is supported by a horizontal bar and set so that the channel above does not overlap. Various height differences between channels have been used. For crop production of lettuce and strawberries 200mm-300mm but for ornamentals it may be less. Channels employed reflect the plants to be grown. Lettuce and strawberries prefer around a 125mm base in a rigid tray and here, there is an application for square line guttering which is rigid enough to straddle the supports but it tends to work out rather expensive. In any case it is still useful to fit a polythene liner to assist cleaning. For ornamentals wider base channels are preferred so that plant placement is not restricted to definite rows.

Fig. 5/17 The circulation tank sited in an outhouse for greater convenience

Two alternative flow systems are employed. There may be an inlet and a return provided for each channel or there may be a single inlet to the uppermost channel which feeds through all the channels down the unit. Because it is preferable not to have more than 20 metres of channel supplied by one inlet, combinations of the two systems are also employed.

Using individual channel inlets, the channels may be fitted equidistant which is an important consideration for crop production when maximising the illumination to each plant. With a single inlet to successive channels the arrangement of the channels one to another is such that gradual narrowing and widening of the height difference between channels occurs, in order that each channel is correctly sloped. This arrangement is advantageous in the smaller greenhouse when it greatly simplifies the solution supply and return and allows the use of much smaller pumps. Additionally the varied height differences between channels may be beneficial for ornamental displays allowing plants of greater and lesser height to be set out advantageously. Figures 5/18 and 5/19 depict alternative 'A' frame arrangements.

Wall tiers

Wall tiers are a novel idea which has come to prominence only because of the development of NFT. Where a greenhouse lies along the preferred E-W axis then a long north wall exists which is necessarily well illuminated by the southern sun. This wall can be exploited for growing plants.

There should be no difficulty in fixing lightweight 125 mm base, or possibly a little larger, channels to the wall. Because of the illumination of the wall the channels may be fixed more or less one above the other. It is not usual to continue tiering below around 60-90cm were the channel might be seriously interrupted by, or interrupt, the ground bed plants.

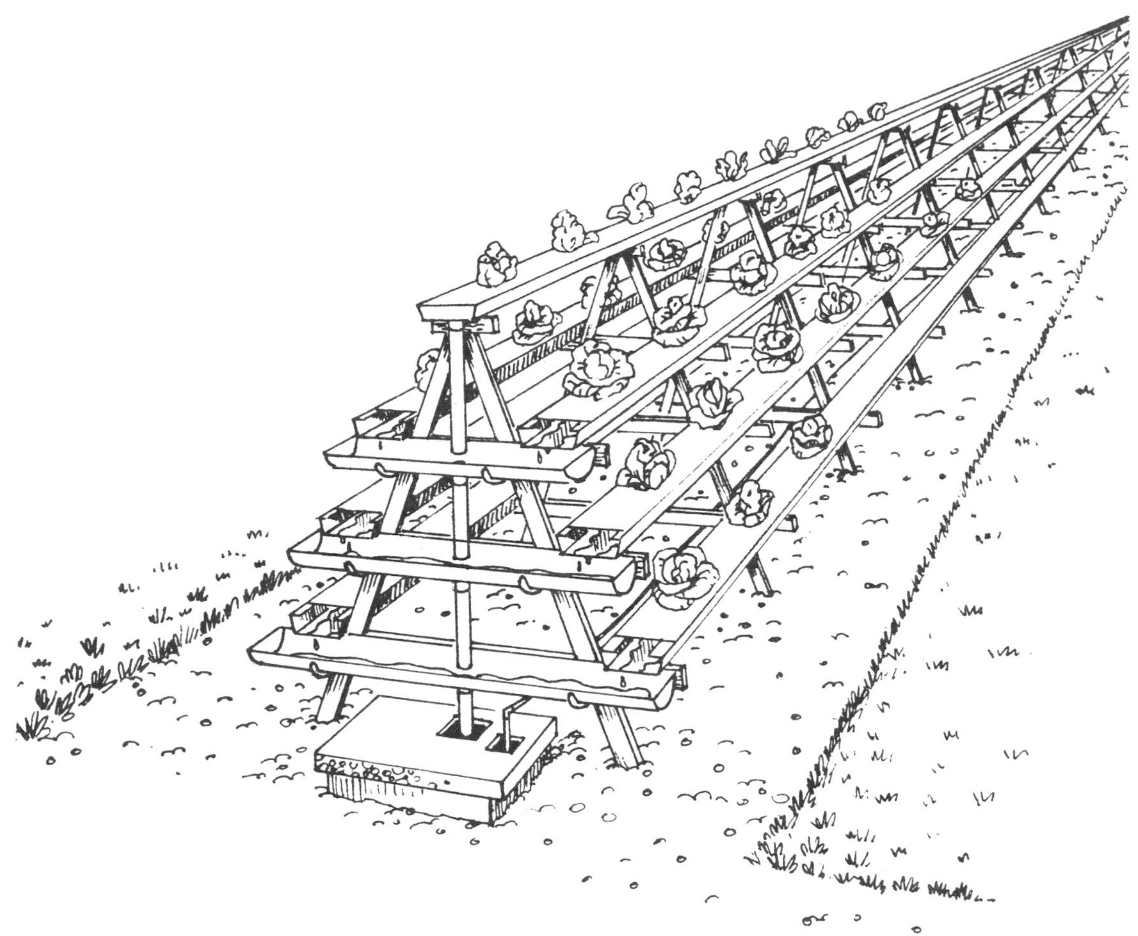

Fig. 5/18 A commercial 'A' frame unit

For smaller sites a single inlet to the topmost channel supplying solution to all channels is preferred. It allows the use of a smaller pump, perhaps the air pressure pumping system. For larger sites it may be just as easy to supply to each channel using a conventional pump especially if the tiered system is an appendage to a much larger unit. Figure 5/20 illustrates a typical wall tier.

Very often plantings are continuous only in the topmost channel(s). Lower channels may be shaded by taller plants in the ground bed during the summer and autumn but be available to take plants in the winter and spring. Not surprisingly successional lettuce and early strawberries are the chief plants grown in wall tiers but there is no good reason why their use should be so restricted.

GUIDELINES FOR CONSTRUCTING NFT SYSTEMS ON SITES WITH SPECIAL REQUIREMENTS

New Greenhouses

When a new greenhouse is planned an opportunity exists to maximise the benefits of using NFT.

Excavate for, and lay foundations at a depth below top soil. Build a retaining wall to ground level or a little above and on this fit the greenhouse structure. The removal of the internal top soil results in a large gain of headroom. As much as 300mm has been reported but take care to ensure that the level is not so low as to attract ground water draining from adjacent land. Usually an insulated concrete floor sloped 1:50 from the door completes the job but leave a space in the concrete for the tank. The best tanks to use are long and shallow so as not to necessitate a great depth of excavation. Extra volume can be facilitated using the auxiliary tank technique shown on page 68. Note, on wet sites, simply continue the retaining wall to a greater height and lay the concrete floor at an appropriately higher level. Finally fit electric supply sockets where they are most convenient.

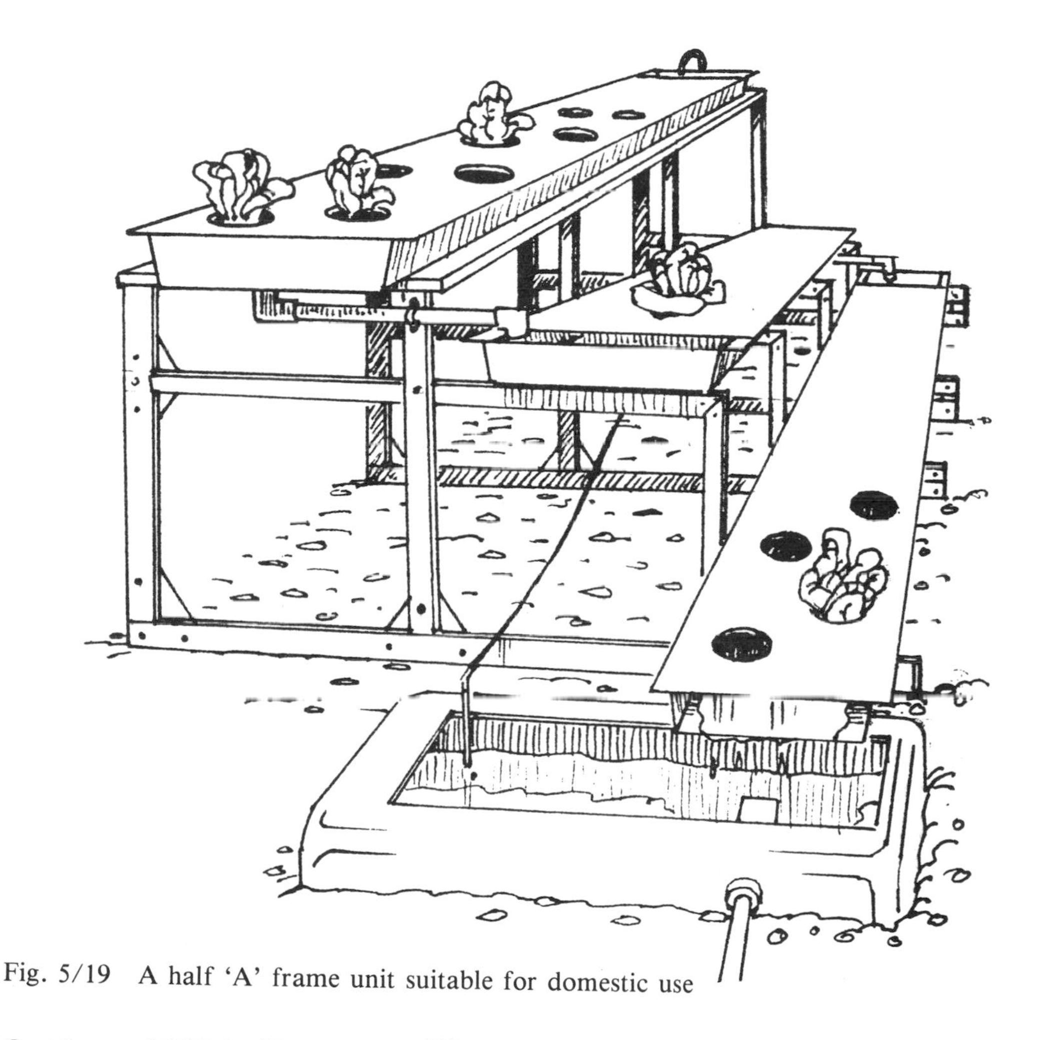

Fig. 5/19 A half 'A' frame unit suitable for domestic use

Outdoors NFT in Temperate Climates

As well as ordinary cultivated areas NFT may be used on sites which would otherwise be difficult or impossible to cultivate. These include, areas of particularly poor soil, hillsides, old buildings and industrial sites and a range of roof spaces and balconies. A possible hillside scheme is pictured in Figure 5/21. The three difficulties associated with these sites are wind, rain and frost.

On ground sites at low altitude wind is unlikely to be much of a problem but at progressively higher levels wind becomes a very significant influence. On some sites it may be possible to fit wind screening which would undoubtedly be beneficial.

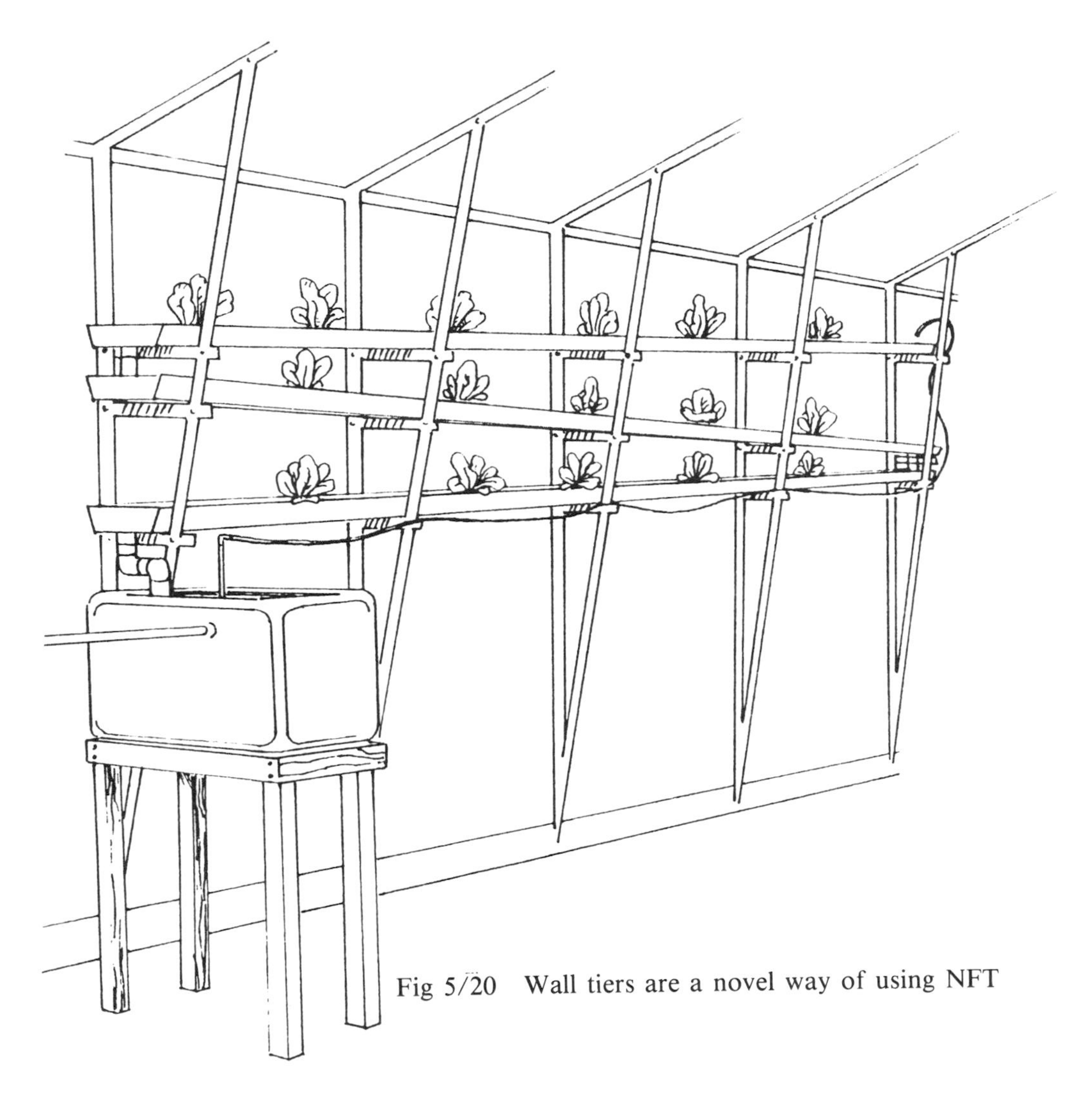

Fig 5/20 Wall tiers are a novel way of using NFT

Generally, it is the channels and the plants growing in them which are subject to wind damage. Accordingly provide secure anchorage for the channels either by fixing to the existing building structure or platform or by laying a heavy stable base on which channel supports can be secured, e.g. transverse or longitudinal ex-railway sleepers or similar. Channels and channel top plates should be secured to the rigid support with stud fasteners or cross bands.

Inlet tubes may be secured by inserting the discharge end into a tight hole made in the centre of a 100-150mm length of 25mm plastic pipe which acts as a toggle and prevents dislodgement, as shown in Figure 5/22. Open channel ends are generally unsuitable though on sheltered sites they may be reasonably acceptable. Instead use waste outlets and rigid pipe for the solution return. As far as the plants are concerned take all reasonable measures to support plants which would normally require support and of course choose plants which are suited to the environment.

Rainwater entering the system is quite innocuous and may even be beneficial. A certain amount of rainwater may be accommodated if a larger than usual circulation tank is employed and run normally at half capacity. Heavy and/or frequent rain will certainly cause overflowing from the circulation tank, though the choice of channel type will markedly affect the amount of rainwater entering the system. Flat topped channels allow large amounts of water to enter whereas flexible tunnel channels are largely rainproof. This consideration should not unduly influence channel choice. On larger outside sites a diverter valve may be fitted to the solution return and operated automatically by rain sensor. This valve serves to channel rainwater to waste before it reaches the circulation tank. On smaller sites such elaboration is unwarranted and it is best to allow excess rainwater to overflow harmlessly to waste.

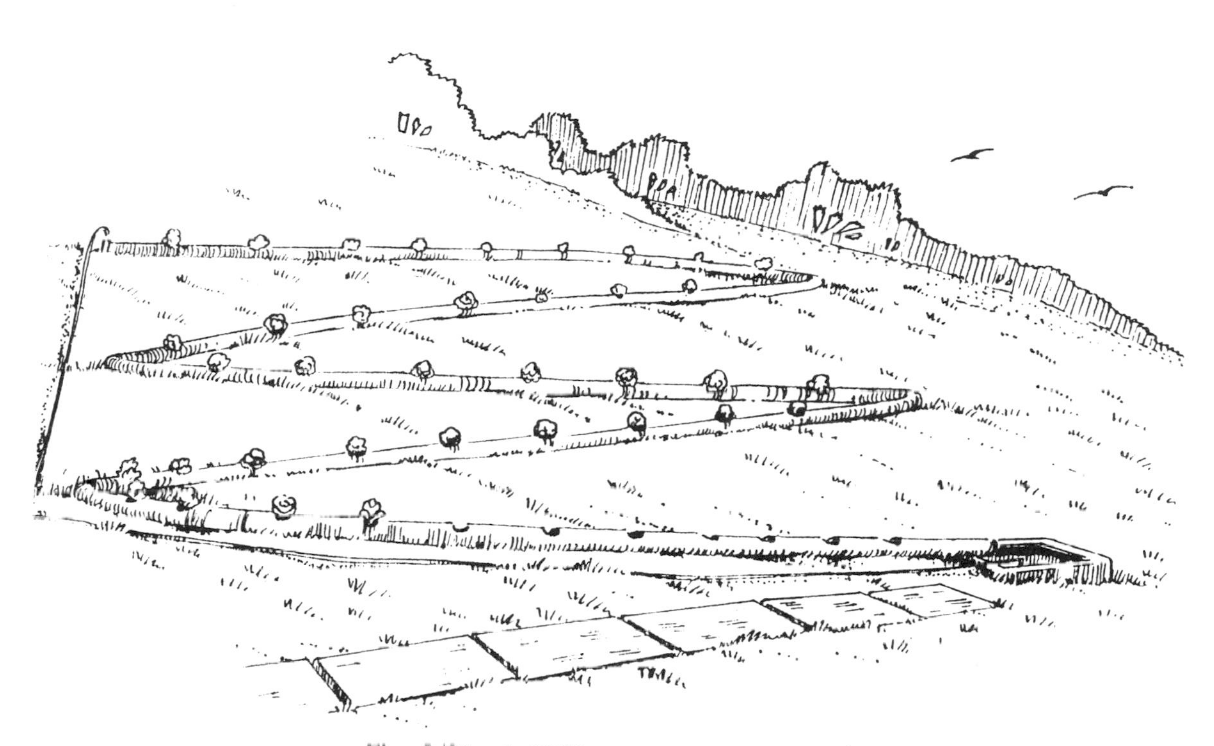

Fig. 5/21 A NFT system on a hillside site

Frost is a problem because it can damage pump, pipework and fittings when the solution becomes frozen inside the system. Accordingly it is generally imprudent to run an NFT system when there is any danger of significant frost, when indeed the system should be drained and the pump removed. In fact this advice should not prove limiting because it is generally uneconomic to run outdoor NFT systems when the maximum day time temperature falls regularly below 15°C. This is about mid-October in the U.K. In the spring, when warm days may be followed by cold nights, the level of frost is insignificant as far as possible damage to submersible pumps and pipework is concerned, and anyhow the unit should be switched off to allow drainage long before nightfall.

In ordinary garden situations outside NFT systems are often run as extensions to permanent indoor units. In these cases it is only necessary to fit a valve on the supply pipe to enable isolation of the outside system. It may also be useful if a manually operated diverting arrangement was fitted to the solution return so that excessive rainwater could be prevented from reaching the circulation tank.

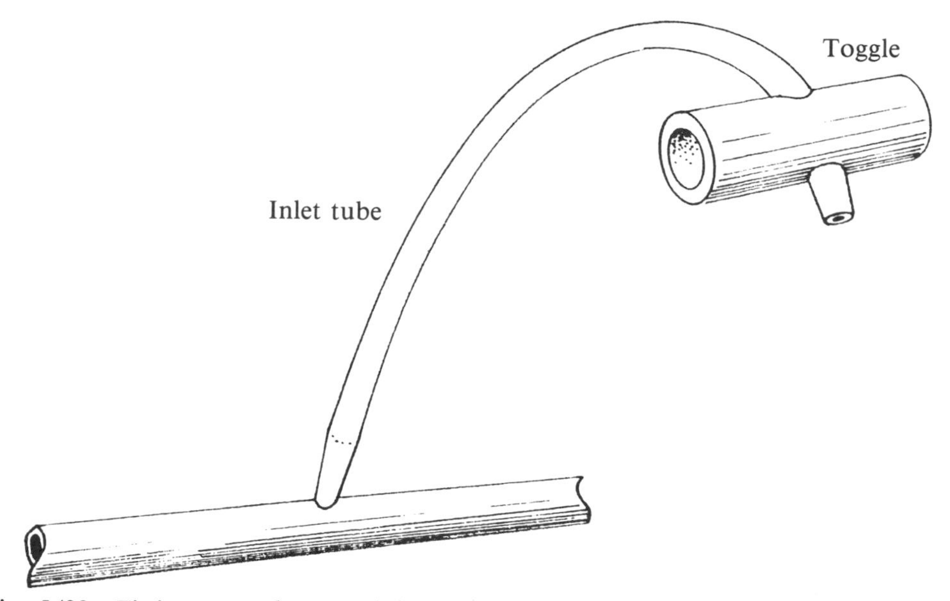

Fig. 5/22 Fitting a toggle to an inlet tube will prevent dislodgement from the channel

If an outside system is run as a separate entity consideration should be given to siting the circulation tank and its accessories in a convenient indoor environment, e.g. garage or outhouse. This arrangement encourages cleanliness, easy servicing, and greatly simplifies electrical connections to pump and heater. Consider also the possibility of using the air lift pumping system whereby the pump may be safely and conveniently sited indoors whilst the tank is placed outside. Of special utility as outside NFT systems are "complete" manufactured units. These have the great advantage of mobility. They can be taken outdoors for the growing season and stored away when not in use. They are ideal for yard and patio use.

Special Adaptations for Hot Climates

To avoid excessive heating of the nutrient solution particular materials and methods are employed.

Channels should be finished with heat/light reflective surfaces. For flexible tunnel channelling this generally means using black/white co-extruded polythene which may also be used as a flat cover over channel top plates. Top plates themselves may be made of insulating material. Where the solution supply and return pipework cannot be buried it should be sleeved with insulation.

It is advisable to use large volume circulation tanks. Even on a large scale as much as 5 litres to each 0.25 sq.metre air space occupied by the plants should be provided to dilute any 'hot' solution. Circulation tanks are best sunk in the ground and not insulated so as to encourage heat loss to the earth. Tank lids may be insulated and fitted with a reflective surface. The use of surface tanks should be avoided if possible. Where header tanks are used they should be insulated and protected from direct sunlight.

Heat is accumulated when the solution is in circulation. Accordingly reduce the opportunity for heat gain through improving the speed of circulation by increasing the channel slope and reducing the channel length. In hot climates a minimum slope of 1.40 is suggested and channel length should not exceed 12 metres.

Adaptations for Fitting NFT Systems on Wet Sites

There are two problems posed by wet conditions, firstly, cold ground water reduces the effectiveness of solution heating, and secondly, rising ground water de-stabilises tanks sunk into excavations. To overcome both these problems the majority of the solution should be held in a main tank fitted above ground. In fact this arrangement bears similarities with the auxiliary and circulation tank system described previously. However on wet sites the lowest tank can be better described as a collection tank. It holds a small volume, 5-20% of the total system volume, consistent with accommodating the pump, if a submersible is used, or the pump intake, if a non-submersible is employed, together with an auto top-up valve. The collection tank should be of tough construction so that weight can be applied to prevent flotation. It can be sited at any point convenient for the channel outflows and access. Figure 5/23 illustrates this arrangement.

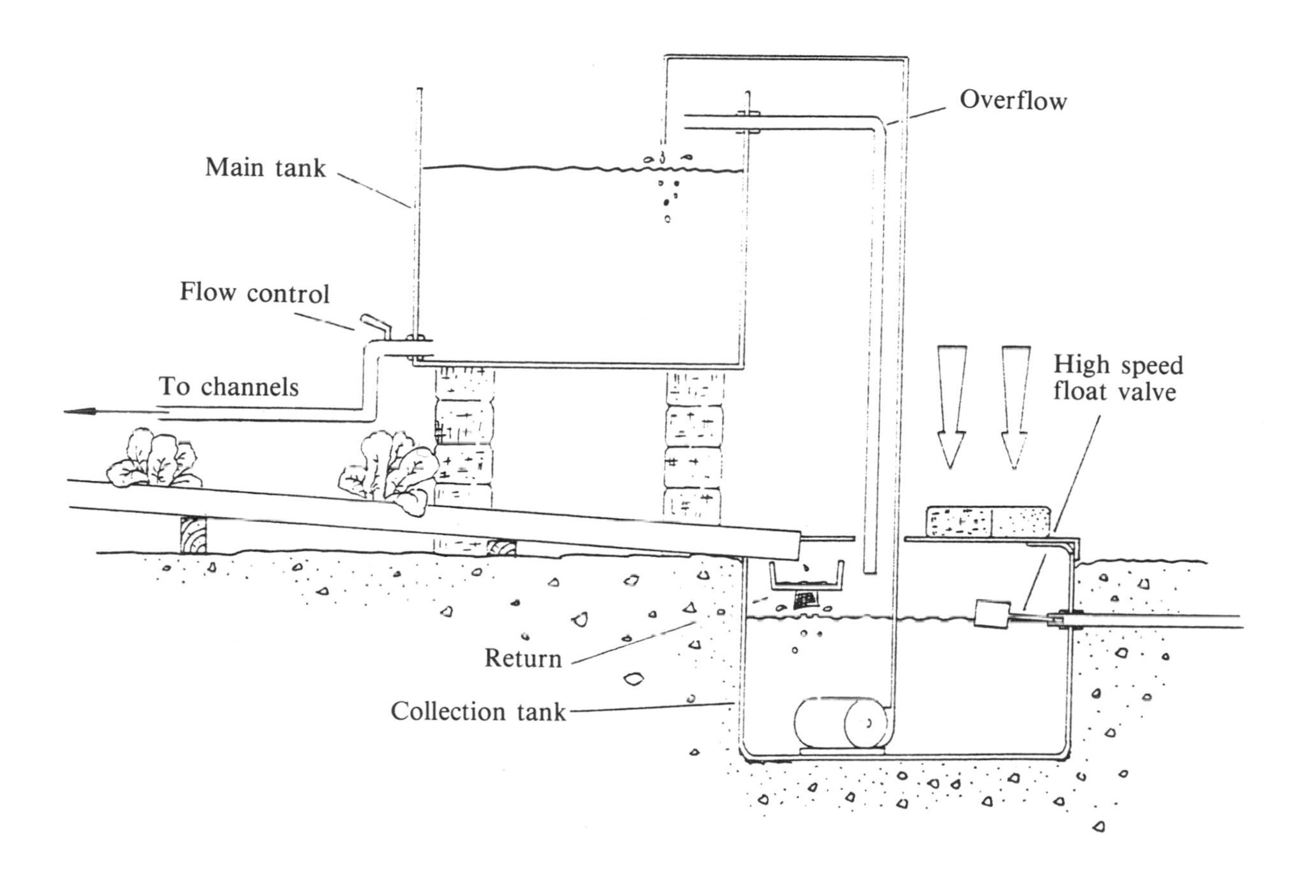

Fig. 5/23 An arrangement of pump and tanks suitable for use when converting a wet site to NFT

The main tank may be sited at any point within, or adjacent to, the growing area. It should be raised clear of any interference by rising water and it should be well insulated if the solution within is heated. Solution is pumped from the collection tank to the main tank through appropriate pipework entering the main tank at, or close to, the top. Delivery to the channels is via tank connector and pipework from close to the base of the main tank. This supply, being a gravity feed system, should be one size larger than the supply from the pump and should be complete with an in-line flow valve. An overflow pipeline of the same diameter as the channel supply is fitted from close to the top of the main tank to the collection tank. Take care that the overflow return does not interfere with the float valve in the collection tank. An over-capacity pump is required so that under normal running conditions excess solution returns through the overflow.

Using this two tank arrangement automatic top-up is highly desirable on small sites and essential on medium and large ones, as otherwise loss of solution volume through take-up by the plants is first manifested as a lowering of the level of solution in the collection tank, causing eventually intermittant availability of solution to the pump. The risk is blockage of the flow by the presence of air in the pipework and/or pump head. It is beneficial if the float valve has a reasonably quick water admittance action. This is generally no problem when the make-up water is supplied by mains pressure but a header tank supply can be too slow unless the header tank is raised somewhat and the orifice of the float valve is sufficiently large. When starting up the circulation, fill the main tank by hose and fill the collection tank to maximum even if this is above the level of the float valve shut off. Open the flow valve to channels and allow the hose supply to make up the volume in the main tank. Switch on the pump only when solution begins to return from the channels. Turn off the hose supply only when solution begins to return from the main tank through the overflow.

Where possible, use raised, even slightly raised, channels on wet sites. This reduces the depth of excavation for the collection tank and accordingly simplifies installation. Where actual flooding occurs it is clearly best if the channels are raised above the maximum flood level, but the occasional ingress of flood water into the collection tank is not seriously detrimental to the system, though it will dilute the nutrient concentration.

Sites where Ground Excavation is Impossible.

Such sites includes conservatories and patios, especially those with decorative floors, as well as numerous sites where the base material is too difficult to excavate. There is no way to avoid the fitment of a circulation tank, however small at the lowest point of the system, consequently the channels must be raised above this minimum height. On many sites this arrangement is itself desirable. To minimise the height of the channels, long but shallow tank/collection ducts are very usefully employed on this type of site. A possible arrangement is shown in Figure 5/24. If necessary extra volume may be added to the unit in the form of an auxiliary tank, see page 68 or, if a large extra volume is required, as a main tank, see page 85.

There is no necessity to site the auxiliary or main tank within, or even adjacent to, the growing area though it may be convenient to do so. Instead, where appropriate, it may be sited wherever it is both convenient to access and not an eyesore.

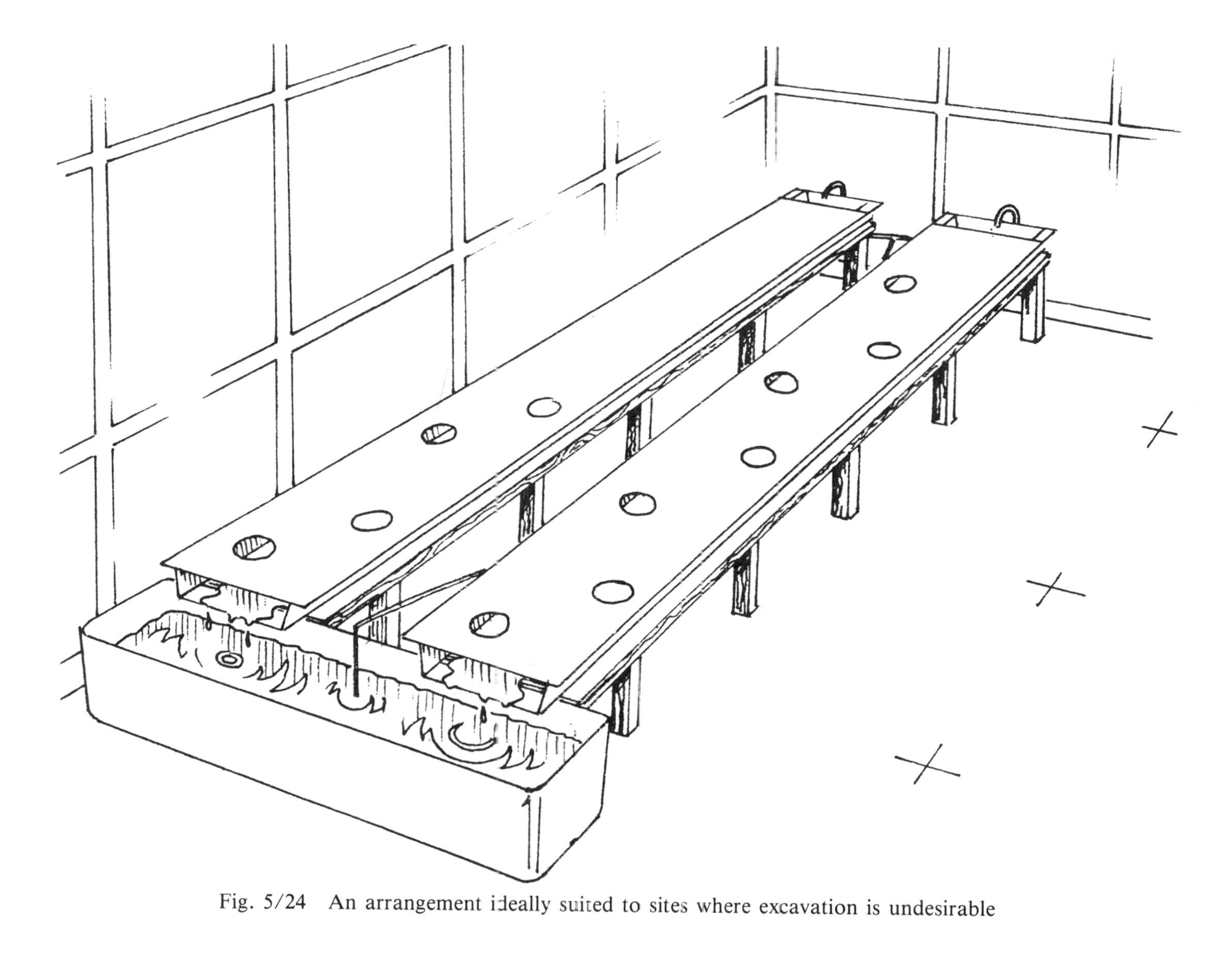

Fig. 5/24 An arrangement ideally suited to sites where excavation is undesirable

CHAPTER SIX

PREPARING PLANTS FOR NFT

When growing in NFT the successful plant produces a root system extraneous to any soil or compost. Accordingly it is vital to eventual success that a plant about to be placed into the nutrient solution is capable of producing an extraneous root system and it follows that any propagation methods which detract from this potential are to be avoided, whilst any which enhance the potential are to be preferred.

IN-SITU GERMINATION

At first sight it seems obvious that if a seed is placed directly into the solution it will have the best chance of successful rooting in the solution. However, with few exceptions, in-situ germination produces poor results. It is useful to examine the reasons for this.

Seed, especially small seed, becomes thoroughly saturated soon after being placed in the flow. The solution is largely airless and the seed dies of oxygen starvation and/or of the encouragement of decay organisms which are well adapted to the conditions. If intermittant or drastically reduced flow is operated in the hope of reducing saturation and admitting air, there is loss of benefit of solution heating and the seed may become subject to unsatisfactory temperatures level and to a serious temperature fluctuation. Additionally there is the considerable work and judgement involved in controlling the solution flow. Another detrimental influence is that nutrient solutions of the strength provided for maturing plants are deleterious to delicate seedlings. Accordingly unless a very weak solution or water only is circulated successful germination and seedling production is unlikely. At the same time it is unlikely to be beneficial to the maturing plants co-habiting the system to subject them to long periods of underfeeding.

Even if the first stages of germination are achieved there is a great loss of seedlings soon after as the root axis and shoot emerge into difficulties. Unless the root axis grows directly into the solution it is often exposed to a relatively dry atmosphere at sub-optimum temperature where it dessicates and dies. This is in contrast to the situation in a good compost where, surrounding the entire seed there is a good mixture of moisture and air. The emerging shoot has an early requirement for light. This is conveniently taken care of by germination in a solid medium as the shoot pushes above the surface but in a closed NFT channel the admission of light would have to be undertaken manually. The act of introducing light will exasperate the problems of the developing root axis.

Finally, by their design and purpose NFT systems are extensive plant growing areas. The conditions required for successful seed germination are often precise and more easily produced in a restricted space, e.g.: a propagator or a seed tray strategically placed to obtain heat. The understanding is that plants so produced will subsequently tolerate conditions to be found on an extensive site perhaps with limited enhancement and of course aided by the advancement of the season.

Success with in-situ germination is not widespread. Generally the larger the seed the more likely is success, so that peas and beans which are both large and undemanding may indeed be germinated successfully in a channel. Greater success is achieved if the seed is first subject to pre-germination before being placed in the channel. This method is common practice with cereal and pulse seed grown for fodder. The process consists of soaking the seed in water at close to optimum temperature so that the seed becomes fully imbibed. For example, this may be 10-12 hours at 20°C for barley. The seeds are drained and the germination allowed to proceed en-masse aided by the heat accumulated in the process of germination. Normally at least one washing through is practiced before the seeds are placed in the channel. This would normally be on the third day.

A second approach is to germinate seeds in or on the root mat of existing plants. Here the technique is to lower the flow to expose a piece of root. Alternatively, the root may be folded up so that a piece remains above the level of the solution. Place the seed in or on this root mat. Considerable germination success has been achieved this way even with small seeds such as lettuce but it is difficult to foresee widespread use.

SEED COMPOST

This, the most common method of seed germination, is also the most successful starting point for plants subsequently to be grown in NFT. This is because the necessities and niceties of successful germination for a huge range of plants have been refined by years of experience and facilitated by the use of composts. Accordingly the adoption of NFT should not ordinarily mean any change of seeding procedures.

POST-GERMINATION TRANSPLANTING

Many seedlings will require one or more transplantings as they outgrow the original space allocation and as they are moved to more extensive accommodation. At this stage certain alternatives present themselves and some of these have special interest to NFT. Other seedlings, of course, require no transplanting having been sown in containers large enough to support the plant over its entire seedling stage. The following notes apply equally to these plants.

Natural Composts

In general no natural compost is unsuitable for NFT. Ordinary soil is probably the least successful. Of course fine peat soils and some sands do suffice as composts but most soils are of doubtful quality, subject as they are to degrees of waterlogging and contamination by infectious material. Accordingly "manufactured" composts, albeit possibly DIY, are the most likely choice. What are the qualities, special to NFT, required of these?

The most important quality is that of binding ability. Subsequently when the plant is placed in the channel complete with its compost block, the block should hold together. Coarse peat is the best source of binding material. Normally whatever else is added to the compost is added in such quantities that the binding ability of the peat is largely unimpaired. There are many trade products of this type available but home made can be just as good. In general sterile or nearly sterile compost is preferred to non-sterile types.

Of course, there are too, many non-peat based composts available. If these materials are used because they suit a particular plant, the benefits of binding may be lost but this might have to be accepted. It may be that the root system of the plant will provide an acceptable level of binding, but it is more likely that the particular subjects would be of hydrophobic tendancy in which case their subsequent treatment in NFT would allow for the lack of binding in the compost.

Additives are fairly commonly used in compost preparation. Wetting agents are detergent-like chemicals which encourage the compost to wet-out rapidly and thoroughly. They are especially useful in commercial horticulture because they cut the time it takes to make up composts and water in transplants and because they increase the efficiency of watering systems. However some doubts have been expressed in the use of composts treated with wetting agents for NFT plants. It is claimed that when placed in the channel the compost block becomes super-saturated which contributes to poor root performance and encourages collar rot. These claims are unsubstantiated but it may be prudent to bear them in mind when assessing results.

Recently, another additive has come to prominence. This is known as a "polymer", and simply, this material is capable of holding a large quantity of water but it does so by binding the water within the molecule. When added to compost, they allow the compost to hold sufficient moisture to maintain plants for long periods without saturation. Polymers are likely to prove beneficial for plants grown in NFT as they, as described, reduce saturation around the junction of stem and root. Also, it is said that the use of polymers increases the air spaces within the compost. At the time of writing there is not sufficient evidence to make a positive recommendation either for or against their use.

Artificial Composts

There is widespread use of lightweight artificial composts such as Perlite and Vermiculite which are designed to combine good aeration with water retention. These materials are not readily bound and therefore are not recommended by themselves for NFT production. The problem is that on transplanting into the channel, substantial amounts of material may break away threatening blockage of the channel, or worse, of the pump. There is no reason why a proportion of these materials should not be added to peat to prepare a compost in the hope of combining benefits of all materials.

There is considerable interest in the use of bound artificial composts. The most common of these is spun molten rock fibre which is sold under various trade names such as "Rockwool" and "Capogro." As well as being available loose when pieces may be mixed with other composting ingredients or placed conventionally in a pot, rock fibre is available in propogation blocks of various sizes and sometimes enclosed within a tight fitting bottomless black plastic film "pot". In theory there is no compelling reason why rockfibre, chiefly in block form, should not be used to grow on seedlings for NFT, but it does pose problems which are not always easy to overcome.

Firstly, the rock fibre does not naturally contain any plant nutrients and artificial fertilizer is not easily dispersed within the block except in solution. Accordingly it is essential from the start to feed seedling transplants with a mixture of water and nutrients. This task sounds simple but in practice there are few enough gardeners and small scale growers with the skill or time to perfect the job. In any case the task is made a little more difficult by the need to counter natural alkalinity (high pH) in new rock fibres.

Secondly, rock fibre is naturally hydrophobic in which form it is used extensively in the construction industry. For horticultural use wetting agent is added and various proportions of hydrophobic and hydrophillic rock fibres are mixed to produce blocks of particular wetting characteristics. However the generally available product wets-out very readily. For small scale plant production this feature may prove a drawback unless a good degree of watering skill is achieved. It should be appreciated that on a large commercial enterprise both the watering and feeding may in fact be facilitated by the predictable nature of the rock fibre.

Finally, in block form, rock fibre does not usually offer the best chance of producing an undamaged root system of the type desired for successful emergence into the nutrient solution. The reasons for this are elucidated in the section "pot type".

FINAL TRANSPLANTING

In the majority of cases final transplanting is into a suitably sized pot of suitable compost. What is a "suitably" sized pot? As far as NFT is concerned the final transplanting should be into a pot, certainly no larger, but generally one size smaller from that which would normally be used. In this way the quantity of bulky material subsequently placed in the channel is limited and at the same time good opportunity is provided for the root axes to reach the periphery of the pot, an essential prelude to entering the nutrient solution. Where seed is sown directly into the pot in which it will grow until being placed in NFT the same advice applies because ultimately the same qualities are required. Of course the advice applies equally to cuttings.

Given below is a list of suitably sized pots based on experience. The list is by no means exhaustive and should be used for guidance only. Variations will occur due to seasonal factors, different pot shapes and the individual preferences of growers.

Tomatoes)		Melons)	
Cucumbers)	90-110 mm	Fuschias)	
Courgettes)		Dwarf Beans (2 plants/pot))	
Peas (4 plant/pot)		Climbing beans (3 plants/pot)	75-90 mm
		Peas (3 plants/pot))	
		Aubergines)	
		Peppers)	
Geraniums)	65-75 mm	Carnations)	50-65 mm
Strawberries		Dwarfbeans (1 plant/pot)	

Lettuce 35-50 mm

Pot Type

Pot types are many and varied. To simplify the issue it is pertinent first to examine groups of alternatives and to consider variations later.

Round against Square

Round pots are conducive to the gentle deflection of the root axes when they come into contact with the wall of the pot. Square pots tend to present the roots with the need to make sharp changes of direction. In fact most plant roots are quite capable of negotiating angles so the apparent advantage of round pots is not so obvious in practice. A reason may be that square pots tend to be manufactured from fairly flexible material, the 'give' being beneficial. Generally fine rooting plants do just as well in square as round pots, but large, sometimes brittle rooted species not so well.

Solid walls against Open (Mesh) Walls

Solid walled pots encourage the root axes to develop around the periphery where they should find moist but airy conditions. This is precisely what is desired because on removing the pot at placement into NFT the root system can make early contact, possibly just by falling, with the nutrient solution.

When root axes reach the edge of open walled pots there is no physical restraint and they may attempt to grow on. This growth is often unsuccessful because of dryness at the periphery due to contact with a dry atmosphere, possibly compounded by fluctuating unsatisfactory temperature. Sometimes, the root may reach a new area of good conditions, perhaps within an adjacent pot, or more likely into the bed below. These roots are likely to suffer damage when extracted prior to transpslanting. Accordingly it is difficult to produce undamaged roots from open sided pots. Still, protagonists of open sided pots argue that they have advantage because the whole pot may be placed in the channel, thereby eliminating the risk of root block collapse and effecting no disturbance to the root which otherwise necessarily occurs when a pot is removed. These advantages are spurious because binding of the root block is achieved by the development of a good root system and by using the correct compost, whilst no amount of delicate handling at transplanting will rejuvenate the damaged root axes typically produced in open walled pots.

There are pots of which a proportion, usually the bottom third, is open (mesh) walled whilst the remainder has a solid wall. There is no obvious advantage in this design over ordinary mesh pots, except that they offer a limited opportunity for root axes to grow around the top closed sides before descending to become obvious in the mesh portion. At this stage the plants, pot and all, may be successfully transferred to the nutrient solution, and it is a technique favoured by some growers.

This practice is fraught with risk. It relies on the successful emergence of a small number of very vigorous primary root axes. If conditions in the channel are not ideal this emergence will not take place and the entire root system will die back due to saturation.

Permeable Pots

There is an extensive range of permeable pots including peat pots and paper pots. Some are easily penetrated by the root axes whilst others are more resistant and have the characteristics of solid walled pots. Generally success with these pots is dependant on the degree to which they perform like solid walled pots. It is best not to anticipate that ultimately the root will penetrate the pot but instead remove the pot on transplanting. If the pot functions more like a mesh pot then success is not likely as the root system is often severely damaged in penetrating the wall and becoming exposed. If plants grown in these pots must be used, and see first "brought in plants", then it is preferable to rip the pot from one side so as to increase the chances of some root emergence.

Blocks

These have become very popular in recent years and they are quite successful for a variety of culture methods including some NFT work. If the blocks are placed separately, with air spaces between, they have all the disadvantages of open walled pots. However it is usual to maintain the blocks in a tight group, perhaps contained within the walls of a seed tray. Only on transplanting are the blocks broken away. This technique is very successful with lettuce and other small plants, when at the stage of transplanting the blocks can be broken without severely damaging the root system. With large plants such as tomatoes there is little chance of limiting damage, firstly because the plants need to be spaced in the propagation area to receive the correct illumination, thereby endangering roots at the block periphery, and secondly because if left unspaced, rapid growth of the primary roots beyond the boundaries of the block inevitably lead to mass breakage on transplanting.

In Summary

For the majority of plants and circumstances, ordinary inexpensive round plastic pots which can be easily removed at transplanting, are ideal for raising plants prior to placement in NFT. Some plants such as ferns make little root growth into the nutrient solution and they grow quite happily contained within a pot. There appears to be some advantage with these plants in employing mesh pots which allow good aeration but the depth of the pot may need to be reduced so that there is not too much opportunity for drying out above the surface of the solution.

BROUGHT IN PLANTS

Probably a majority of plants matured in gardens and small holdings are brought in from specialist growers. Clearly such plants will not always be in containers thought suitable for NFT, though a large number will be. Where a choice exists it is obviously the latter which should be preferred. Some plants may be in a larger than ideal container. Here, provided root growth has developed satisfactorily at the periphery, and check that this is so by removing a sample plant from the pot before purchase, these plants may be chosen with confidence.

If no other choice exists, but plants in unsuitable containers, then choose undersize plants, remove the container gently and re-pot in a preferred pot. With certain species, e.g. tomatoes, it may be beneficial to transplant a little deeper so that new roots, known as adventitious or stem roots, may be encouraged to form around the base of the stem. From these vigorous roots a satisfactory root mat may be produced in NFT. Block grown plants will often benefit from being transferred to suitable pots. Allow sufficient time for an abundance of strong white roots to become present on the outside of the propagation block before transferring late transplants to the nutrient solution, even though this may mean some delay in setting out the plants.

Plants brought in as bulbs and corms such as onions, gladioli and hyacinths, need not be transplanted at all. Instead they may be placed directly in the channel. However it may be beneficial to start them in pots because the block so produced can assist plant support and because it will allow later transfer back to a pot if the plant is subsequently taken elsewhere for decorative effect.

Strawberries provide an interesting special case. In the garden maiden runners for fruiting in the greenhouse, are rooted in 65 mm pots sunk in the ground. When the new plant is severed from its parent it should be in an ideal condition for transplanting to NFT in due season. Brought in strawberry plants may arrive as pot grown specimens, but more likely they will be free rooted runners taken from very sandy soils. In these cases, subject to season, the plants may be placed directly into the nutrient solution where the old root system acts as a supportive structure. If plants arrive before the time to transfer to NFT simply heel-in the plants in a well drained position outside. With the possible exception of raspberries, other plants which arrive free rooted should first be potted up before being placed in the channel. In particular, cauliflower and cabbage benefit because of the useful support provided by the compost block.

IN-POT TREATMENT

Generally, the treatment of seedlings and transplants should proceed according to usual practice. There are two points of particular interest which have come to prominence with the development of NFT, but which in truth, apply equally to all cultivation methods. Firstly, watering from the top is preferred because it encourages roots to form and stay within the boundaries of the pots, whereas base watering encourages roots to emerge from the pot where they may enter material, e.g., capillary matting, from which they are not easily removed without damage. Secondly, it is preferred if plants are produced which are rather "tight" or "hard" as against "lush", this advice applies particularly to crop plants such as tomatoes. To produce such plants, water should be withheld a little so that drying out occurs between waterings. Of course never reduce water to the extent that the root system is damaged.

THE ROOT CONDITION OF PLANTS READY FOR TRANSFER TO NFT

In the case of pot grown plants naturally producing vigorous white root systems, by far the majority of plants being prepared for NFT, simple guidelines may be set out. White roots should be abundant on the outside of the propagation block when removed from the pot. They should bind the block so that it can be handled easily without crumbling though some loss of material from the top, where roots have not grown, would be acceptable. The tips of the major root axes should be alive, usually indicated by greenish yellow colour and pointed finish. Dark or black blunt root tips are probably dead. Very often most axes are alive but a few black tips are present. This is perfectly acceptable.

In cases where a white root system is not produced or the plants are dormant they may be placed in NFT as soon as they are large enough to handle, and can be comfortably accommodated in the channel. It shculd go without saying that where growth is expected, environmental conditions must be acceptable.

CHAPTER 7

PLANTING OUT INTO NFT

PREPARING THE SYSTEM PRIOR TO PLANTING

Whenever reasonably practical, it is useful if a new NFT unit is run with water only for up to 48 hours before placing any plants in the unit. In this way leaks may be detected and made good. A difficulty occurs in completing the circulation for test purposes if flexible tunnel channelling is employed, and also if spreader mat is used to bridge channel outflow and return duct. In the former instance it should be possible to complete the circulation by leaving the channel open but within a channel support. In the latter case it should be possible to lay a short length of spreader mat at the outflows and secured with a stone or other weight within the channel. At the end of the test circulation pump to waste, this will remove any contaminants which may have been picked up by the water from the surfaces of the construction materials. Prior to transplanting, refill the circulation tank with clean water and switch on the solution heating if appropriate.

PLACING SPREADER MAT AND PLANTS IN THE CHANNELS

Plants having vigorous white root systems

Using Flexible Channelling

It is usual to lay spreader mat in flexible channelling immediately prior to planting out. A planting out sequence is illustrated in Figure 7/1. The method is straightforward and does not require particular skills. Firstly, lay the channelling, inside surface uppermost, open and centrally placed on the prepared slope. Secondly, run spreader mat along the length of the centre of the channelling. Where appropriate allow excess material at the outlet end. Wet out the spreader mat possibly using a watering can and rose. This process adheres the spreader mat to the channelling and subsequently provides substance and form to the base of the channel. Thirdly, place the plants in position on the spreader mat. Finally, beginning at one end, bring up the edges of the channelling such that they meet above the centre, so that the propagation blocks become enclosed within a tunnel and from which the shoots protrude between adjacent edges of the channelling. Secure the edges with suitable fastenings, e.g. staples, but care should be taken not to damage the protruding stems. The best approach is to fasten once directly behind the stem and then again in the centre between the plants, this way the plant obtains immediate support but the channel is lightly vented and inspection access is available.

As an alternative spreader mat and plants may be set out simultaneously. Here, a strip of spreader mat sufficient to cross the base of the channel is placed in position. The mat is secured by placing the plant and the edges of the channel are drawn up as before. This way there is no need to wet out the mat manually as it is certain to intersect the water when circulation is begun. The method is regarded as having time saving advantage on large sites. Figure 7/2 shows this alternative method.

Flexible channels tend to become crinkled at the base during planting out. It is useful to secure one end either by employing a helper or by placing one channel end under a weight so that after planting out the whole channel can be stretched to remove crinkles.

Using Flat Topped or Open Channels

When using narrow base channels spreader mat may be dispensed with, provided there is reasonable surety that plants subsequently set out will not be left isolated from the flow. Where spreader mat is employed it should first be laid the length of the channel,

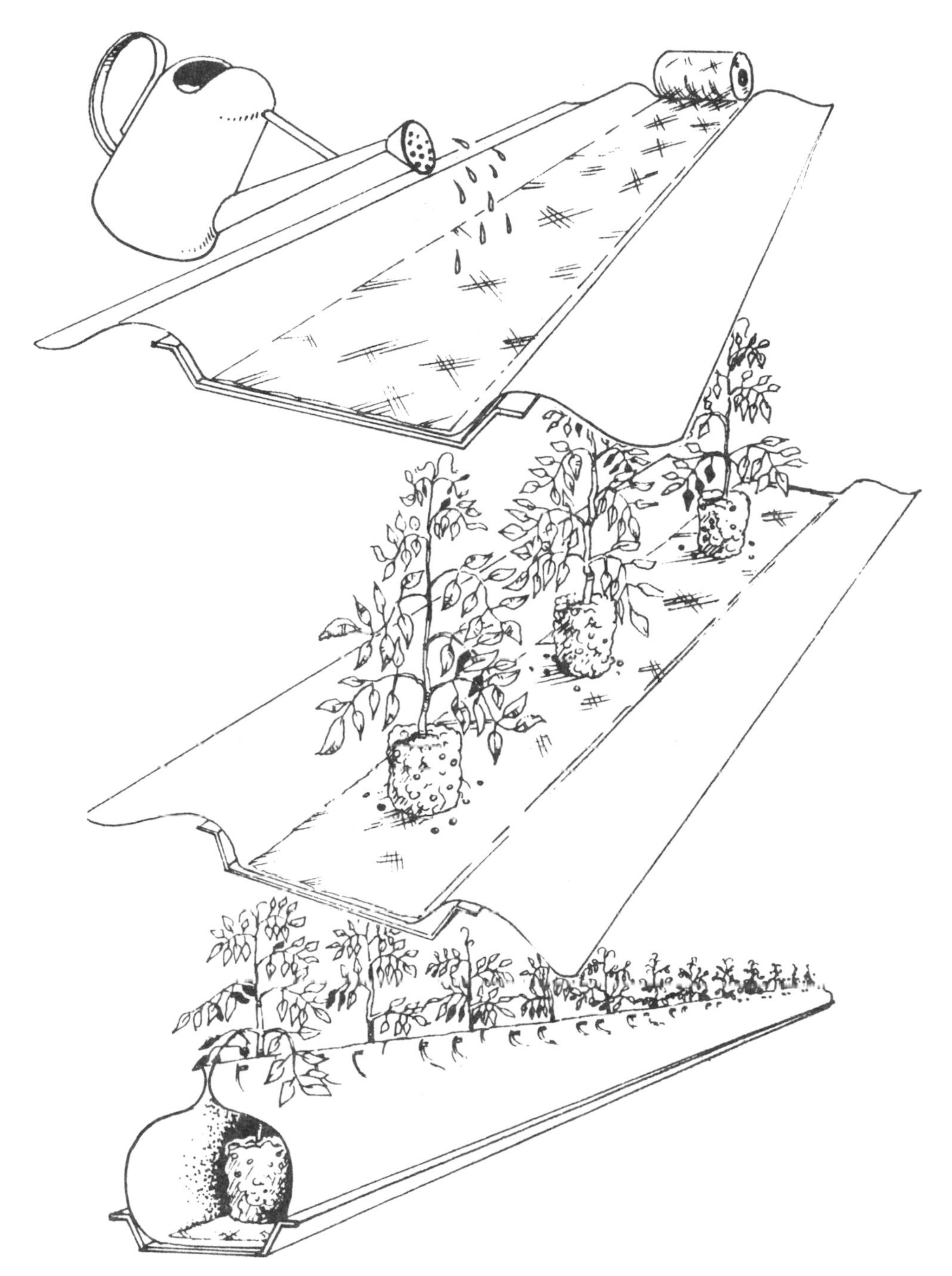

Fig. 7/1 A method of using flexible channelling when setting out plants

more or less covering the base. If necessary use parallel strips of mat to achieve the desired coverage. The spreader mat may be wetted out or left dry. At planting out, place plants in position using open channels, as shown in Figure 7/3, but introduce plants through accommodation holes cut in the top plate when using the more widely employed closed channels, as shown in Figure 7/4.

The accommodation hole should be cut to give a clearance of around 6-15mm to assist in ventilation, but if by chance a larger hole is cut or an old top plate with larger holes cut for a previous crop is employed, it is not a matter of concern, for a base cover, see over, may be fitted.

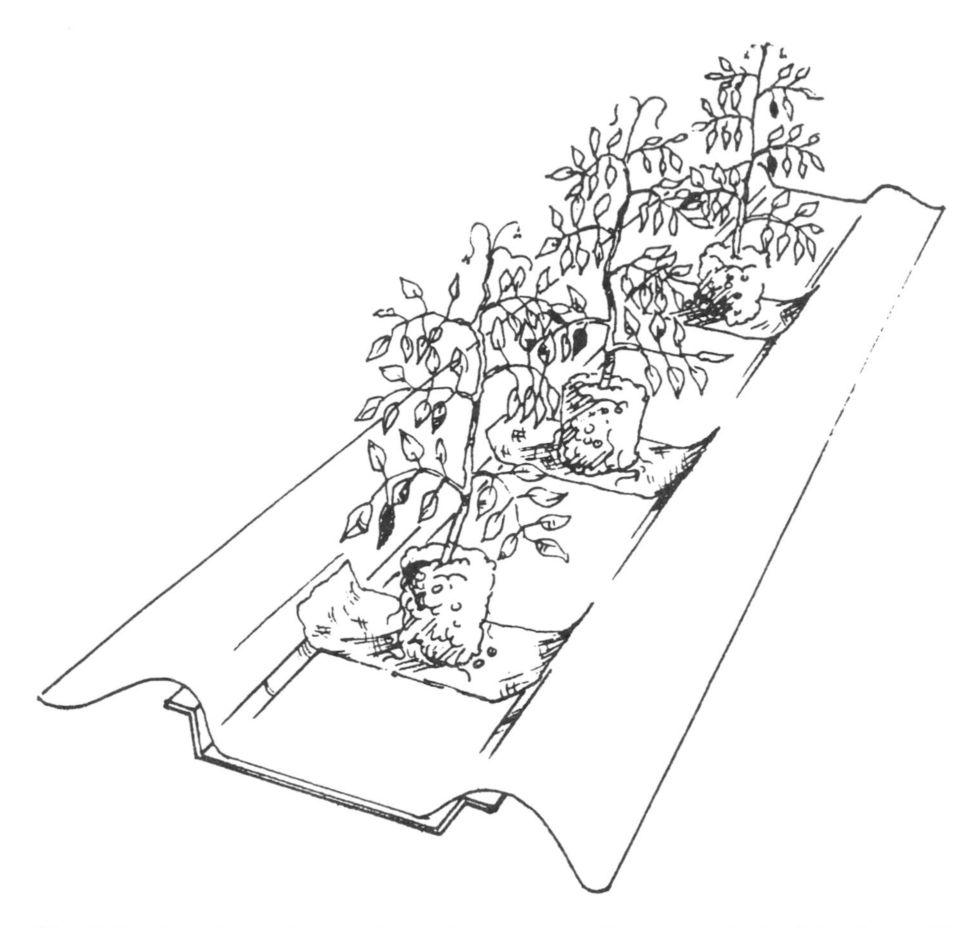

Fig. 7/2 An alternative method of using spreader mat with flexible channelling

Where the propagation block stands proud of the channel top plate it may be desirable to place a base cover over the block to prevent drying out of the root system in this exposed area. Black polythene sheet, black on white in hot climates, is ideal for use as a base cover. Cut a square sufficiently large to cover generously the propagation block, make a slit to the centre and then cut out a small diameter hole. Fit around the base of the stem and fasten the loose edges of the slit. The method of fitting base covers is pictured in Figure 7/5.

Dormant Plants

Setting out dormant plant material is precisely the same as setting out plants with vigorous root systems, i.e. the plant material is placed directly on the spreader mat at the correct planting distances. It is sometimes inadvisable to place the material in such a position as it might dry out from the top during periods of sunny weather. This applies particularly to free rooted strawberry and raspberry plants and similar species in flat topped channels where it is beneficial to tuck the plant under the top plate, but not so far as to make it difficult for subsequent shoot growth to find the light. Alternatively base covers may be used. Bulbs and corms are generally not subject to drying out and are usually placed so that when the shoot emerges it does so directly into the light though sometimes it may be desirable if the shoot is encouraged to extend by restricting the light. In this case the accommodation hole may be covered. Dormant plants in compost blocks generally benefit from being exposed at the top during dormancy as this allows the base of the stem to dry from time to time. However not all plants, ferns in particular, should be exposed to long periods of dryness even when dormant.

Fig. 7/3 Plants set out directly onto spreader mat in an open channel

Hydrophobic Plants

These plants are treated in a distinct manner. Typical plants are carnations, geraniums or calceolarias. They should be subject to periods of drying out and this is most easily facilitated by the use of intermittent flow. Accordingly it is desirable, but not essential, that hydrophobic and hydrophillic species are not mixed in the same channel.

To take advantage of intermittent flow it is advised to provide a means by which the drying process, during the flow-off period, is controlled. This is best achieved by adding a limited amount of solid material in the base of the channel. Accordingly place a layer of coarse sand or grit about 5-8mm deep in the base of the channel, then add 20-25mm of small stones or gravel. Next, using plants in just the same root condition as other white rooted species, set out the plants through the top plate and into the gravel and sand so that the base of the propagation block lies on the base of the channel. The top of the propagation block may advantageously stand proud of the channel to encourage drying, but if it does not do so then the same effect is produced by making the accommodation hole nicely larger, a clearance of 25mm all round will suffice. This method of planting out hydrophobic plants is illustrated in Figure 7/6.

Note that, if intermittent flow is envisaged the circulation tank should not be filled to capacity at start-up but instead filled to a maximum of 75% so that drain back during the flow-off period can be accommodated.

Fig. 7/4 Using closed channel plants are introduced through holes cut into the top plate

Fig. 7/5 Use of a base cover to prevent drying out of an exposed root

Fig. 7/6 The preferred method of setting out hydrophobic plants

When hydrophillic and hydrophobic plants occupy the same channel, thereby reducing the option to use intermittent flow, considerable success can still be achieved by modifying the conditions in the immediate vicinity of the hydrophobic plants. Here raise the propagation block clear of the circulating stream by constructing a mound of solid medium, ideally stones 6-12mm diameter, over the mound place a layer of spreader mat which should also contact the flow. This acts to bring some solution, in addition to that arising from the stones, to the top of the mound. If the mound is made about the same height, or a little greater than the ultimate depth of the root mat produced by the hydrophillic species in the channel giving a mound height probably 10-20mm, then subsequently additional flow can be made to contact plants placed on the mound by raising the flow rate for short periods.

ARRANGEMENT OF PLANTINGS

Monocrop plantings should present no queries as the plants are set out at preferred planting distances. Where a double row of plants is placed in one flat topped channel then it is usual to stagger the row, but if double density is set out in flexible tunnel channelling it is proper to complete the planting in one straight line so as to assist the closing of the channel.

Mixed plantings present some options. The overriding influence is that of light. Plants should be placed so that they receive the illumination they require. Accordingly, tall plants should not shade sun loving small plants but they may be strategically placed to provide shade where it is required. Where shading is to be avoided, large and small plants may occupy the same channel length if plantings are made into flat topped channels in two rows, the tall plants to the back and the small plants to the front from the sunward side so that good illumination is provided. Figure 7/7 depicts this arrangement. Notwithstanding illumination considerations, where plants with both large and small root systems occupy the same channel it is desirable if the large rooted plants are placed at the inlet end so that the root mat they produce does not tend to cause a dam to form in which small root systems may be drowned.

Fig. 7/7 Using flat topped channel to set out plants of contrasting habit

CIRCULATION: THE EARLY DAYS

At anytime during or just after transplanting the circulation may be switched on. It is decidedly advantageous that at switching on, the water temperature should be acceptable. If the water is too cold it may be necessary to add a quantity of hot water. The alternative, of heating the water after circulation has begun, may be extremely slow during periods of very cold weather.

Irrespective of plant type it is recommended to circulate water only at first, as this encourages rooting. Also it prevents the wasteful use of nutrients if, early on, a serious leak occurs or alterations to the circulation system become necessary. Moreover most propagation blocks already have nutrients present and these soon leech into the circulating water where they may cause the solution nutrient concentration to rise alarmingly if there exists already a base nutrient level.

Plants having vigorous white root systems

Root activity should be obvious within 24 hours of the circulation being switched on. This activity will often manifest itself as growth of root axes into the water. Usually these axes will be seen to begin horizontal development at the base of the propagation block, but it is also quite possible that root axes will continue to develop from where they have come to lie after falling free of the propagation block at transplanting. Alternatively fine root hairs will be seen to develop on the outside of the propagation block. This is a sign of good root activity and larger root axes should be seen to enter the solution within a further period of not more than 48 hours.

Transplants should be inspected daily, or as often as reasonably practical, to assess the state of development of the root system. When it is obvious that a root system has begun to develop satisfactorily it is in order to add nutrients to the water. However in order to rid the system of nutrients which may have leeched from propagation blocks it is advised that the original circulation water is first pumped to waste. Before circulating the new solution it should be checked to see that it is at an acceptable temperature.

Treatment of Rooting Failure

If root growth is unsatisfactory it is not good enough to do nothing. The early development is a critical stage in the growth of the plant, unless the root system enters the flow at this stage, growth will never be satisfactory. What are the causes and cures of roots failing to enter the water?

By far the largest proportion of failures is accounted for by plants being placed in the system before they have reached an acceptable state of root development in the propagation block. In these cases, on placement in the flow, the propagation block becomes thoroughly saturated causing the roots within to be deprived of essential oxygen. From this situation there is little or no chance of ever producing successful root growth and the plants must receive attention. The best treatment is to remove the plant from the system and repot, treating the plant in the same way as brought in plants in unsatisfactory containers, page 92. Obviously, give the repotted plant the best available conditions and do not overwater. After 10 days or so, a plant suitable for transplanting back into NFT may be produced. However with plants prone to bolting e.g. cauliflower, it is unlikely that treatment will be successful and it is best to discard the plants and obtain new ones.

Alternatively an intermittent flow regime may be introduced. With this technique the propagation block is given an opportunity to drain within the channel and this should enable new roots to develop. The technique is problematic. On a small scale it is expensive or impossible to automate the on/off-flow periods. Instead the task must be performed manually and this can be a most irritating chore. However on larger sites the adoption of the intermittent flow technique may save considerable labour and inconvenience. Using the technique, first, give the plants a full 24 hours off-flow for the saturated block to drain. Subsequently, the flow should be off during the hours of darkness plus 1 or 2 hours on either side and may remain off during very dull and wet weather. During the rest of the time if the solution is switched on for 10 minutes in every couple of hours a more than adequate degree of wetting will result. Gradually as roots emerge onto the spreader mat the time and frequency of on periods should be increased.

Generally the intermittent flow technique of encouraging rooting in failed plants is applicable only if the treatment is necessary for all or most plants in the unit or at least, in one channel. Firstly, because no or very little nutrient should be present in the water when using the technique, thereby occasioning a threat to healthy vigorously growing plants within the unit. Secondly, because the off-flow period may result in drying out of extensive root systems produced by healthy plants.

When there is some doubt as to the degree of fitness of a root system for transplanting to NFT, but yet the shoot is very well developed, then the use of a modified intermittent flow technique may be beneficial. As an example, some dwarf beans produce a root system which does not readily branch and bind the propagation block. In good conditions this is hardly likely to deter successful root entry into the flow, but often conditions at transplanting, very early or late in the season, are poor. In such cases switching the flow off during the period of darkness plus 1 or 2 hours either side and during cold overcast weather encourages successful rooting. This particular practice is easy to institute in the domestic situation and the small holding and can be operated even if more vigorous successfully rooted plants occupy the same system or channel.

The second most common cause of failure of initial rooting is a too low water temperature. If there is a serious shortfall in water temperature, root activity is immediately stifled, the propagation block saturates and the roots will die back just as in the case of too early transplanting. The treatment accordingly is the same, except that if the intermittent flow technique is employed the water temperature must be raised and the air temperature should be checked to ensure adequacy.

However, in many cases observation of the root system reveals the root axes "trying" to enter the flow. New white roots appear on the outside of the propagation block and grow down the side of the block or sometimes grow out into the adjacent air space, usually at a sharp angle, but in neither case do they make much headway after contacting or coming close to the water. Figure 7/8 pictures this condition.

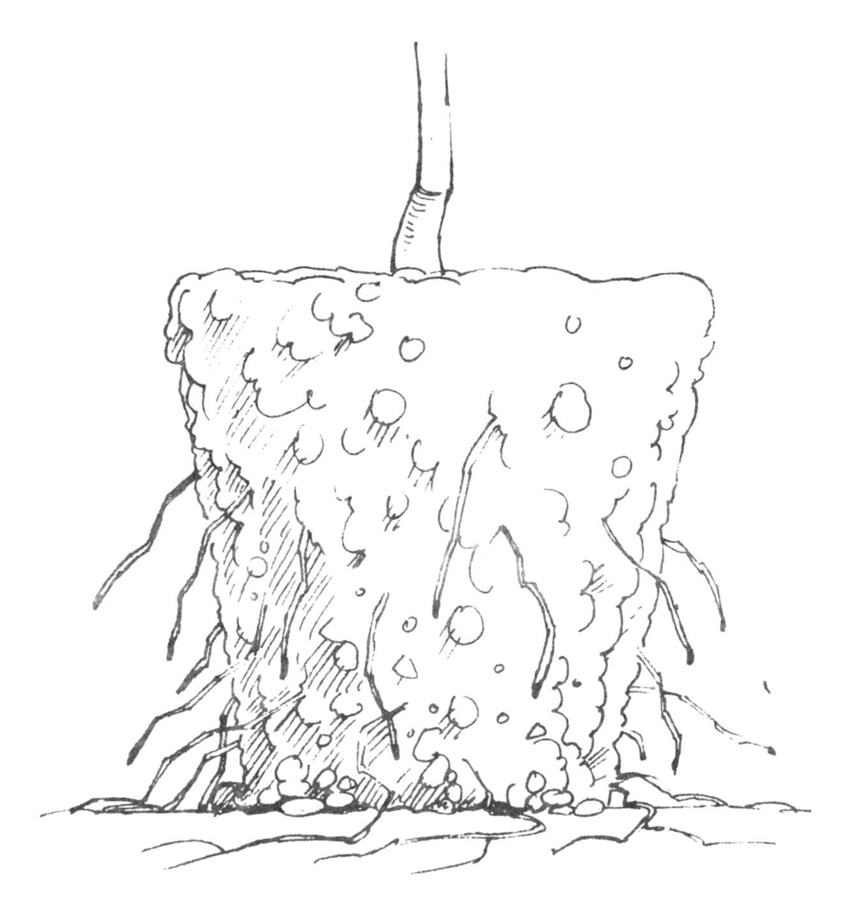

Fig. 7/8 Stultified growth of root axes typifies the solution being too cold

These symptoms typify the water temperature being marginally too cold, perhaps being too cold for just a portion of the time, most likely at night. In these cases raising the water temperature can effect a spectacular cure within 24 hours. Do not be reluctant to raise the temperature 3/4°C to test the effect and do not reduce the flow rate. In fact in stubborn cases it is beneficial to raise the flow rate at the same time as increasing the water temperature. Do not add nutrients to the water until the growth of the root system is satisfactory.

Other causes of initial root failure which have their origin in the particular requirements of NFT include, the collapse of the propagation block due to the use of an unsuitable medium, the placement of the plants in pools of water due to uneveness of slope and finally, due to the addition of large quantities of nutrients to the water. This latter is unreasonably common. Even amongst fairly experienced NFT growers there is a tendancy, which must be resisted, to add nutrients to excess.

Finally, initial root failure may be the first noticeable symptom of plants being set-out in an unsuitable environment. Commonly the introduction of NFT is coincidental with an effort to "bring the season forward" or to grow more demanding plants. In these situations it is essential to ensure that the shoot environment is satisfactory as well as that of the root. However occasional reversions of the weather should not by themselves be sufficient to prevent successful rooting and in this case look towards one or other of the alternative causes. Needless to say, a spell of particularly fine weather may bring plants through when otherwise the betting is that they would fail, such successes should be treated with caution.

Specialist Techniques

So far plants subjected to intermittent flow have been so treated in order to encourage root development. However there exists a specialist intermittent flow technique which is designed to maintain the top growth of crop plants in a predetermined desired condition, whilst so restricting nutrient solution to the root that root growth and development are greatly inhibited. At first this seems a violation of the principles and preferred practices which have thus far been set out.

Some commercial U.K. tomato crops are set out in the channels during early/mid winter when they are subjected to low light levels but reasonable (heated) temperatures. In these conditions even 'hard" transplants soon begin to produce lush 'soft' growth if the root system develops rampantly into the nutrient solution. To counteract this tendancy the plants are subjected to an intermittent flow at such a level that the root is not encouraged to extend beyond the propagation block. Most of the block and certainly the surrounding spreader mat, is allowed to dry out before a short on-flow period is begun. The off-flow time is simply that time which it takes for the desired degree of dryness to be reached. This depends of course on the weather and illumination. The on-flow time is that time it takes to thoroughly wet out the blocks, it may be 10-20 minutes or sometimes longer. Later, when light conditions improve and when the crop has fruit trusses set and developing, continuous flow is gradually instituted allowing the root system to develop in the conventional manner. The method has also been used successfully with cucumbers.

Two most pertinent points arise. Firstly, even after a month, maybe two, of intermittent root restricting flow, the root system grows out when full flow is introduced. How is this so? Root growth and shoot growth are competitive. Under good light and temperature conditions the shoot will generally have the advantage. Under poor conditions the root is usually advantageously placed. Accordingly in any season, first root growth is preferred, but progressively as the season improves shoot growth becomes ascendant. Note that, this specialist intermittent flow regime is practised during the winter, so that sufficient early season remains after continuous flow is started, to allow and encourage satisfactory root growth and development into the nutrient solution. The later the season at setting-out the less satisfactory is the technique, but equally the less need there is to use the technique. Accordingly the private gardener or small grower is unlikely to benefit from using this technique simply because the season is too far advanced at the time of setting-out.

Secondly, the technique demands regular examination of the state of dryness of the propagation block to determine when to switch on the flow. There are reasonably priced sensors which do this job automatically, but in general the demands of the technique for constant attention or automation make it unattractive to small scale NFT users. The question arises then, are there any alternative techniques suitable for domestic and small scale growers which can be used to prevent growth becoming "soft" after very early season transplanting? This is important because of the willingness of some individuals adopting NFT for monocrop production, to attempt particularly early cropping. In fact there are two options available to the early starter. By early we mean setting-out, using plants at the correct stage for setting-out, before the end of the first week of March in the U.K. Midland counties. Commensurately a little earlier or later in progressively southern and northern regions.

Firstly, the grower can increase the concentration of the nutrient solution thereby restricting water uptake and "hardening" top growth. For details see page 108. Secondly, the grower may practice a regime half-way between the specialist intermittent flow and full flow. In this case not only is the off-flow time much reduced but also the duration of the treatment. Using this method, set out the plants as usual, switch off the circulation only during the hours of darkness plus 2 hours on either side and during cold dull weather. Later assess the state of "hardness" to determine if a somewhat more restricted flow is necessary. Close to the end of flowering of the first truss begin a change to continuous flow taking four or five days to complete. Using this schedule the flow restrictions are likely to be operative for two to three weeks. If a greater time is required then insufficiently developed transplants have been used or else environmental conditions have not been good enough to promote the correct development of the shoot. Finally a word of warning, do not combine this modified intermittent flow technique with the increasing nutrient method as this can lead to serious reduction of fruit set and development.

Dormant Plants

In an intensive cultivation area it is unlikely that dormant plants would be housed in NFT channels for long periods. Instead placement of the plant material in the channel is usually designed to break dormancy. Therefore placement should coincide with the onset or provision of environmental conditions conducive to the growth of the dormant plants. Since there is often little contact between the air space and the dormant plant material, it being contained entirely or mainly within the channel, water heating is an important facility when starting plants into growth during periods when ambient temperatures are too low.

It is usually unnecessary to subject dormant plant material to continuous flow. A common practice is to circulate water during daylight and even then only on days with reasonable brightness. Once growth begins more continuous flow may be instituted but, especially early in the season, it may be beneficial, by protecting plants from undue saturation, to switch off the flow at nights and during very inclement weather.

Water only should be circulated around dormant plants. The time it takes for the plant material to initiate new roots is very variable depending on the degree of conduciveness of the conditions and the state of dormancy of the material. In general, new root growth should be apparent within 14 days of setting out. With bulbs the new root growth occurs around the base of the bulb, with plants on their old roots such as strawberries, new root growth occurs from along the length, usually towards the tip, of the old root system where it contacts the flow. When it is obvious that roots have successfully entered the water, nutrients may be added to the water.

In extensive cultivation areas dormant plants may be set out in channels a long time, perhaps months, before dormancy is expected to break. These plants are generally shrubby perennials but herbaceous plants too may be so treated. In these cases water only is circulated for as long as is required to keep the propagation blocks from drying out. This may be not at all in winter, perhaps only an hour or two a week in early spring but later somewhat greater flow periods may be required. In general dormant plants of this type begin root development before shoot development so that even early on in the year when the shoot appears still quite dormant root activity may be significant. It is important to watch for this development, because the new roots should not be damaged by excessive dryness. Accordingly once root growth begins the flow-on times may have to be increased. However a greater increase in flow-on time will become necessary when the plant shoots develop and water begins to be lost from the leaves. At this stage nutrients may be added to the circulating water.

As for their future attention, once root growth has developed satisfactorily and nutrients have been added to the circulating water, it is appropriate to classify once dormant plants into either vigorous rooting types or hydrophobic plants. In the case of the latter the provision of solid medium in the channel (see page 97) is preferably taken care of at planting out, but it may be added as necessary during early growth.

Hydrophobic Plants

The key to success in establishing these plants in NFT is to resist the temptation to overwater. Before re-starting flow check that the propagation block around the base of the stem has dried. It need not be powdery dry but the remnants of the compost should be fairly friable. The time taken for drying is dependant on the season, the temperature and the weather in addition to the size of the plants at setting out. During deep mid-winter in northern areas no flow may be started for several weeks, but if large plants are set out in good conditions later in the season then a short on-flow period, about 1 hour, may be required each day or two.

In general, satisfactory shoot growth is the best indicator of health in hydrophobic plants. It is not easy to assess the state of root development though if the aggregate is gently disturbed it may be possible to see new fine roots which have developed from the propagation block. Sometimes these can be found within a few days of setting out but at other times it may be months before they become obvious. When shoot growth is apparent add nutrients to the water.

The same general principle applies where hydrophobic plants have been set out with hydrophillic types. The flow in the bed beneath the propagation block should be sufficient to just moisten the base of the block. If it is too little then increase the flow, if it is too wet, decrease the flow. If adjustments to the flow cannot be made, add sand to increase wetting, or take away aggregate to form a water escape channel to increase drying.

The most common symptom of failure to establish is stem base rot. This is a fungal attack facilitated by overwatering of the propagation block to the point where the block is continually wet at the stem base. Plants do not, as a rule, recover and should be disposed of. Prevent re-occurrence by reducing wetness. Stem base rot in transplants is significantly increased in poor environmental conditions and when plants have been handled roughly.

CHAPTER EIGHT

NUTRITION

In this chapter the nutrition of plants in NFT systems will be explained in respect of the typical two component, A and B, nutrient and phosphoric acid described in Chapter 4. Although nutrition and nutrition programmes excite comments such as, "too complicated", and "you need to be a chemist", nothing could be further from the truth. In practice no knowledge of chemistry is required or is even desirable. All feeding programmes are simple. It is good attention to the method which produces the most rewarding results.

No matter whether manufacturers or DIY nutrients are used, it is essential to have a high degree of confidence in the nutrient composition of the product. Especially amongst 'new' NFT operators there is a remarkable tendency to suspect the composition as being responsible for any and all difficulties which occur, when in fact difficulties are only very rarely attributable to this cause. Very much more likely causes of difficulties are overdosing of nutrients and heavy-handedness with acid. Accordingly, a golden rule may be constructed, viz., when in doubt add less nutrients; not more, add less acid; not more.

STOCK SOLUTIONS

Nutrient Stock Solutions

Most DIY nutrients will have been prepared as concentrated solutions, but manufacturers nutrient packs will certainly arrive as dry powders. Though it is possible to use these dry powders directly in any nutrition programme, it is much preferred if stock solutions are prepared. The reasons for this are:— Firstly, weighings, especially of small quantities, are time consuming and tedious. Secondly, dry powders need to be effectively sealed after each weighing to prevent them taking up moisture from the atmosphere. If they do take up moisture they become soggy or else cake, which makes them awkward and irritating to handle, but does not affect their nutrient value. Thirdly, and most seriously, dry powders, added directly to the water in the circulation tank, take some time to dissolve and become dispersed evenly in the system so that it is impossible to obtain immediate accurate readings of nutrient solution conductivity, and it is unwise to make fine adjustments of pH. This problem can be overcome if, before addition to the circulating water, dry powders are pre-dissolved in a little warm water. But this process simply adds unwanted tedium to, what should be, a swift and easy routine.

When making up stock solutions, use sufficient weight of powders that will meet nutrient requirements for a reasonably lengthy period. This may be as much as a seasons supply for a small domestic unit, but perhaps more like a month for a small commercial system. Where dry powders are taken from a bulk supply, ensure that the correct weight ratio of powders A & B is taken.

Obtain two containers of approximately 4-5 litres volume for each 1 kg. weight (total of A & B) of dry powders. Therefore, if a manufacturers 2.5 kg (A & B) pack of nutrients is to be made up into stock solutions, two containers, each of not less than 10 litres, are required. If the containers are of different sizes it doesn't matter, simply mark them each at the required identical volume. The dilution figures given above assume a reasonably quick usage of the stock solutions so prepared. If a seasons supply is made up in one dilution then the preferred dilution rate should be approximately double, i.e., 8-10 litres water to each 1 kg weight of nutrients (total weight of A & B). The reason for this is that whilst dry powder nutrients have an indefinite shelf life so long as they are kept dry, nutrients in solution are affected by chemical reactions which may cause precipitation and loss of availability. The speed of these reactions is governed by the concentration of the solution, the more concentrated the solution the faster the reactions. Stock solution containers are preferably of plastic. Metal containers are best avoided, though enamelled buckets are suitable. If light can penetrate the walls of the containers algae may grow in the stock solutions, so if black or other dense colour is unavailable, containers may be painted black on the outside or simply stored between use in a dark place. Lids are useful, but alternatively the containers may be covered with black polythene sheets or similar. Mark the containers A and B.

Fill the containers to the required volume, the same volume in each container, and add the correct weights of nutrients, A to container A., B to container B. Stir vigorously, or shake to dissolve. If a little hot water is used in filling the containers the powders will dissolve much more readily. Occasional difficulty is experienced in dissolving nutrient B when it has caked due to the action of moisture on a phosphate ingredient. In this case, break up the cake before adding to the water. When completely dispersed, stock solutions are ready for use.

Acid Stock Solution

Phosphoric acid is fairly easy to use in the concentrated form. However, it is undesirable if a large container of acid is employed for small outgoings as this encourages accidents and overdosing. Instead, either decant a convenient volume of acid from the large supply to a suitable MARKED plastic bottle with a good cap, or preferably, make up a weak solution in a plastic bucket. A convenient dilution on small sites is around 250 ml. acid to 5 litres water, but on commercial sites 2 or 3 times this concentration would be more convenient. Add acid to water, never water to acid. Mark the dilution 'Phosphoric Acid' and keep acid and acid solutions out of the reach of children.

NUTRITION PROGRAMMES

There are three entirely effective nutrition programmes available to NFT users. The conductivity programme, the discharging programme, and the simplified topping-up programme. The conductivity programme is the original and basic programme. It is equally effective on any scale of enterprise, but because it requires a conductivity meter, which is a not inconsiderable expense, alternative programmes have been developed for small scale users. For these users, the discharging programme has a history of success. It has advantages because, not only is specialist test equipment not required, but neither are auto top-up facilities which can sometimes be a significant expense, or which can be difficult to fit when space is at a premium. More recently the simplified topping-up programme has been described. This offers the small scale user some of the features of the conductivity programme, but without the expense of a conductivity meter. However, header tank auto top-up facilities are highly desirable when using this programme.

THE CONDUCTIVITY PROGRAMME USING SOFT WATER

The following materials should be on hand.

1. A conductivity meter.
2. A thermometer.
3. Nutrient stock solutions A & B.
4. A jug, cup or plastic measure.
5. An acidity test kit.
6. A supply of phosphoric acid. Preferably as a dilute solution.

Basic method

Determine the conductivity factor (CF) of the water/solution in the system. Determine the desired CF, of the nutrient solution. If the CF of the water/solution is below the desired CF add equal volumes of nutrient stock solutions A and B until the nutrient solution CF is raised to the desired CF. If the solution CF is higher than the desired CF dilute the solution until the desired CF is attained. Later check the pH of the solution and adjust using phosphoric acid if necessary.

Detail

The CF is normally found by setting the conductivity meter to the temperature of the solution to be tested. Some meters have automatic temperature compensation. Other meters have no compensation mechanism, in this case, take readings always at a similar temperature.

The desired CF is the CF deemed to be appropriate to the plants in the unit at that particular time. Using properly formulated NFT nutrients, a nutrient solution more or less conforming to the composition of the optimum solution given on page 51 is produced with a CF of around 20. This may be referred to as the standard CF value, but this figure cannot be used universally as the desired CF. The factors affecting the desired conductivity are:— age, health and fitness, type and mix of plants in the unit, and environmental conditions.

Age

Young plants generally benefit from a period of establishment at low CF. There are two reasons for this. Firstly, root systems must be allowed to supply the water demands of the shoot, but at progressively higher CF values water uptake is inhibited. This effect is compounded in young plants because the root system is usually poorly developed. This is especially so in the early stages of establishment in NFT, when the majority of the root system may be contained and operate within and around the rather poor conditions of the propagation block. Secondly, young plants are often subjected to relatively poor environmental conditions on being set out early or late in the season. This causes a stress which exposure to standard CF can exacerbate. Therefore, the desired CF for young plants may be set as low as 5. As the plants establish and mature, the desired CF may be raised.

There is a circumstance where the general advice to lower CF for young plants is not followed. In adequate temperatures, but low light levels, excessively lush growth may be produced at low CF's. Young plant growth may be 'hardened' by subjecting the plants to high CF values, in fact as high as CF 40. In this instance, the plants are generally allowed at least 1 day per week at low CF and this may be facilitated by running the unit at about 25% of solution capacity so that a great dilution can be had, on the appropriate day, simply by topping up the system with water. Later, the new large volume can be made up to high CF and the volume gradually run down over the succeeding days. The practical operation of the method is easier on large sites, but certainly it can be implemented on small sites too. The method is inappropriate during periods of high illumination, say after the first week of March in Midland UK counties as then serious semi-permanent interference with the plants water uptake operations may be inflicted.

Mature plants with good root systems are able to tolerate, and sometimes benefit, from the provision of a nutrient solution at higher than standard CF. It is generally agreed that provided undue stress on the plant, due to interference with water uptake is avoided, high CF solutions increase the quality of fruit and flowers. It is unlikely, all other aspects being considered, that the CF would be raised above 30 on account of an allowance for maturity.

Plant Health and Fitness to Environment

Provided young plants occupying an NFT system are healthy and fitted to the prevailing environment, it is beneficial if the CF value of the circulating solution is gradually raised towards standard, and thereafter maintained, subject to other considerations. However, this desirable condition may not always be achieved. From a variety of causes, some self-inflicted, such as using ill-prepared plants, others external, such as aphid attack, plants may grow but not as well as hoped or anticipated. In these cases run a lower CF regime until such time as the stress on the plants is relieved.

In the same way environmental conditions may be so poor as to impose a stress on the plants. This is particularly true of early plantings, which may be subject to unreasonably cold conditions, perhaps just at nights, for considerable periods. This condition commonly occurs in domestic greenhouses during April and May when tomato plants, set out early, are stressed for perhaps six weeks or more by low night temperatures. In these and similar circumstances, run NFT systems at lower than standard CF. Note that overcast conditions do not impose a stress on plants. Such conditions reduce growth rate and water loss through transpiration and therefore generally make it easier for the root to keep up with the shoots demand for water and nutrients.

Type of Plants

Some plants lose water rapidly from their leaves, others do not as water loss is restricted by adaptations. Though it is a generalisation, it is useful if such plants are described respectively as hydrophillic and hydrophobic. Hydrophillic plants make enormous demands of their root systems for water and they perform poorly when water is deficient. As water uptake is progressively inhibited by increasing solution CF it follows that hydrophillic plants should not generally be exposed to high solution CF. However, some hydrophillic plants produce very large root systems which serve to meet the very large demand for water. Such plants can tolerate, and sometimes benefit from, higher solution CF, tomatoes are a particular example. Other hydrophillic species, e.g. strawberries, rarely produce root systems large in proportion to their foliage and, accordingly, they are always suspect if exposed to high solution CF. Hydrophobic species take up little water, but of course they still require nutrients. They appear to benefit from high solution CF.

Mix of Plants

It is a common occurrence for plants, at differing states of maturity and of diverse type, to be cultivated in the same nutrient solution. Fortunately, with mixed plantings, the selection of desired CF is straightforward. The rule is that low CF always takes precedence. This allows young plants to be set out successfully at any time, it provides a break, from water uptake stress, for high performing high CF plants from which they often benefit, and it provides a useful opportunity for the nutrient solution to be discharged so that in succeeding weeks the CF value can be gradually increased. Whenever possible, coincide raising the CF with periods of dull weather, as under bright conditions additional stress would be imposed on the low CF plants.

Environment

First time users of NFT are often amazed at the differing volumes of water removed from the system by the same plants, but in contrasting environmental conditions. In bright light and good temperatures, water usage is much greater than in low light and only adequate temperature. It is obvious then, that in bright light and good temperatures, plants are susceptible to water stress and that this may be compounded if a high solution CF is run concurrently. Accordingly, it is possible to devise a simple rule of thumb. Under conditions of bright light and good temperatures the solution CF should be lower than under poor light and adequate temperature.

In practice, with small scale NFT, changes in solution CF due to prevailing conditions are not often made on a daily basis. In part, because it is not always easy to alter the solution CF so rapidly, in part, because plants are generally excellent at adapting to transient, but reasonable, changes in conditions. Instead changing the solution CF is mainly practiced in response to periods of particular weather. Therefore, during hot dry spells decrease the solution CF by 5-8 points and take advantage of dull wet spells to raise the solution CF by a similar amount to improve quality.

Solution temperature has a large impact on the plants ability to take up water and consequently on desired CF. In bright light and good atmospheric temperature, raising the solution temperature can relieve water uptake stress by increasing root activity and therefore enable the unit to be run at a somewhat higher CF. In the same way, young transplants may be encouraged to root into the solution by raising solution temperature and this may also allow the solution to be run at higher CF.

Adding Nutrients to Raise CF

The volume of stock solutions A and B required to raise the CF of the circulating solution to the desired CF is proportional to the volume of the system and the concentration of the stock solutions.

Remember to use equal volumes of A and B unless there is specific reason to do otherwise, see later. However, if one measure of each stock solution is added and dispersed in the system, then a further CF reading can be taken and the uplift of CF attributable to the measure may be used to achieve the same uplift with further additions because the effect of nutrient additions on CF is additive. It is useful to have some idea of the volume of stock solutions required to make the required uplift of CF at any time, because it enables the system to be 'dosed' without the need to wait while nutrient additions are dispersed in the system. Incidentally, if a paddle is used to mix additions made into the circulation tank, dispersal of the nutrients throughout the unit is much more rapid.

A fine degree of accuracy is not required. A difference of several points between desired and achieved CF is insignificant and it is time wasting to attempt to achieve exactly the desired CF. The order in which the stock solutions are added to the circulating solution has some significance if considerable quantities of stock solution are added, such as maybe the case at system start up or after discharging solution. Here it is best to add solution A first and allow this to disperse before adding solution B. In this way any possibility of precipitation of calcium and phosphate caused by local high concentrations in the circulation tank is avoided. When adding small quantities of stock solution then it is immaterial which order the additions are made. How often should nutrients be added to the system? This depends on the rate of decline of the solution CF, which in turn is dependent on many variables conveniently summarised as the number and type of plants, the volume of the unit and the environmental conditions. Nonetheless, provided the unit has been constructed within the guidelines of plant capacity and volume given earlier, changes in solution CF will be gradual. Note that if the solution CF falls rapidly in a system automatically topped-up then a leak should be suspected.

On commercial and semi-commercial sites, and indeed with larger domestic systems, a daily routine of monitoring and, if necessary, adjusting CF may be instituted. Where auto top-up facilities are not fitted, make-up water should be added to the system at least 1 hour before monitoring CF so complete mixing in is achieved at the time of monitoring. The best time to monitor and adjust CF is in the evening because the plants will then be exposed to the highest CF during the night and morning, whilst during the heat of the day the CF will have declined a little due to take-up of nutrients from the solution. Of course, if the unit is manually topped up this effect will not occur, nor is it so important a feature that daily life need be disrupted if evening monitoring is inconvenient. With many domestic and some semi-commercial systems daily monitoring is inconvenient. In these cases simply monitor CF when most convenient.

Monitoring the CF of the nutrient solution should be a simple task done without aggravation. If the unit is difficult to dose because changes in CF are very rapid, insufficient volume has been allowed. At an early stage add extra volume as an auxiliary or maintank. If the CF is so stable that no additions are required within a reasonably short time, i.e., no CF change within 2-3 days when immature, but growing, plants occupy the channels, then the system volume is too great. It is generally easy to reduce volume by setting the auto top-up valve lower. Later in the season when mature plants use more nutrients, some or all of the original capacity may be reinstated.

Periods of operator absence, e.g., holidays and illness should not pose a serious problem. Usually it is inappropriate to detail the use of the conductivity meter to another person unfamiliar with the aim or operation of the unit. Instead it may be best if instructions are given to add a particular volume of stock solution, e.g., 1 cup full of A and one of B, on particular days. The amount being determined by experience with error on the side of caution. It is even more opportune if these volumes are already taken from the stock solutions and stood in jars convenient to be emptied into the circulation tank on the nominated day.

Diluting the Nutrient Solution

Under conditions where the nutrient solution is automatically topped up with water then a gradual decline in solution CF will be apparent. However, in the absence of auto top-up, the general tendency is for the nutrient solution to become more concentrated, raising CF, as water is preferentially lost from the system by transpiration and evaporation. In bright light and hot conditions this tendency to concentrate can become quite marked. Additionally, as the volume in circulation declines, further preferential losses of water may result in rapid upward movement of solution CF. To obviate this effect, periodic dilution of the solution is necessary. This is easy enough to achieve, simply add water manually to bring the volume in the circulation tank back to the original. Do this each day during periods of rapid growth and water loss, but less frequently during periods of little or no growth when water losses are comparatively small. After so adding water, allow at least one hour for the solution in circulation to become thoroughly mixed before testing the CF and making adjustments as necessary. Therefore, in systems run without auto top-up facilities, two site visits are required to check and adjust solution CF.

There are circumstances where it may be advisable to dilute the nutrient solution by a greater degree than is brought about by making up the solution volume, These include:—correcting nutrient overdoses, making an early allowance for a change to fine weather and reducing stress on plants, such dilutions are greatly facilitated if the circulation tank is normally operated at around 75% of capacity so that dilution water can be added without the need to drain away and waste nutrient solution.

Checking and Adjusting the Solution pH

Allow additions of nutrient stock solutions A & B to become thoroughly dispersed in the system before checking the solution pH. Normally at least one hour should be allowed. In practice a convenient routine is to check the pH in the morning, having adjusted the CF the previous evening.

Always be cautious when adding acid to the nutrient solution. Where only small adjustments in pH are required it may be safer, from the point of view of alleviating the risk of overdosing, if diluted acid is used. The operator should aim to become so familiar with the acid quantities that in making an adjustment of pH just one addition of acid is required, otherwise checking pH can become something of a chore given that around 1 hour should be allowed for mixing in between addition of acid and re-checking pH. Dispersal time is reduced if the solution is stirred after adding the acid.

Run the solution at a pH between 6.0 and 6.5. Under-dosing is unimportant, simply use a little more acid at the next regular addition. Overdosing by a small amount to about pH 5.5 is not serious. In this case allow the pH to climb back during subsequent days but rectification may be effected immediately if more water is added to the system at the time of overdosing. Overdosing to below pH 5.5 and those occasional overdosing cases where the pH stays doggedly at, or a little above 5.5 require the solution to be discharged. There is no reason why the discharged solution should not be used elsewhere in the garden, the fact that the pH is low does not affect its suitability when applied to soil or compost.

Where an NFT system is topped up with water via a header tank, the water contained in the header tank may be treated with acid as necessary so that the nutrient solution is maintained at the correct pH. However, it is advisable to check that this is so when monitoring solution CF. This method can save significant work and is especially useful during regular operator absences.

On some sites, using very soft water or exclusively rainwater, the solution pH may never rise above 6.0 and may indeed decline to below 5.5. In these cases it is necessary to dose the unit not with acid but with alkali so that the solution pH is raised above 5.5. Sodium Hydroxide can be used for this purpose.

Discharging the Nutrient Solution

Using soft water supplies, the desired CF may be maintained by regular additions of nutrients for a very long period, but eventually these additions become less frequent, or the decline in CF becomes less noticeable so that nutrient usage gradually declines. This is indicative of a build-up of useless salts in the solution. Salts of sodium, chlorine and sulphur are most usually implicated and their sources are both the water and the nutrients. It is preferred if the solution is discharged before there is any serious build-up of these salts, and to achieve this the general recommendation is to discharge the solution at intervals not exceeding 10 weeks. The period may be reduced if at any time the plants appear to be suffering a stress or as a prelude to holidays and enforced absences.

It is also generally appropriate to discharge the solution more frequently if alkali has been added to raise solution CF. On sites where this procedure is followed, the solution life should not exceed 5 weeks, at least until the operator has become fully conversant with the running of the unit.

It is useful to observe closely the growth of plants immediately after discharging solution and while running a new solution. Sometimes a significant growth increase is noticed, usually coupled with increased water uptake and nutrient usage. This observation suggests that the discharge interval has been too long and an appropriate adjustment is required the next time round.

EFFECTS OF HARD WATER ON THE NUTRIENT SOLUTION

Hard water is water which contains a high level of dissolved salts. The two most common salts are those of calcium and magnesium. An everyday manifestation of the presence of these salts is the furring of kettles. As described, electrical conductivity, monitored as CF, increases as nutrient salts are dissolved in the solution. It follows then that natural salts dissolved in water add to the CF. The CF of the water before nutrients are added is known as the base CF. Use the conductivity meter to measure base CF taking care to use a representative sample, i.e., from a pond or other open water source.

Collect from 'open' water not from puddled edges, from the tap; run the tap for a minute before collecting the sample. If your CF meter is not temperature compensated adjust the sample temperature to around 20°C before taking a reading.

Results and Actions

Reading CF	*Action*
0-3 inclusive	follow soft water instructions
4-8 inclusive	follow hard water instructions
9 or above	refer to special adaptations

What is the effect of hard water on the nutrient solution? Hard water adds to the CF of the solution without commensurately increasing the nutrient value. What is more, it does so according to the quantity of water extracted by the plants. An example will serve to illustrate this process:— An NFT unit has 30 tomato plants and 180 litres of solution in circulation. The water base CF is 6. At start-up nutrient stock solutions have been added to raise solution CF to 20. Therefore, at start up 14 CF points are due to nutrient additions and 6 are due to the water. If we assume that during a typical summer week these tomato plants use 180 litres of water (they may use more during hot weather) then at the end of the week an additional 6 CF points will have been added to the solution by the make-up water. Therefore, assuming the solution is maintained at a CF of 20, 12 CF points will be attributable to the water and only 8 points to the nutrients. This status is barely acceptable. At the end of the following week the position would stand as only 2 CF points due to nutrients and 18 due to water. Clearly this status would be unacceptable.

In practice the position is not as critical as the example concludes because much of the base CF is due to salts, which also function as sources of nutrients, so that some are taken up by the plants. The actual addition of CF to the solution by the make-up water is probably about half of that which would be attributable if the full impact of base CF was allowed for. Using the prior example the 180 litres of make-up water taken in the first week would account for just 3 points of the solution CF so that the status of the solution would be:— 9 CF points attributable to the water (6 + 3) and 11 CF to nutrient additions. At the end of the second week 12 CF points would be attributable to the water (6 + 3 + 3) and 8 to the nutrients. This is a significantly improved position when compared with the original calculation.

However, the situation may be made substantially more critical by two separate influences. Most importantly the solution volume. In the example, if the circulation volume was reduced to 90 litres then the addition of CF points due to make-up water would be doubled. Accordingly never underspecify the system capacity when using hard water and, if necessary, add extra volume by fitting an auxiliary or main tank. Less important is added CF due to acid additions which may total 2-4 CF points per week even with adequate volume. But this addition is of course of mainly useful nutrient, namely phosphate. Still, using hard water supplies, there is a tendency for phosphate levels in the solution to rise, thereby adding unnecessarily to CF. This tendency may be alleviated if phosphate free nutrients are used.

THE CONDUCTIVITY PROGRAMME USING HARD WATER (BASE CF 4-8)

The sum of the affects of using hard water make-up supplies is that, after nutrient additions to a predetermined level, desired CF, subsequent changes in solution CF do not solely reflect the removal of nutrients from the solution by the plants. This situation manifests itself as stable solution CF when make-up water CF additions more or less equate with nutrient losses, or as rising solution CF when make-up water CF additions are greater than nutrient losses. Sometimes the solution CF may fall if marginally hard water is used. Irrespective of the manifestation the effect is a gradual decline of the nutrient status of the solution. This decline must be arrested and the following procedure demonstrates how this is done.

At System Start-Up

Fill the circulation tank with clean water, heat as/if necessary, begin circulation and bring the system to operating capacity. Check, and note, the base CF of the water in the circulation tank.

Add phosphoric acid to reduce water pH close to desired pH, i.e., between 6.0 and 6.5. The amount of acid used will depend on the hardness of the water. It is useful to keep a record of the amount of acid required so that future treatment of the same volume, after solution discharges, will be rapidly accomplished. Do not overdose, avoid lowering the pH much below 6.0.

Determine desired CF using the parameters described previously for soft water. Add half of base CF, the resultant is target CF viz:—

desired CF plus ½ base CF equals target CF.

Add nutrient stock solutions A & B in equal volumes, unless specifically desired to do otherwise, to achieve target CF. Add nutrient A first and allow this to disperse a little before adding B. Allow time between nutrient additions and monitoring CF for the nutrients to disperse throughout the system. This process may be encouraged by stirring the solution in the circulation tank. When target CF is achieved check solution pH and adjust if necessary.

Maintaining Solution Nutrient Status

Soft water may be used as make-up water for the system. This is commonly done when a supply of rainwater is available. In this case subsequent monitoring and adjusting of solution CF and pH is exactly the same as the soft water procedure. Sometimes sufficient rainwater is available to supply a proportion of make-up water requirements. Useful amounts may be a half or a quarter. In these cases assume a proportional reduction in base CF of the make-up water e.g., hard water base CF 4 but half rain water used, adjusted base CF 2. Again, hard water base CF 8 but quarter rain water used, adjusted base CF 6.

Record the volume of make-up water entering the system. If the system is manually topped up this is of course very easy. If the unit is supplied via a header tank calculate the drop in header tank water level as volume. With large header tanks it is useful to construct a dip stick for rapid volume measurement. If the unit is supplied by mains, a water meter may be fitted which records accumulated water consumption. These meters are not especially expensive, but on small sites the header tank method is more convenient in most cases. When a significant volume of make-up water has entered the system, itself an indication of plant growth and activity, calculate a new target CF adding an allowance for the CF attributable to the make-up water. Examples best illustrate this procedure.

Example 1

Base CF of make-up water	6
Solution volume in circulation	210 litres
Original target CF	13
Make-up water used	70 litres

Therefore make-up water volume is ⅓rd. of solution volume and contributes proportionally to the solution CF. i.e., 6 divided by ⅓ = 2.

Result, add 1 point to target CF because the assumption is that ½ of the CF attributable to the water is useful nutrient. Original target CF 13 plus 1 = new target CF 14. Now add nutrients A & B to bring the solution to the new target CF.

Example 2

Base CF of make-up water 8 but quarter rainwater used therefore true make-up water base CF	6
Solution volume in circulation	90 litres
Original target CF	20
Make-up water used	90 litres

Therefore make-up water volume is equal to the solution volume and contributes accordingly to the solution CF i.e., 6.

Result, add 3 to target CF because the assumption is that ½ of the make-up water CF is attributable to useful nutrients. Original target CF 20 + 3 = new target CF 23. Add nutrients A & B to achieve new target CF.

As with soft water, the ideal time to monitor and adjust solution CF is during the evening, but the advantage is only marginal, the important consideration should be one of convenience. Again as with the soft water procedure, check and adjust pH at a time other than when checking and adjusting CF. This is often conveniently done in the morning. However, solution pH rises much more rapidly when hard water is used as make-up water so that on large installations it may be advantageous if the pH is monitored during the morning and again in early afternoon. This increased monitoring should not be necessary or be even desirable with domestic units where control of the rise of pH is achieved by employing a more than adequate solution volume.

The institution of the procedure described results in solution CF gradually increasing. In part the rate of increase is due to the rate of removal of water by the plants which in turn is very much influenced by plant size and growth rate. Therefore, the procedure has an inbuilt protection of immature and stressed plants which necessarily do not remove large quantities of water. A potential problem occurs when plants preferring a particularly low CF, such as transplants, are set out to occupy channels with fast growing plants. In this situation it is advised to set out the low CF plants coincidentally with a change of solution so that they are exposed to the lowest available CF. If necessary for example, because of reluctant rooting, the system may be run for a day or two with no nutrients added to provide an extended opportunity for successful establishment.

Notwithstanding occasional considerations such as the above, the hard water procedure satisfies the dual requirements of meeting the nutritional requirements of all types of plants with an excellent degree of simplicity and convenience.

Discharging the Solution

Eventually the target CF will be raised to an unnacceptably high value. Generally this occurrence dictates the time the solution should be discharged. The frequency of discharging will be regulated by the rate of water removal by the plants of course, but also and particularly by the hardness, manifested as base CF of the make-up water. It is pertinent to examine the original example this time allowing for the affects of different weather types on water usage, to determine what actually happens.

Remember, system capacity 180 litres. 30 tomato plants.

At start-up. The base CF = 6, desired CF = 20, therefore target CF = 23.

At the end of the first week of average weather 180 litres of make-up water have been used. Using the procedure described a new target CF of 26 is calculated.

At the end of the second week of predominantly cloudy conditions only 120 litres of make-up water have been added. This results in a new target CF of 28.

At the end of the third week of very bright and warm weather 240 litres of make-up water have been used. This results in a new target CF of 32.

The general advice, found to have great practical utility, is to allow the rise in CF to continue until it passes a value 50% greater than the original target CF. In the example, this would be CF 34 (23 plus 11), and would probably occur at the end of the 4th week. This length of solution life, which is typical, should pose no problems and indeed many small scale NFT users in hard water districts prefer to discharge solution rather more frequently, say every 3 weeks during the normal growing season. The practice is encouraged if the old solution can be profitably used elsewhere. Naturally, most hard water supplies are found in localities with alkaline (chalk) soils where old NFT solution is especially valuable for application to ericacious beds, specimen rhododendrons and indeed lawns. It is not uncommon to find NFT growers in chalk localities deliberately changing the nutrient solution more frequently than necessary to provide sufficient for regular garden uses. Other occasions where the solution may be changed more frequently are because of the onset of a particularly hot spell of weather or as a prelude to holidays and enforced absences.

What are the opportunities for extending the life of the solution in hard water areas? In fact, there is precious little theoretical or monetary advantage in being able to do so, though where the old solution is pumped to waste the question often arises.

Some monocrop growers adopt the procedure of discharging the solution when the target CF reaches twice the desired CF. In the example this would be at solution CF 40 allowing a gain of 2/3 weeks in solution life. In practice the scheme is allowable only where environmental conditions are maintained close to optimum for the particular plants. This requires an excellent level of management and more often than not, environmental control equipment normally associated with the commercial grower. However, the scheme is certainly viable where these conditions are satisfied.

Assessing the Nutrient Status of the Solution

Use of the foregoing procedures should ensure that NFT systems running hard water contain sufficient nutrient levels to maintain healthy growth. However, doubts may still exist when large, fast growing, high water using plants such as tomatoes or cucumbers mainly occupy the system.

An attractive method of assessing nutrient status in these circumstances is to use a Nitrate Test. In general there is little point in testing for the individual nutrient levels of the solution because it is slow, costly and confusing. However, the major nutrient nitrate may be semi-quantitatively determined at just acceptable expense by the use of a simple immersion colour comparison test (much like the pH tests). The appropriate method of use is as a check on total nutrient status as indicated by the level of nitrate. The argument being that as a balanced nutrient is always added, sufficiency of one major nutrient is a good indicator of sufficiency of others. Coupled with the previously described method of nutrient additions in hard water areas this is a very reasonable assumption. Accordingly, if the nitrate test is employed, check the solution nitrate level at system start-up and re-check occasionally during the life of the solution, say each week. Assess whether nitrate level is being maintained, is declining or is rising and if appropriate, make a small adjustment to target CF. For instance, if a 3 point rise in target CF each week resulted in a decline in nitrate level then institute a 4 CF point rise. Note that this increase may produce an earlier time for discharging the solution.

The nitrate test method of assessing nutrient status is more useful on large sites than small ones because on large sites the changes in nutrient level are more dramatic. In the vast majority of cases no assessment of nutrient level is required or is even desirable.

SPECIAL ADAPTATIONS FOR VERY HARD WATER SUPPLIES

The principal problems with very hard water supplies, base CF 9 or above, are these: First, because of the very high level of natural salts present, there is a large oversupply of those which are also nutrient salts, so that a smaller proportion are removed from the system due to take-up by the plants. Second, large amounts of acid are required to neutralise the salts. The result is that start-up solution CF, already high due to high base CF, is quickly increased by make-up water and acid additions, and there is reduced scope to assign these CF increases to useful nutrients. The practical significance is that the full base CF must be allowed at system start-up when calculating a target CF and when maintaining nutrient levels in the solution by setting a new target CF. Accordingly, when using very hard water supplies, calculation of target CF uses the equation:— desired CF + base CF = target CF. Consider the effect of this with our example where 30 tomatoes used 180 litres of water/week. System capacity 180 litres, desired CF 20 but base CF (of water supply) 10.

At start-up target CF (desired CF + base CF) is set at 30. During the first week 180 litres of make up water have entered the unit resulting in a new target CF of 40. Clearly, the use of very hard water results in a rapid rise in solution CF necessitating early discharging of the solution. Additionally, the solution may be heavily loaded with phosphorus due to acid additions.

What can be done to alleviate this state of affairs? Part of the answer is to use phosphorus-free nutrients relying entirely on acid additions for nutrient phosphates, which are in fact more than ample. The effect of this is to allow a reduction in desired CF by about 10% because weight for weight phosphate-free nutrients supply more of the other nutrients. A further reduction in desired CF is allowed to take account of the fact that desired CF, as described in the original soft water scheme, is assumed to reflect nutrient additions alone whereas, in fact, a small proportion is attributable to the base CF, low but definitely present, of soft water. After allowing for these two factors, desired CF may be reduced by 20% when calculating target CF and using very hard water. Although in theory this action does not affect the reserve of nutrients in the resulting solution, in practice some reduction probably does result. This is because the calculating of desired CF is essentially subjective. For this reason it is advised that monitoring and adjusting solution CF should be more regularly attended to when using very hard water compared to alternative sites using somewhat softer supplies.

The next objective is to reduce the dramatic effect of make-up water on solution CF. There is no alternative, assuming no rainwater is available, but to raise the volume of the unit. Doubling the volume has a most useful impact. Consider the sum of these changes on the example:—

> 30 tomatoes use 180 litres water/week, system capacity 360 litres, desired CF 16, base CF 10.
>
> At system start-up target CF (desired CF plus base CF) 26
>
> At end of first week 180 litres of water is used adding just 5 to target CF. New target 31.
>
> Similarly at end of second week, new target 36 and so on . . .

The rise in solution CF has been reduced to 5 points/week and from a lower start, resulting in discharge becoming due during the third week. However, because of the extra volume, the system contains a substantial pool of nutrients. An additional half week or so of solution life may be gained by shutting off the make-up water supply when target CF reaches or becomes close to discharge value. Allow the solution volume to drop by around ⅓rd before discharging.

With this modified scheme excellent results may be obtained even using very hard water though the frequency of solution discharge is certainly increased and there is some loss (waste) of nutrients at discharging. However, neither of these seriously threatens the smooth running or economics of the unit.

THE DISCHARGING PROGRAMME

Basic Method

Using the discharging programme a quantity of nutrients is added to the system and the unit is run without further additions of nutrients for a pre-determined period and then discharged. The pH of the solution is adjusted as necessary at start-up and during the life of the solution. After discharge a new solution is made up and the cycle is repeated. Make-up water is added manually or automatically as appropriate during the life of the solution. No instrumentation is required to undertake the discharging programme, but a measuring cup or jug is useful if stock solutions are employed.

Detail

The quantity of nutrients added is basically that amount which will produce the optimum solution, page 51. It may be referred to as the standard solution and it is varied somewhat according to the circumstances and demands of the plants. How is the quantity of nutrients A & B that will produce the standard solution determined? If manufacturers' nutrients are used, this information will be included with the instructions. If D.I.Y. solutions are used the amount will have been determined previously when formulating the nutrient mix.

Dry powders may be added directly to the circulation tank as there is no need to check nutrient concentration subsequently. However, it is preferred if they are separately dissolved in a little warm water before being added to the system. Where, for greater convenience, stock solutions A & B are used, calculate the volume of stock solutions required to deliver the correct weight of nutrients. An example will suffice to describe this procedure. Suppose a 1.25 kg pack of nutrients A & B is made into two 5 litre stock solutions and suppose a standard solution is achieved for the volume of the system according to the manufacturers' instructions by the addition of 56g A and 112g B. The volume usage is determined by:—

Total pack wt. 1250g. Total nutrient usage 168g
1250 ÷ 168 equals 7.3.

Therefore there are 7.3 complete doses in each stock solution. Round the figure up or down to the nearest whole number, in this example 7. Therefore each charging of the system to obtain standard solution is achieved by adding 1/7 (one seventh) of 5 litres of each of stock solutions A & B, i.e. 700 ml. Stir stock solutions before use. When adding nutrients to the circulating water add stock solution A first and allow a little time for this to disperse before adding B.

Just as if using the conductivity programme, the standard solution cannot be used at all times, though using the discharging programme there are fewer opportunities and usually less need to make large variations. What variations should be made? Certainly an allowance should be made for transplants. The allowance depends somewhat on the proportion of transplants in the unit. If the whole unit contains newly set out plants then the quantity of nutrients A & B may be reduced by about half for the first solution and by about ¼ for the second. The third solution may be at standard strength. If a quarter or more of the space in the unit is occupied by mature plants, then the first solution only would be adjusted and then by a ¼ reduction. Because, using the nutrient discharging programme, the nutrient concentration is not maintained at a high level, it is quite in order to set out a small number of transplants amongst mature plants without reducing the nutrient solution concentration. In this case, particularly in soft water areas, it may be beneficial if the setting out is done during the second half of the life of the solution when the solution concentration is at its lowest.

Some allowance may also be made for plants under stress. Two particular instances serve as common examples; firstly, plants, especially tomatoes, cucumber and the like set out early in domestic greenhouses when conditions remain poor for long periods. Secondly, when the time for making up a new solution coincides with a period of very hot weather. In these, and similar circumstances, the nutrients A & B may be added, half at the start of the new solution, and the balance at the beginning of the second half of the life of the solution.

Greater than standard quantities of nutrients may be used when the unit contains a proportion, ½ or more, of high CF plants such as mature or maturing tomatoes or carnations. In these cases an increase of ¼ to ⅓ in nutrients added may be made and there is some advantage in adding the nutrients in two lots as described above.

The most consistent variation in nutrient additions is the allowance which should be made for the type of water used. For hard water users the standard solution is appropriate but for soft water users the usage of nutrients may be increased by about 25%, the advantage being a useful extension of the life of the solution. The procedure for determining the amount of nutrients to be added may be neatly summarised by examples:

Example 1. Hard water, average conditions, mixed crops.
- (1) Determine standard solution.
- (2) No adjustments necessary.

Example 2. Hard water, very hot weather, some transplants entered in the unit.
- (1) Determine standard solution.
- (2) Apply 25% reduction due to transplants.
- (3) Add half quantities of A & B at start of cycle and the remainder at the beginning of second half of cycle.

Example 3. Soft water, mature tomatoes in good weather.
- (1) Determine standard solution.
- (2) Apply 25% increase due to soft water.
- (3) Apply 25% increase due to crop type and condition.
- (4) Add half quantities of A & B at start of cycle and remainder at beginning of second half of cycle.

Example 4. Soft water, all new transplants.
- (1) Determine standard solution.
- (2) Apply 25% increase due to soft water.
- (3) Apply 50% reduction due to transplants.

Notes: for the purposes of the nutrient discharging programme, water which furs kettles should be regarded as hard water and all other water as soft water.

The Life of the Solution

This is calculated by reference to the space occupied by the plants and to the volume of the system. These in turn are representative of the removal of nutrients from the system and the quantity of nutrients added at start-up.

Just as used previously, the air space occupied by the plants is the most accurate measure of occupation of the system as this neatly compensates for most of the differences between tall, strong growing plants and short, less vigorous types. As an example:— If one side of a 3 metres × 2.4 metres greenhouse has been converted to NFT with two 300mm wide flat topped channels running the length, then, when fully planted with tomatoes, the air space occupied by the plants is the area of the entire half house allowing for the central pathway, i.e. 1.1 metres × 3 metres = 3.3 square metres. If the same channels were planted with successional lettuce in staggered rows then the air space occupied by the plants is only the same as the channel cover i.e., 300mm width of channel × 3 metres length of row × 2 number of channels, equals 1.8 square metres. Clearly the tomatoes would be expected to run the solution down more rapidly than the lettuce and the procedure given below reflects this expectation.

The volume of the system is normally known. It is that volume which was used to calculate the quantity of nutrients added. The relationship between the air space occupied by the plants and the volume of the unit is:—

Soft water $\frac{\text{Litres}}{\text{sq. metres}} \times 0.6$ or $\frac{\text{galls}}{\text{sq. ft.}} \times 30$ equals life of the solution in days

Hard water $\frac{\text{Litres}}{\text{sq. metres}} \times 0.48$ or $\frac{\text{galls}}{\text{sq. ft.}} \times 24$ equals life of the solution in days

The figure arrived at can be applied to all systems where summer conditions are present, either because it is summer or because the environment is enhanced to become summer-like, e.g., extending the season by the provision of a greenhouse. In U.K. midland districts, summer conditions are said to prevail in unimproved greenhouses from early May to mid-September. This is extended a week or two in southern districts and marginally reduced in more northern areas.

During less growth promoting conditions, i.e. those of early spring and autumn, the life of each solution may be extended by 50% and the same applies to improved winter conditions, i.e. where heat and/or light are applied to induce some growth when growth would otherwise not occur. During the middle of the U.K. summer in greenhouses or indeed in tropical and subtropical climates when similar conditions occur, the solution life should be reduced by about 25%.

When operating the discharging programme it is most acceptable if the dischargings are contrived to coincide with a convenient time, e.g., at weekends or perhaps at 10 or 11 day intervals. This convenience may be gained by discharging a day or two earlier than the theoretical time, or indeed a day or two later, when perhaps a small amount of nutrient may be added during the second half of the solution life to compensate for the extra time. Alternatively, and often more conveniently, adjust the system volume to adjust the discharge date.

Discharging the Solution

At, or about, the predetermined time discharge the nutrient solution, preferably not to waste, but instead put to good use elsewhere in the garden or greenhouse where the residual nutrients may be used. On making up another solution ensure that it is at a reasonable temperature, perhaps by adding some hot water, before starting circulation.

It is not necessary to drain the system absolutely dry, indeed in soft water areas the next charge of nutrients may be added directly to the tank without any discharge at all, but complete discharge should be reinstated the next time. In hard water areas this practice is not recommended, but still may be usefully employed if a recharging falls due when holidays or other absences necessitate that the discharge operation would be carried out by a person unfamiliar with the system. In these cases simply measure out the required weight/volume of nutrients to be added and leave instructions as to the date of addition.

How much nutrient is wasted if the discharging programme is employed? Of course on many hard water sites no waste may occur as there is excess demand for used solution for use elsewhere. Even in soft water areas it is a rare site indeed which has no use whatsoever for used solution. The technique described for calculating the solution life assumes a fairly high and sustained level of nutrient removal. Therefore wasted nutrients are those nutrients not taken up by plants because growth is less than anticipated. The most common cause of this is poor environment, either continuously so, e.g.

because of shading, or transiently, e.g. because of dull cold weather in summertime. Over a season a reasonable estimate of the additional nutrients discharged from the system using the discharging programme compared to the conductivity programme is 12½%. On most small sites the monetary value of this nutrient is low indeed.

pH Monitoring and Adjusting

In soft water areas check the pH of the solution at start-up, after allowing time for the nutrients added to become dispersed in the unit, and adjust if necessary. Thereafter check pH at regular intervals. It is likely that frequent additions of acid will be unnecessary and this will be reflected in the frequency of pH checks.

On hard water sites the pH should be adjusted to close to optimum, 6.0-6.5, before the addition of nutrients at start-up and again after the nutrients have been added and time allowed for dispersal. Subsequently, test for pH regularly and adjust as necessary.

If the unit is fitted with auto top-up facilities from a header tank then control of pH may be achieved by treating the header tank water with acid so that on make-up water entering the system the correct acidity is maintained. If the system is not automatically topped up, a large quantity of make-up water for manual addition may be stored and treated with acid in a conveniently sited butt or other container. Where space allows, this procedure can be saving in both time and pH test materials and is especially useful when the system is topped up by a person unfamiliar with the unit, as then the tasks of checking pH and adding acid may be dispensed with.

THE SIMPLIFIED TOPPING-UP PROGRAMME

Basic Method

Nutrients are added to the water in circulation and to the make-up water so that the nutrient level in the system is maintained at, or close to, the required concentration.

Detail

The quantity of nutrient added to the water at system start-up is determined and varied exactly in the same way as for the discharging programme, but ultimately reduced by 20%. This reduction provides for any concentrating up of the nutrient solution, either transiently during a very hot day, or gradually over a period, due to preferential uptake of water by the plants.

As with other nutrition programmes, when using hard water supplies, it is best to adjust the pH of the water in circulation before adding any nutrients. Also check and adjust the pH as necessary after adding nutrients. When using soft water it is sufficient to check and adjust the pH after the nutrients have been added. Similarly, when using hard water, the nutrient A should be added first and allowed to disperse before adding B. This procedure need not be adhered to when using soft water.

After start-up add nutrients to the make-up water. The most convenient units for doing this are those fitted with header tank auto top-up facilities, when it is necessary only to add nutrients to the water in the header tank in ratio according to the volume held in the header tank. If the system is manually topped up it is necessary to measure the make-up water requirements of the solution in the circulation tank and then add nutrients according to the volume required. In this case, the replenishing nutrients may be mixed with the make-up water or added directly to the circulating solution. The least convenient topping-up method for use in conjunction with the simplified programme is auto top-up from a mains supply, when it is necessary to fit a meter on the supply so that the volume of make-up water used can be determined. In this case replenishing nutrients are added directly to the circulating solution in quantity proportional to the make-up water used in the period since the last addition of nutrients.

The quantity of nutrients added to the make-up water is determined and varied just as for the discharging programme, but for the simplified programme, whereas at start-up a final reduction of 20% was applied, for the make-up water a reduction of 50% is in order. If this procedure is followed, the concentration of nutrients in the circulating solution should be maintained at, or close to, the original concentration or decline slowly. When adding replenishing nutrients, either into a header tank or directly into the circulating solution, the same sequence of pH adjustment and nutrient additions should be followed as was practiced when nutrients were first added to the circulating solution.

If desired, adjustments to the nutrient concentration of the circulating solution can be brought about by altering the quantity of replenishing nutrients added to the make-up water. For example, if the nutrient quantity added to the make-up water is ultimately reduced by less than 50%, or perhaps not reduced at all, then the concentration of the circulating solution will tend to rise gradually as more concentrated make-up solution is introduced. Such an alternative may be useful, for example, after setting out plants and starting the solution at low concentration. Gradually, as the plants root out and begin to remove water and nutrients from the system, the solution concentration will tend to increase.

Check and adjust the solution pH as appropriate irrespective of checks which may have been made at the addition of replenishing nutrients. Just as with other nutrition programmes very few, perhaps no adjustments need be made when using soft water supplies, whereas frequent adjustments may be found to be necessary when using hard water.

Using the simplified topping-up programme, the life of the solution may be extended beyond the time normally allowed if using the discharging method. In theory, in soft water districts the solution life could be as long as if using the conductivity programme, but in practice, so as to avoid the possibility of uncontrolled rise in solution CF, the solution should be discharged at 6 week intervals. In hard water districts 3/4 weeks is a reasonable maximum. It is always sensible to pay particular attention to the growth and health of the plants immediately before and after the solution has been discharged and replaced. If there is a noticeable increase in water up-take, a feature easily determined when using the simplified programme, this is indicative of too great a delay in changing the solution.

The simplified topping-up programme has much to recommend it. It is especially convenient to many domestic NFT users because it reduces the number of occasions when discharging is necessary and reduces the costs of nutrients. However, consider also that this may not be an advantage where ex-NFT solution is in demand. The programme also offers reassurance to NFT users because there is a regular input of nutrients into the system which is found to be satisfying. On a larger scale the simplified programme may be preferred to the conductivity programme because it eliminates most of the calculations for accounting for hard water. Instead the programme embodies the principle of applying nutrients only to replenish those removed by the plants.

Mitigating against the simplified programme on very small sites are tiny weighings, if dry powders are used, or small volume measures if stock solutions are used. In the latter case, the problem can easily be overcome by using greater dilutions when making up stock solutions, so that the volume required for a given quantity of nutrients is increased to the point where ordinary domestic measures may be used. In the case of dry powders, these are always tedious to use irrespective of the nutrition programme employed. On larger sites the simplified programme does not give the same fine control as can be achieved with the conductivity method.

ADJUSTING THE POTASSIUM/NITROGEN RATIO

Nutrient formulations such as those described in Chapter 4, and used in accordance with any of the nutrition programmes described, produce nutrient solutions where potassium (K) and nitrogen (N) are supplied in the ratio about 2:1. This ratio has been found to produce good results in an extensive range of plants and a variety of conditions. It is not at all unusual for NFT users to use nutrients giving a 2:1 K/N ratio throughout successive seasons. However, experience has also illuminated areas where improvement in performance may be attained by manipulating nutrient usage to alter the resultant K/N ratio in the solution.

Situations where there is a potentially increased demand or use of nitrogen compared to potassium occur mainly at the post transplant vegetative stage of maturing plants. In these situations it may be appropriate to use nutrient solution with K/N ratio reduced towards 1.5:1. The growth promoted by reduced K/N ratio tends to be very soft and lush especially in poor light conditions such as early in the season, or where shading is applied. Accordingly, it is important not to persist with reduced K/N ratio when lush growth is not required. In practice, apart from summer foliage crops such as lettuce, which may be grown entirely in reduced ratio solution, the technique tends to be restricted to the immediate post transplant period and as an occasional boost to mature plants showing lack of vigour. A common example of this latter situation are crop plants producing successional fruit such as tomatoes or peppers. Here the demands of initial heavy fruit load reduce the vigour of the leading shoots, but it is best if vigour can be restored to provide the foundations for subsequent fruiting.

Development of fruit, fruit size, colour and flavour in crop plants and flower size and quality in ornamentals, may be enhanced by increasing the supply of potassium compared to nitrogen. Accordingly, at appropriate times, it may be beneficial to use nutrient solution with K/N ratio increased to around 2.5:1. Although there are occasions when the increased ratio may be used continuously, for example, when melons are ripening and no further crop production is expected, in many situations continued use of high ratio solution results in loss of vigour of vegetative growth which may subsequently affect yield and performance. More balanced growth may be restored by reverting to normal ratio solution.

How is the K/N ratio adjusted? Because NFT nutrient is formulated in two components, nutrients A & B, rich respectively in nitrogen and potassium, adjustments to the K/N ratio of the nutrient solution are easily achieved by altering the relative amounts of nutrient A & B used. The precise manner of adjustment varies according to the water supply, a slightly different method being adopted in soft water areas compared to hard water areas. As in the case of equal nutrient additions made according to any of the nutrient programmes described, absolute accuracy in determining the altered rates of use of nutrients A & B is neither necessary nor desirable. Always err on the side of caution and note that the best assessment of the result of altering the nutrient solution is the response of the recipient plants.

Soft Water or where using Rainwater

a). Reducing K/N ratio. Increase the quantity of nutrient A and maintain the quantity of nutrient B. The increase in N required to change a K/N ratio from 2:1 to 1.5:1 is 20%. In common nutrient formulations only about ⅔rds of the nitrogen supplied to the solution is supplied by A and therefore it is necessary to increase nutrient A by more than the 20% to make a full adjustment. In theory an increase of about 30% would be required to make a full adjustment. In practice a 20-25% increase in A is usually ample and effective.

b). Increasing K/N ratio. Increase the quantity of nutrient B and maintain the quantity of nutrient A. The increase in potassium required to alter the K/N ratio from 2:1 to 2.5:1 is 25%. As nutrient B is the sole source of potassium simply increase usage of B by up to 25%.

Hard water Areas

Adjusting the K/N ratio is slightly more problematic in hard water arcas because increasing the quantities of A or B without making some compensatory reduction elsewhere, increases also the solution CF. This tendency should be avoided. Accordingly, only if a low nutrient level is being run, e.g., because a crop is recently transplanted, is it in order to alter K/N ratio solely by increasing the quantities of nutrients A or B as in the case of soft water. In all other situations, likely to prove the large majority, the alternative method below should be employed.

a). Reducing K/N ratio. Increase the quantity of nutrient A and decrease the quantity of nutrient B. As nutrient B also supplies nitrogen there is some offset of the gain of nitrogen produced by the increased use of A, but this is not proportional and further, the K/N ratio is improved in the desired direction by the decline of potassium attributable to reduced use of B. Using common nutrient formulations increasing the weight or volume of nutrient A by up to 20%, and reducing B by equivalent weight/volume, effects the desired adjustment without substantially altering the overall solution concentration.

b). Increasing K/N ratio. Increase the quantity of B and reduce A by an equivalent weight or volume. If nutrient B is increased by only 10-15% and equivalent weight or volume reduction applied to A a dramatic change of K/N ratio results. This is because as well as increasing potassium due to increased use of B, there is a simultaneous marked reduction of nitrogen due to decreased use of A.

Altering Nutrition Programmes to Accommodate Adjustment to K/N ratio

The conductivity programme

Here make the required volume adjustments when transferring stock solutions to the circulation tank. In soft water areas solution CF may be raised above desired CF by the extra nutrients added, but in hard water areas the adjustment should be accommodated within the target CF. This will automatically occur if the hard water procedure given above is used. Adjustments may be made at anytime. If at start-up with a new solution, then complete adjustments to the new K/N ratio is achieved immediately, whereas if only the replenishing nutrient additions are altered the change to new K/N ratio is gradual. This latter is probably preferable especially when increasing K/N ratio.

The procedure to be followed is:—

a. Soft water. Aim: To decrease K/N ratio to about 1.5:1.

Method: To each measure of stock solution B use 1¼ measures of stock solution A. Adjust to desired CF or may go above.

b. Soft water. Aim: To increase K/N ratio to about 2.5:1.

Method: To each measure of stock solution A use 1¼ measures of stock solution B. Adjust to desired CF or may go above.

c. Hard water. Aim: To decrease K/N ratio to about 1.5:1.

Method: Increase usage of nutrient A by up to 20% and make a corresponding reduction in the use of nutrient B. Adjust solution close to target CF.

d. Hard water. Aim: To increase K/N ratio to about 2.5:1.

Method: To each measure plus 10% of B use measure less 10% of A, or use the 'field' method; to each measure of B use measure less 20% of A. (This latter is mathematically incorrect, but the error is so small as to be insignificant). In either case adjust solution to close to target CF.

The discharging programme

Here, when the system is charged with nutrients the weight or volume added reflect the alterations required to adjust K/N ratio. The solution life should not be altered even in soft water areas when a greater total weight of nutrient is used.

a. Soft water. Aim: To decrease K/N ratio to about 1.5:1.

Method: Use normal quantity plus 25% of A and normal quantity of B.

b. Soft water. Aim: To increase K/N ratio to about 2.5:1.

Method: Use normal quantity of A and normal plus 25% of B.

c. Hard water. Aim: To decrease K/N ratio to about 1.5:1.

Method: Calculate 15-20% of the normal quantity of A whether using dry powders or stock solutions. Add the resultant weight or volume to the normal dose of A and subtract it from the normal dose of B.

d. Hard water. Aim: To increase K/N ratio to about 2.5:1.

Method: Calculate 10-15% of nutrient A whether using dry powders or stock solutions. Add the resultant weight or volume to the normal dose of B and subtract it from the normal dose of A.

The simplified topping-up programme

The alterations are exactly as for the discharging programme, but here the altered nutrient weights or volumes may be used from start-up and continued during topping-up, or they may be introduced with the topping-up water at anytime in the life of the solution. As in the case of the conductivity programme, there is considered a slight advantage, when increasing K/N ratio, to introduce altered nutrient weights or volumes with the topping-up water, thereby effecting a gradual change.

Plate 1

A series of plantings at 2 day intervals demonstrates the remarkable root growth of tomatoes when set-out in NFT. Note the advanced state of the shoot at the time of setting-out

Plate 2

Primary root axes emerge from the propogation block and enter the solution stream. They grow both above and below the spreader mat

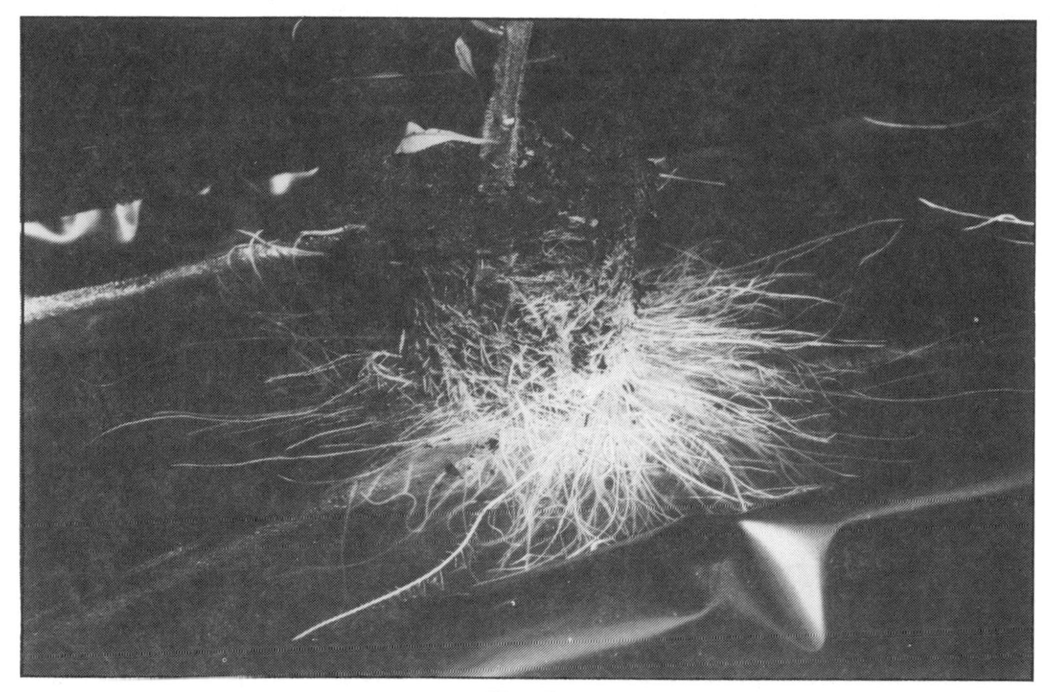

Plate 3
The primary root prominent at the bottom left shows the onset of secondary root development

Plate 4
From the centre of the propagation block a strong primary root emerges. Subsequently it will grow into the solution where it will make a substantial contribution to the total root development

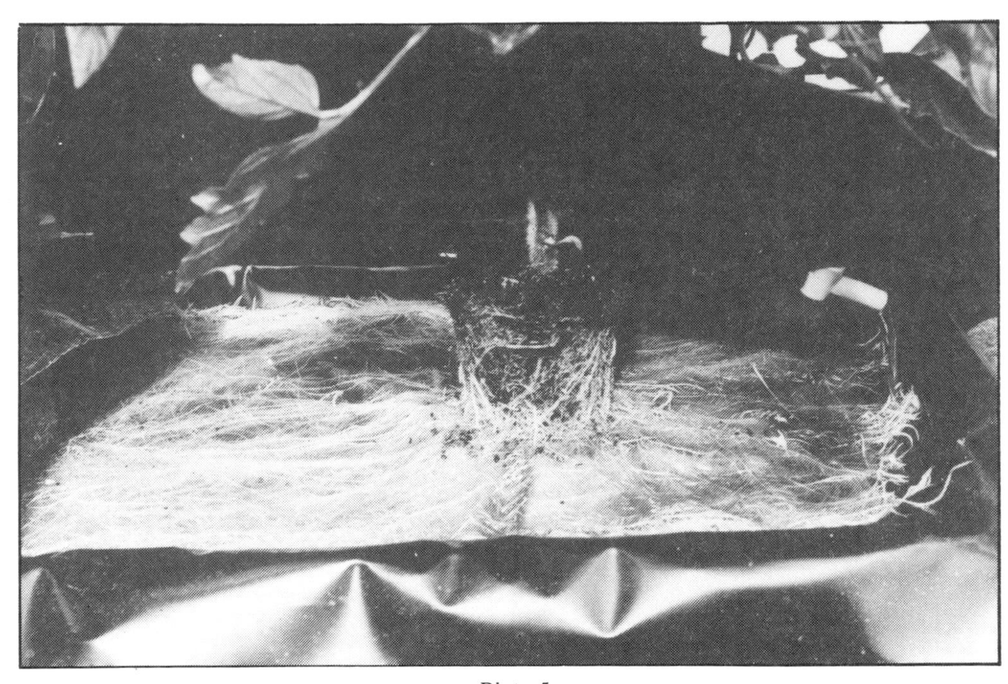

Plate 5
Growth of primary and secondary roots continues, eventually covering the channel base and forming a 'root mat' typical of plants grown in NFT. Note the solution inlet at the right hand side

Plate 6
An impressive stand of NFT grown tomatoes

Plate 7
Root growth of an NFT grown strawberry plant. The new seasons roots (lighter colour) are clearly shown below the older roots (darker colour)

Plate 8
A NFT wall tier giving the promise of an excellent crop of strawberries

Plate 9
Root growth of lettuce in NFT. Note the propagation block and the accommodation hole cut in the channel top-plate

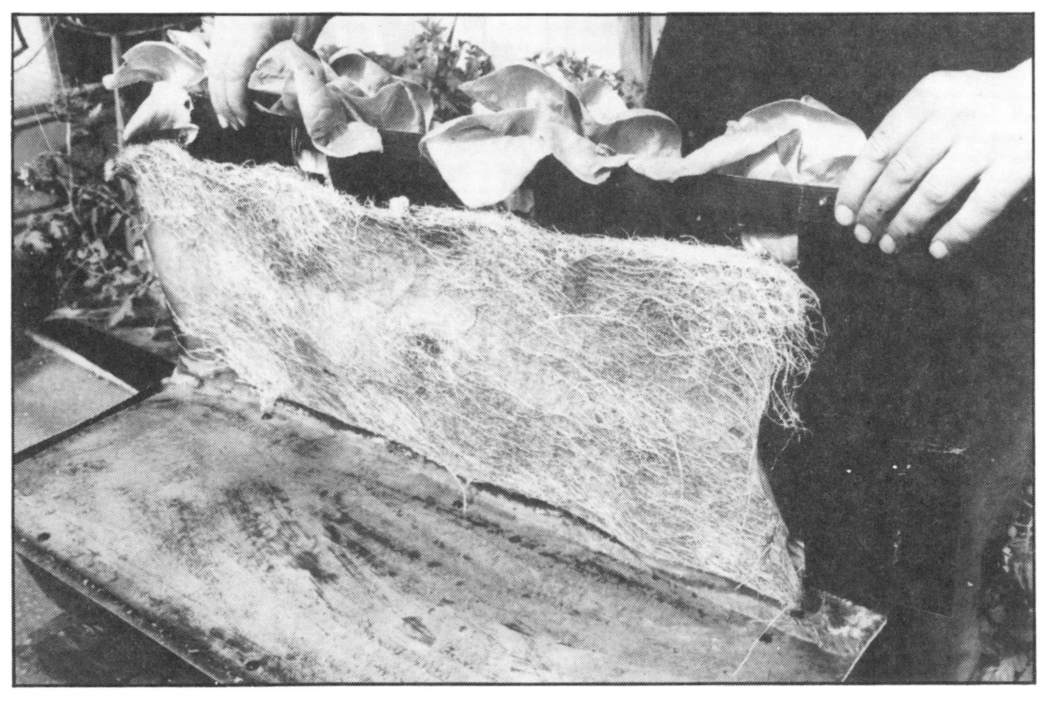

Plate 10
The root mat of a crop of lettuce grown in a "GRO-TANK" NFT unit

Plate 11
A fine bed of NFT grown lettuce

CHAPTER NINE

ROOT GROWTH OF PLANTS GROWN IN NFT

TYPICAL ROOT GROWTH

After emerging from the propagation block primary root axes establish quickly in the nutrient solution, making extensive growth. Direction of growth is influenced by the direction of emergence, but also by the direction of flow so that commonly greater root growth occurs 'with' rather than 'against' the solution stream. This effect is influenced by species, hyacinth roots for example grow mainly 'with' flow, whereas roots of tomatoes are hardly affected by flow. Initial root growth is not always straight. Roots which eventually show a high degree of branching often undergo slow or sharp direction changes, sometimes actually rising a short distance from the solution. Primary root axes which do not readily branch such as are produced by onions, generally pursue a straight path. If spreader mat is employed primary root growth may be under or over the mat depending on plant species and mat type. This characteristic is unimportant except where heavy weight bench watering mat has been inadvertently used, when, if root growth is confined beneath the mat it may detract subsequently from the efficiency of the root system, due probably to oxygen deficiency in turn due to restricted contact between the root system and the atmosphere.

Root hairs are often present a little way back from the tip of the developing axes wherever the axes remain in contact with the atmosphere. This may be at any point in the channel mainstream, or particularly where the primary axes reach the edge of the channel and typically grow a little up the side and out of the solution. Secondary roots emerge as branches from primary axes. These are smaller diameter roots and their growth rate and direction tend to be more haphazard than that of the primary axes. It is common to see secondary roots growing vertically from the solution for perhaps 2.5cms when they are often accompanied by profuse development of root hairs. Other secondary roots normally growing in the solution emerge occasionally from the solution when they intercept an existing root. At these points more root hair production is usually evident. As with primary axes, when secondary roots reach the edge of the channel, they tend to continue to grow out of the solution for a short distance before the root tips die of dessication. This is indicated by dark stub ends.

Eventually a root mat is formed. Where primary and secondary roots grow simultaneously this is of an interwoven nature when it is usually possible to trace the path of individual primary axes but they may not be withdrawn. Root mats produced by primary axes alone tend to form as a rosette or fan with limited weaving and, from which root axes may be withdrawn, though with these types the primary roots are often brittle. Also the root mat often consists of interwoven primary and secondary roots of adjacent plants. There appears to be little or no antagonism between the roots of different plants of the same or different species.

In all cases, the growth of one root upon another, the presence of roots around the propagation block, and growth at the edges of the channel, result in a proportion of the root mat being permanently in close contact with the atmosphere. Bunches of root hairs are typically present and are indicative of root health and activity. Root colour is usually white or off-white, perhaps locally reddish due to the presence of iron.

FACTORS AFFECTING ROOT GROWTH AND ACTIVITY

Age and maturity

In the typical plant, root and shoot growth follow a predictable relationship. At first root growth, if measured by dry weight gain, is equal or almost equal to shoot growth, but very shortly a progressively greater proportion of dry weight is accummulated by the shoot and at maturity the proportion of the plant total dry weight attributable to the root is quite small, often less than 10%. This innate physiological growth relationship of root and shoot manifests itself dramatically when plants growing in NFT are observed.

At first a period of rapid root growth is noted, but soon root growth slows. This is because, during the vegetative phase of shoot growth, root extension growth gradually declines. However, because of the presence of greater numbers of root axes, with the natural development of more primary and secondary roots, the root mat continues to develop, albeit at a reduced rate. For plants which stay in the vegetative phase during their useful life, such as lettuce or cabbage, such is the entire character of root growth. For these plants, the root mat should always appear bright and vigorous and root hairs should always be found without difficulty.

As the shoot enters the reproductive phase, and particularly at the maturity of flowers, root growth slows more appreciably. In some species such as chrysanthemums the root system remains bright and there is obviously some continued root growth. In many other species, the root mat does not continue to develop and indeed, there may be some noticeable reduction in bulk and brightness. This observation emphasises the importance of early root growth, clearly in many species a more or less finite root system is produced upon which the plant relies during maturity.

At maturity the root may decline rapidly, as in the case of dwarf beans, so that when the plant is removed from the channel the root system breaks away. In other cases the root system remains intact, appearing to be preferentially maintained by the shoot. This has been noted particularly in melons. Perennial plants may begin to lignify some root tissue, noticeable in strawberries and carnations. Where subsequently actual dormancy occurs a considerable amount of root formed during annual growth is sloughed. This is particularly noticeable in shrubby perennials and corm and bulb forming plants.

Environment

The Shoot Environment

The effect of the natural relationship between shoot growth and root growth is modified by the external environment. Adequate light and temperature enhances shoot growth, seemingly at the expense of root growth, whilst poor light and temperature promote root growth at the expense of shoot growth. Accordingly, in season, first root growth is promoted when light and temperature are poor, but later shoot growth is stimulated as light and temperature improve. Where plants are grown in normal season, this influence of environment is complimentary to the natural growth of plants as described beforehand, but if plants are grown out of season, the influence of environment is often contradictory to the natural growth of the plants. This has important consequences because it means that the later in the season plants are set out, the less well developed will be the root system before the dual influences of improving environment and the maturing of the plant curtail further root growth. There is no doubt that this is at least a partial cause for the generally relatively poor performance of some late sown plants, irrespective of the method of cultivation. As far as NFT is concerned, these observations emphasise the need both to manage plants in such a way as an adequate root system is produced, and where appropriate to take advantage of the fact that root activity may be influenced by management to produce the best results with any given root system.

Earlier, mention was made of plants which produce a finite root system upon which they rely during maturity. In the context of the influence of environment an interesting observation has been made. Late sown plants of this type, e.g., tomatoes, generally produce a smaller root mat than their earlier sown counterparts, but due to the lateness of the season they are required to continue cropping with the support of the smaller root mat for a shorter period. Accordingly, and apparently inadvertently, a proportional relationship between root size and cropping period is achieved.

The Root Environment

The chief influence on root growth is that of temperature. Many plants have a somewhat lower optimum temperature for root growth than for shoot growth, and this is not surprising given that soil temperature is generally lower than air temperature during the growth of most plants. With many plants grown in NFT it is easy to modify the root environment with the aid of solution heating such that the roots are at least as close, or indeed closer, to their optimum temperature than the shoot is to its optimum. Under these conditions root growth and activity will be enhanced when compared to plants grown in an unmodified root environment.

The influence of nutrient concentration on root growth is less certain. Certainly low nutrient concentration increases root activity in the sense that water uptake is improved, and there is some evidence to suggest that there is also an improvement in root extension growth, though possibly the quality of growth is poor. Under conditions of high nutrient concentration, root activity, as measured by water uptake, decreases but root growth of good quality is improved. It is doubtful if these observations of the relationship between root growth and activity and nutrient concentration can be usefully used to manipulate root growth in NFT, however the condition of good, even excellent root growth, together with hard, usually curled, shoot growth may be taken as a symptom of excessive solution concentration.

Plant Species and Variety

Considering the massive variety of leaf and flower forms, there is remarkable uniformity of appearance and habit of the root systems of even diverse plant species. Some variation in diameter of the individual root axes is obvious on examination of roots growing in an NFT channel, but the greatest variation is simply that of extent.

Popular crop plants such as cucumber, melons, tomatoes and courgettes would be expected to, and do, produce large root mats. It is not uncommon to find an inidividual primary axis of a cucumber plant in excess of 2.4 metres long, whilst the root mat formed by such a plant may fill a channel 30cm wide to a depth of 3.0cm for fully 1.2 metres channel length with extension growth beyond. Two plants which regularly produce smaller than expected root systems are peppers and aubergines. It is probable that this shortcoming is more apparent than real because in fact, neither plant produces a leaf area comparable with say a cucumber or tomato, at least under U.K. conditions. Nonetheless root growth of peppers is noted as being difficult to start into the solution, whilst less than expected root growth of aubergines may, in part, be due to the glaucose nature of the leaves which reduce water losses.

A feature of root growth associated with large rooted hydrophillic species is the rather disturbing phenomenon known as 'root death'. Root death may become obvious when the fruit load on the plant is at its maximum, day length is long and daytime temperature high, that is, the conditions least conducive to root growth and conversely most encouraging to shoot growth. The condition is first manifested by a change of root colour from whiteish to mid-brown but soon, on close examination, some secondary roots are seen to have died and break away at the slightest touch. In extreme cases only a skeleton of primary axes remain, more often only a proportion of secondary roots are lost but even this results in a general loss of bulk and springiness of the root mat. Later some re-growth occurs and this generally increases as environmental conditions become more favourable for root growth, namely longer nights and shorter cooler days. Root death is not caused by an infective agent, instead it is considered a fairly normal physiological condition displayed by many plants. Of course in soil or substrate grown plants root death goes unobserved, whereas in NFT at first siting it strikes immediate alarm.

In my experience root death is typically apparent in well grown crops of tomatoes and much less so in other species and circumstances. Although the presence of root death may necessitate some alteration to the regime in the channel, as detailed later, in order to effect a continued high rate of cropping, as the condition is associated with good crops it is perhaps best to regard it as benign.

Amongst other crop plants, peas particularly form larger than expected root mats and accordingly they are amongst the easiest plants to grow in NFT. Indeed, for newcomers to NFT they are well worth a try, not least because they provide an excellent illustration of growth and development in NFT whilst being an undemanding plant. Additionally, as they may be grown 'out of season' in a greenhouse it is possible to crop peas before setting out the main production plants, so any educational exercise need not impinge on the regular season.

Of the beans, dwarf beans are scantily rooted and less well branched than comparable plants. Interestingly, root nodules formed by nitrifying bacteria on legumous plants are produced in NFT just as in soil. Of course, if bizarre legume species are grown, innoculum may not be present in the circulating solution whereas the common pea seems to become 'infected' very readily.

Two very different plants are characterised by root growth forming two distinct stages. In maize (sweet corn), a typical root is formed by strong primary axes initiated from the tap root. In strawberries early root growth forming a typical mat arises from the partially lignified primary roots of the previous seasons growth. Subsequently, in both species a new extensive phase of root growth occurs, in maize from primary adventitious roots initiated in the stem base, in strawberries new primary roots grow from the crown. The yield success of both these crop plants appears to be largely dependent on the success of this second stage of root development. It is highly likely that the same can be said of other plants which display a similar rooting characteristic.

Under normal conditions conducive to healthy growth, hydrophobic plants never produce root systems comparable in extent to those produced by tomatoes and the like. However, most continue to develop the root system over a long period so that eventually a quite extensive, though usually fine, root system is produced.

Choice of variety can certainly affect root growth as demonstrated by laboratory and field experiments, but without recourse to accurate measurements, it is more often than not difficult to determine varietal differences. Sometimes vigorous rooting varieties are noted for being quick to establish in the solution, but generally such distinctions are inapparent.

CHAPTER TEN

MANAGEMENT OF THE ROOT ENVIRONMENT

SOLUTION HEATING

Although solution heating is rightly regarded as a very useful tool in NFT management, it is by no means essential to the success of an NFT installation. As far as the UK is concerned, it is obvious that a wide range of temperate plants can be successfully grown at ambient temperatures in greenhouses, or outdoors in due season, and without any need for solution heating. Furthermore, the enhanced temperatures naturally occurring in greenhouses as the season improves, are themselves quite sufficient to produce truly excellent plants of the 'hot house' type, particularly common greenhouse crops such as tomatoes and cucumbers. The adoption of NFT does not imply that a change to artificial heat input is essential. A further important point is that while solution heating may be used to improve performance, it does not necessarily do so because it may not offset bad management elsewhere, for example poor ventilation. Alternatively, good practice elsewhere may well offset all but uneconomic gain induced by solution heating.

The use of solution heating to promote root growth is not restricted to the encouragement of rooting into the solution from propagation blocks, or the breaking of new roots from dormant plants, at setting-out, as described in Chapter 7. In these cases, if the ambient solution temperature remains below a threshold point at which root growth is seriously impaired, then solution heat must continue to be applied if sufficient root growth is to be made during the establishment of the plant to satisfy subsequent shoot demands. However, it seems that less heat is required to maintain continued root growth than is necessary to stimulate root entry into the solution.

Where ambient solution temperature is sufficient to promote normal growth of the roots, but for one reason or another, root growth is below par, then solution heating is usefully applied to rectify the matter and again the solution heating should be continued until the quantity of root growth is satisfactory. An example of this situation is where initial root growth is restricted by damage to some primary root axes in the propagation block. Here, remaining undamaged primary axes, and subsequently produced secondary roots, should be encouraged during establishment to make up for lost root growth.

In any situation where the root mat has developed adequately, it is inappropriate to continue solution heating on the grounds of encouragement to root growth alone. However, heat should be reinstated if and when root quantity again becomes inadequate. The classic case of this situation is the occurrence of "root death" but roots may also be lost due to waterlogging, continued overdosing with acid, and just possibly due to disease. In these situations encourage the growth of new roots by raising the solution temperature close to optimum and maintain this regime until the extent of root growth is again satisfactory. In the event of an especially serious occurrence of "root death", this might be for a considerable period as even the provision of optimum root temperature may stimulate only modest root re-growth because of the inhibiting effect of hot, bright environmental conditions and the dominant state of the shoot with a heavy fruit load.

Root activity should be considered entirely separately from root growth, though both may be stimulated by solution heating, and it may be that the need to improve growth and activity is coincidental. Solution heating applied to improve root activity is motivated by the desire to improve shoot performance. The chief observation used to determine the level of root activity is the water status of the shoot. Accordingly symptoms of water stress whether they be immediate, such as wilting or lack of leaf turgor, or resultant such as small fruit or failure of pollenation, are all suggestive of low levels of root activity and may possibly be corrected by instituting solution heating. In contrast leaf turgidity and successful pollenation are indicative of good root activity. A particular indicator of good root activity is the presence in many plants of guttation droplets on the leaves. These are water droplets released through valves on the leaf surface and usually noticeable in the early morning. Often they are most abundant at the edge of the leaf and may cause a line of scorch at the leaf margins when the droplets act as magnifying lenses for sunlight before being evaporated away. Guttation does not occur, at least to the naked eye, in plants with effective leaf adaptations to reduce water loss, but in many other plants including most common cultivated species, guttation can be found. The presence of guttation is especially useful in the management of indoor strawberries. These plants rarely produce a large root and seem particularly subject to water stress. Accordingly maintain root activity so that guttation droplets are evident.

Hardness of shoot growth is certainly attributable to water stress and indeed, as described, it may have been deliberately brought about by underwatering or by raising solution nutrient concentration. Though increasing root activity by raising solution temperature may mitigate hard growth, it will not, by itself, normally reverse the condition. Instead application of solution heat should be coupled with reduced solution concentration. Where hard growth has been caused by serious overfeeding then water only should be run until the growth type is reversed. This practical example serves to illustrate that no one tool of management need be used in isolation and that generally there is more than one method of effecting any management aim.

It is often quite easy to foretell the occurrence of situations where water stress may occur and to pre-empt it by the early introduction of solution heating. Just such a situation is the onset of hot bright weather, especially in early summer when it may be accompanied by cool nights. Here, during the morning ambient solution temperature may remain well below optimum, whilst air space temperature and brightness improve rapidly, resulting in water stress and loss of growth when excellent growth might justifiably have been anticipated. In this case, the early application of solution heating can effect a quite spectacular improvement. This is an area were growth improvement due to the use of NFT is actually identifiable because other methods of cultivation cannot match this degree of control of the root environment.

There are a few limited opportunities for the use of solution heating to offset expensive space heating, where otherwise root growth appears satisfactory and solution heating would not be employed.

After setting out early in the season and after successful emergence of the roots into the solution, plants may be subjected to a period of cold brought about by change of weather. Generally daytime temperatures, though less than satisfactory, rise to a point at which some growth may be made, but serious problems occur because of exposure to long nights at low temperature. Ideally space heating might be provided to maintain satisfactory growth, but on many domestic and small scale commercial sites it is simply uneconomic to apply such heat. In these cases solution heating provides a relatively low cost alternative for the partial alleviation of hostile conditions by maintaining the activity of the root system, which in turn helps to maintain the shoot in passable condition, probably by allowing the shoot to make more of the limited growth opportunities in the daytime. However, it seems that prolonged exposure of the shoot to unsatisfactory conditions could overwhelm the beneficial effect of solution heating and therefore it is wise to set a limit to the expected gain by using this procedure. Accordingly, if planning an earlier season, allow for very few days earlier on account of solution heating alone and do not count on solution heating bringing the plants forward in difficult conditions, but only to maintain them so they may be able to take good advantage later at the onset of better conditions.

Occasionally circumstances occur where root activity, as judged by water status, is satisfactory but uptake of nutrient is less so. Such a situation might occur during periods of low ambient daytime air temperature, especially late in the season, resulting in low water requirement but coincidental with a large shoot load of buds, or unripened fruit, perhaps best typified by tomatoes during October. Here nutrient uptake, particularly that of phosphorus, might be inhibited by low solution temperature. Applying solution heating in these circumstances may allow economic cropping to be continued where otherwise pulling out would be more appropriate as space heating would certainly be uneconomic.

Sometimes ambient solution temperature may become too low for good nutrient or water uptake because of the impact of two cooling influences. These are, first, the effect of cold ground water which, even quite late on in the season, can seriously reduce solution temperature, as ground water rarely exceeds 14°C in the U.K., and second, the effect of evaporative cooling which can reduce solution temperature by up to 1-2°C. Evaporative cooling occurs at those points where a water surface contacts a mobile atmosphere. Accordingly it is particularly significant in the first half of any season when foliage coverage is least, when root systems have not developed to form a continuous mat, and especially where the propagation block is exposed to the atmosphere. Apart from the last circumstance, which might be rectified by the provision of base covers, evaporative cooling is unlikely itself to cause uptake difficulties, but combined with the influence of cold ground water, the effect on hot house plants can be quite disastrous. In these conditions solution heating is clearly necessary. If the requirement persists then alterations to the installation are obviously necessary so that ground water influence may be excluded, but often the heat requirement is transient being necessary only during, and just after, spells of particularly inclement weather on some sites.

Where only very modest heat inputs are required to achieve improved growth, such as in the protected growing of temperate plants very early, very late, or in winter conditions, then an opportunity exists to make these heat inputs via solution heating rather than by space heating apparatus. In these circumstances solution heating offers advantages because the NFT system provides a means of efficient heat distribution as well as being easy to control and competitive to install. Certainly root growth is advanced, possibly beyond the extent it might normally grow, if space heating was employed, but this root growth is regarded ultimately as beneficial. At the same time shoot growth is promoted, especially vegetative growth, and accordingly the technique is most usefully employed where leaf production is desired, e.g., in winter lettuce production or during the immature stages of the growth of fruit and flower producers, and this of course often neatly coincides with the very environmental conditions which necessitate the heat application.

Given so many opportunities to use solution heating what are the possibilities of deleterious effects on plant growth in NFT by over use? In fact applying heat for too long or running too high a temperature is likely to be uneconomic rather than injurious, but there are minor exceptions. Take tomatoes as an example. It is known that tomato root growth is close to optimum at 22-25°C, but exposure to long periods as high as 31°C does not appear to pose serious problems to the plant provided that the shoot is exposed to roughly corresponding temperature. This situation occurs quite naturally in the tropics. If the same solution temperature was used under early U.K. season ambient, or even somewhat uplifted, air space temperature, then the growth made would be soft, open and largely vegetative, and not conducive to a good crop. The degree to which growth is deleteriously affected depends on both the duration and the differential of the root and shoot temperatures. Other plants respond in much the same manner as tomatoes, but the degree of response may not be so dramatic.

A particular case where overheating the solution may generate problems is where mixed plantings of temperate and hot house plants have been made. It is suggested that manipulation of the growth of the hot house plants by solution heating would surely have a damaging effect on the quality of growth of the temperate plants. Indeed there is evidence of this, but the effect is proportional to the length of time the high temperature solution is circulated. A short exposure to high temperature solution as well as achieving, at least in part, the desired effect on the growth of the hot house plants, may also be beneficial to the temperate plants because it promotes leaf growth, but not so much that excessive softness is induced. There is no doubt that in some plants this additional leaf growth is usefully used resulting in a better plant. Of course where specialist plants are grown it would be unwise to subject them to a regime which might be harmful on account of coincidental occupation of the system by plants of grossly different character. This is clearly a circumstance where two units are better than one.

TESTING FOR AND ADJUSTING SOLUTION TEMPERATURE

If unheated solution is continually monitored it will reveal a cycle of gradually rising temperature during the day and gradually falling temperature at night. A similar fluctuation occurs with air temperature, but here the peaks are higher and the troughs are deeper, and also the cycle is somewhat in advance of that of the solution temperature. Accordingly, it is appropriate to check solution temperature during the early daytime period, as then temperature shortfall is most likely to be evident.

Solution temperature may be raised to a predetermined value thought to be appropriate to the plants in the unit, or it may be raised by a predetermined uplift - the temperature increment method. Using either method the heat may be continuously available or it may be restricted to particular periods only i.e., time switch controlled. In the case of raising the solution temperature to a predetermined value the solution temperature is usually raised close to optimum, in the belief that this will have the most beneficial impact on growth. The method is particularly appropriate and successful in monocrop production and where the shoot environment is maintained to a high standard in respect of light, temperature, ventilation and where applicable, carbon dioxide concentration. Clearly these requirements are most often met by the commercial grower on large modern sites. On other sites the method tends to be wasteful of heat and may promote soft growth because the air space environment is simply not good enough to make the best of optimum solution temperature.

The temperature increment method is highly appropriate to sites with known limitations of air space environment and where mixed plantings are made. That is, the majority of domestic and semi-commercial units and indeed to a good number of fully commercial sites where low-cost production is imperative. Using this method, during periods of expected rapid growth a significant, but limited, uplift of solution temperature is used to achieve particular management aims, e.g. greater root activity. Typically such an uplift would be in the order of 3-6°C. The advantages of the method are that the heat applied is all effectively used at the root zone and that heating costs are limited. Additionally the method does not require the provision of heaters and ancillary equipment capable of supplying and controlling the largest heat demand that might be made if a regime of continuously close to optimum solution temperature was introduced, but instead only the equipment required to give the desired temperature uplift. There are, therefore, savings in heating equipment and installation costs. A further feature of the increment method is its responsiveness to changes in air space conditions, so that without the need for adjusting the equipment the solution temperature tends to be highest during fine bright conditions and lowest during cool overcast weather. This is precisely in line with requirements. The heater may be allowed to operate uncontrolled, but there is a potential waste of heat when during the later day period the solution temperature may naturally rise close to optimum. If a thermostat is set close to optimum the heater can be cut out during this period.

At other times when rapid growth is not expected because air space conditions are not conducive, the temperature increment method will prevent the solution temperature becoming too low for root activity or growth. Again the heater, of sufficient capacity to give a useful increment, may operate uncontrolled, but if a thermostat is fitted some costs may be saved during those occasions when external heat raises the solution temperature to a useful point. However, it is surprising how few are these occasions, for example in the U.K. autumn, once weather conditions have generally deteriorated to the point where rapid growth is no longer promoted.

What is the best temperature for running an NFT nutrient solution? Regrettably there is no easy answer. The problems in determining an answer are best illustrated by an example:

If tomatoes are grown in a modern glasshouse with adequate ventilation, and fully controlled air space temperatures, together with carbon dioxide enrichment then the solution temperature would normally be maintained at very close to optimum if maximum yield is to be produced, i.e., 23-25°C. Because of the adequacy of the air environment very little heat will be required to maintain this temperature. If the same solution temperature was applied to mid-season tomato crops in an average greenhouse with all its limitations of ventilation and air space temperature, it would certainly be uneconomic and maybe deleterious. A better temperature would be 19-22°C. Under average summer conditions this would not require excessive heat inputs. In the same greenhouse late in the season if this temperature regime was maintained, it would become seriously uneconomic as the difference from ambient temperature increased. Better now to reduce the thermostat setting to the range 15-18°C providing a useful input but restricting costs.

This example illustrates some of the factors which need to be considered in determining the level of solution heating. It is by no means a comprehensive example and should not be taken as a blueprint for tomato production. When setting a solution temperature or when heating for particular temperature uplift, or when applying heat for a particular period of the day, take note of all the prevailing conditions and have in mind a tangible objective.

ECONOMICS OF SOLUTION HEATING

Although running an NFT system normally incurs costs for pumping the solution, these are very small compared to the potential expense of solution heating, for even the smallest heaters use far more power than the system pump. It isn't possible to give figures of economics because sites and circumstances are so varied. Clearly the commercial grower has very different economic values than his private gardener counterpart, and even if they grow the same plants their use of solution heating is likely to be contrasting. However, there are a few facets of solution heating which are worth noting and affect its economy and operation generally.

First, solution heating is very efficient. Except in the case of ground water contacting the circulation tank, nearly all heat applied to the solution is made available to the plants. Ground water is likely to be much more of a problem on small sites when it is the single most common cause of inefficient, uneconomic solution heating, and a serious contributor to poor results and high costs.

Second, the uses and misuses of solution heating indicate particular reasons for use. Unless there is a reason for persisting with solution heating the heater should be switched off. This sounds trite and obvious, but experience suggests that practice is very different. There is a tendency to leave heating on irrespective of the circumstances, under these conditions it is likely that significant costs may be incurred without any compensating growth advantage. The preferred mode of solution heating from both the growth and economic view is controlled limited inputs.

Third and finally, consider the true value of extra production. It is a fact that too ambitious plantings prejudice success. For example, starting the season uncommonly early seldom produces encouraging results but incurs significant extra costs which are not recovered. Accordingly make changes from normal procedures only gradually and with experience gained from season to season. Work to a plan which dictates and limits costs.

ADJUSTMENTS TO FLOW

Interrupted Flow

The use of intermittent flow technique with hydrophillic plants has so far been restricted to early management. It is inappropriate to cut off the flow during the daytime during any period of rapid growth once roots have extended into the channels, except for very short duration such as at discharging. However, switching off the flow during periods of reduced or insignificant growth can be a very useful technique because it provides an opportunity for reducing excess moisture around the base of the stem and the root, thereby restricting the possibility of disease. Additionally the technique is known to promote root growth and may beneficially affect root activity. Periods of reduced or insignificant growth include the hours of darkness and other periods when temperatures or light are inadequate. As a result the circumstances where the flow may be advantageously interrupted are quite varied, but note also, that many times excellent results have been achieved without any interruptions to flow.

Wilting, as a result of insufficient root or root death, may be alleviated by switching off the flow at night. Of course, as this condition usually occurs in summertime during long days, the opportunity for switching off is limited, but is nevertheless useful. If a crop is open to receive early morning sunshine then it is imperative that the flow is reinstated before dawn. Some growers institute night time shutting off as standard procedure because it is felt it acts as a preventative of excessive root death as well as ensuring adequate root quantity. The evidence for this is not conclusive. However, during the later season when growth rate has declined and with it the demand for water, there is an opportunity for switching off flow each night to allow the propagation blocks to dry and to reduce dampness surrounding the plants. Similarly if plants are overwintered in the nutrient solution, especially lettuce and other plants set out late for early production the following season, then it is advantageous if the flow is switched off at night and indeed at other times where there is no possibility of growth and where some reduction of root zone and atmospheric moisture is desirable.

The greatest difficulty of interrupted flow regimes is the complication of switching off and on. On some sites there is no difficulty, but in the domestic situation it can be an unnecessary chore unless the operation is automated. Where automation is introduced ensure that the stopping and starting of flow is compatible with any solution heating programme simultaneously employed.

Where hydrophobic plants occupy channels especially prepared with aggregate, intermittent flow is the rule rather than the exception. Here the on-flow time is gradually increased to allow for increased water uptake due to larger plants and improvement of the season, so that by mid-summer the on-flow time may indeed be all day. Later, as the season declines, the on-flow time is reduced so that by late autumn or early winter, just an hour or two on-flow per fortnight is ample in poor conditions. There is no doubt that these desirable changes in on-flow times do worry inexperienced NFT growers, especially as it is not possible to give precise day by day or week by week instructions. Fortunately absolute accuracy, as in other aspects of NFT, is not necessary. Occasional failure to switch off at night in mid-summer or indeed failure to switch on promptly at other times is most unlikely to have a noticeable affect on the plants. Two parameters are utmost. Always allow the propagation block to dry, at least at the top, before restarting flow and judge the effectiveness of the regime by the growth of the plants.

Flow Rate

The majority of NFT systems are run through the season with no adjustment to flow rate, but there are occasional circumstances where flow rate may be altered with useful effect.

The interaction between solution heating and flow rate has been described. In mixed plantings heat may be preferentially applied to those channels occupied by plants most responsive to solution heat, if on introducing the heat, flow rate in these channels is increased while a corresponding reduction in flow is made in other channels. This approach also facilitates the adequate heating of a system by a heater of moderate output and this may have significant cost advantages. Large adjustments are possible, the limitation is that flow should not be reduced below about 125ml per min. (250ml in summer conditions) in the reduced flow channel. It is advised that later, when the heat is removed, the flow rate in all channels should be returned to the original.

There is known to be some growth and activity response by root systems to changes in flow rate, but it is often difficult to use this to advantage because the response is so varied. For example, in similar circumstances, both increasing and decreasing flow rate have apparently stimulated root growth. It is probable that increased growth with increased flow rate is due to an accompanying increase in applied heat. Accordingly, in some cases of root death or wilting, brought on by insuffiency of roots, it may be worth increasing flow rate whilst at least maintaining solution temperature if the means to do this are available. Root stimulation by reduced flow rate is probably due in part to the growth response of the plant sensing reduced water availability and in part due to a local improvement, by contact with atmospheric oxygen, of a section of the root system. Certainly in summer conditions if temporary wilting occurs frequently it may be worth trying to stimulate new root growth by reducing the flow rate temporarily. Of course the advantage of flow rate adjustment over flow interruption is that the control need not be so precise and automation is not required. The disadvantage is that in many cases the benefits are not so obvious, but still they may be sufficient to obviate the need for more dramatic action.

Enforced changes to flow rate may occur in two distinct situations. Firstly, when a root mat develops to the extent that the channel overflows. In this case reduce flow to the maximum point at which no solution is lost plus a small safety margin. It is unlikely that the plants will show any growth response. Secondly, on account of pumping difficulty or failure. Here conserve solution supply to the channels, e.g., from a header tank, by closing down the flow to a fast drip. Do not pour large volumes of cold mains water into channels at any time as this will certainly provoke wilting which may be irreversible. Instead allow water to stand, preferably in the greenhouse where it can warm up, or alternatively add some hot water.

CHANNEL AND ROOT MAINTENANCE

Concerning Root Growth and Activity

With many plantings the roots produced remain undisturbed and unattended during their occupancy of the channel. However, there are a number of actions which can influence root growth and activity and which are rightly regarded as very useful management tools.

Many plant roots appear to function very poorly when large areas are exposed to the atmosphere. This is a fairly well known problem of soil cultivation when for one reason or another soil is lost from around the base of the stem and a part of the upper root is exposed, but it would hardly have been thought to be equally applicable to plants growing in NFT where there is an abundance of water available to the root system. It seems that the atmosphere immediately surrounding exposed roots may be sufficiently dry as to encourage water loss. Where this occurs to any great extent, water stress is induced and growth is reduced. Any problem is potentially greater in summer than in winter because the atmosphere is then more likely to be dry and the water demand of the plants is greater. Hydrophillic plants are more or less exclusively at risk, hydrophobic plants appear to benefit from some root exposure, but in theory it seems possible that this could be taken too far.

To prevent root exposure problems occurring as the season and temperature improve, ensure that the fastenings of flexible channelling keep the channel closed as high as possible around the stem bases, but do not fasten so tightly that abrasive damage to the stem is induced. With flat topped channels, fit base covers when the plant type allows this to be done. Strawberries and plants with similar growth habits tend, by increasing weight of top, to pull their roots out of the channel and expose the crown. Check these plants and where necessary push the crown firmly under the channel top plate.

Surprisingly exposure problems can extend even into a closed channel where the atmosphere immediately above the solution would surely be moist. Plants producing very large root mats such as cucumbers and melons, may push layers of roots well above the surface of the solution where they lose water to the detriment of the plant. Covering these roots with a polythene sheet is an effective method of promoting beneficial activity, probably because it both prevents moisture loss to the atmosphere and encourages water movement to the roots by capilliarity and condensation.

Later in the season as atmospheric moisture levels increase and shoot demand for water decreases, any problem of root exposure is obviated, but there is the potential at least of too much dampness at the top of the roots. This situation is entirely analogous to that causing stem base rot in hydrophobic plants. In practice there seems no need to loosen channel fastenings or to remove base covers, though if stem base rot was a problem this would certainly be advised. Clearly if a new planting was made in these conditions base covers would not be required.

A number of plants naturally produce adventitious roots which are simply roots emerging from the stem. Already the special case of maize has been mentioned, but in other plants these roots may appear well above the propagation block when they make limited growth, but rarely enter the solution. In general there does not seem any particular need to encourage these roots, but if plants are in difficulty because of insufficiency of root it may be worthwhile attempting to lead them to the solution. In some cases all that is necessary is to lift or fit a base cover somewhat higher up the stem or to fasten flexible channelling at a higher level, perhaps by arranging for it to be supported in position. A more sure method is to fit a sleeve of plastic sheet or toughened paper around the stem and resting on the propagation block. Fill this with compost and moisten as necessary. The method is illustrated in Figure 10/1. Roots soon emerge into the new pot and travel via the propagation block into the channel.

Long trailing plants such as tomatoes may be encouraged to root from high up the stem by layering and especially by inducing a bend at the point where rooting is desired. With judicious training these plants can be rooted into the channel some distance along from the propagation block, as shown in Figure 10/2.

An advantage of adventitious roots is that they seem to be produced and grow reasonably readily, when the growth of the main root is at its least. Accordingly, they do provide another option for management in difficult circumstances.

Another occasional practice which quite surprisingly has been shown to be beneficial, is the technique of root folding. Here the root mat is folded under, either at the edges or perhaps so much that the propagation block has to be lifted to receive the root fold. This technique, shown in Figure 10/3, appears to stimulate root growth, which is probably related to the bending of the root axes, and also to increase root activity which is probably due to increasing capilliarity within the root mat. Clearly the technique is not a standard procedure, it may be tried when there is a suggestion that under good conditions growth is less than expected. Obviously plants with brittle roots should not be subjected to this treatment.

Control of Algae

At any point where light contacts the nutrient solution algae are certain to develop.

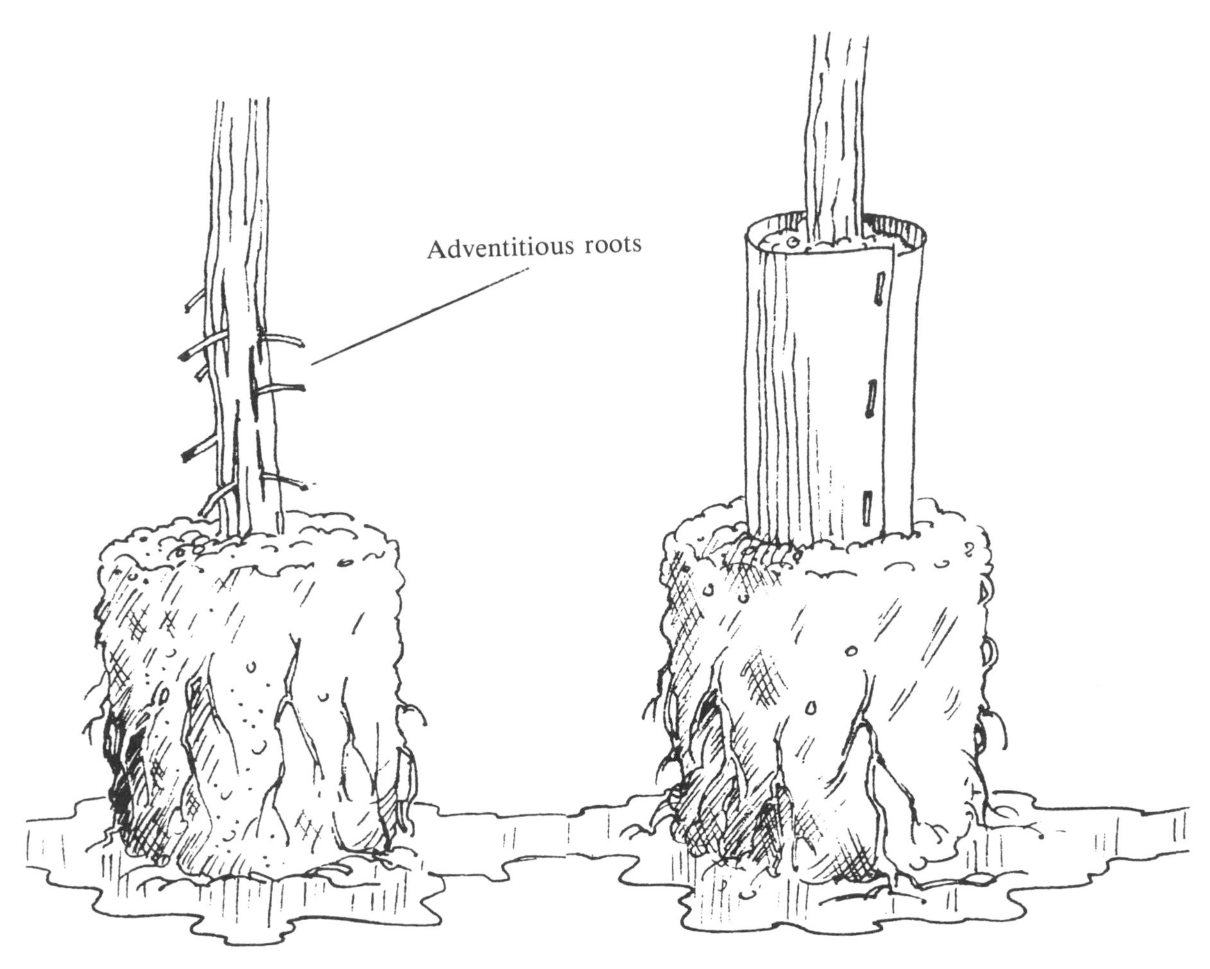

Fig. 10/1 Adventitious roots may be encouraged to enter the solution by fitting a sleeve of compost

The degree of build-up is proportional to the intensity of the light. The damaging effects of algae are: they use a small amount of nutrient, they threaten blockage of the system, they overlay root systems preventing contact between the roots and the atmosphere, and they are unsightly. Note that algae may also be slightly beneficial in that in certain conditions they add oxygen to the solution.

In the channels algae may be limited to small growths at the ends if the channels are kept closed. Unused spaces cut in channel top plates are best blocked off with non-transluscent board of which the top plate material is ideal. If a particularly neat finish is required, it should be possible to keep the cutouts so they can be fitted back when necessary. Open channels encourage algae, but large scale growers are prepared to live with this because of the time savings in setting out and harvesting plants. With open channels algae develop soon after setting out and build-up rapidly. Later, as the foliage of the plants gradually inhibits light incidence onto the solution surface, the algae die away leaving a brown scum, though usually some pockets of green growth remain. After harvest, the root systems, scum and any remaining growths are simply swept away in one operation.

Algae should hardly be present in any circulation tank which is normally kept covered. In uncovered tanks, the greatest danger is build-up of algae on a low pressure float valve, either blocking off the supply or keeping the valve from shutting off. Algae growing in header tanks may also block the float valve when they are drawn into the supply tube. To prevent this a filter fitted in the header tank is extremely useful.

Fig. 10/2 Some plants may be encouraged to root from the stem by layering

The greatest presence of algae is usually to be found in open return ducts and at open channel outflows. Fortunately these are the areas of least potential harm, though it is often a good idea if some effort is made to reduce the build-up by covering these positions with a loose plastic sheet. Occasional removal of algae from open ducting is useful but when doing so be careful to remove all debris as these dislodged pieces are most likely to block the return duct outlet and filter. Check and clean the filter soon after removing algae.

Do not add chemical algaecides to the nutrient solutions. They are all harmful to many plants, and toxic to some. Instead institute limited and reasonable preventative measures as outlined and do not become over concerned about the presence of small amounts of algal growth.

Avoiding Blockages

Apart from algae, the most common causes of serious blockages of the flow result from failure to empty the filter, and the growth of the root system into channel outlets.

The filter is most likely to become blocked whenever there is disturbance in the channels. This is especially true at planting out when loose compost and other debris may fall into the channel, but it can also occur at the removal of plants and indeed during inspections of root systems, particularly if roots have been sloughed due to root death. The filter may also accumulate an amazing assortment of insect life which, unusually, may increase in number until a blockage is affected.

At channel outlets, root systems which threaten the solution return system must be trimmed. With cucumbers trimming may be necessary three or four times in a season but as root trimming is quick, no major difficulty is presented. Roots growing from open channel ends into open return ducts do no harm at all and in fact may assist in maintaining security of flow at that point.

Fig. 10/3 Root folding may increase root growth and activity

In-Season Uprooting and Removal of Root Systems

Here a number of options are presented. The most usual case is the harvesting of successful crops when the plants are often removed in one operation, that is, shoot and whatever root comes with it. After completion of harvesting the channel may be opened and debris swept up and removed. It is usual to switch off the flow during this operation. Sometimes the fact of the roots being intertwined results in potential damage to the top growth as a good grip and tug is necessary to remove the plant. In this situation, such as occurs on harvesting lettuce, it is better if the top, the product, is first cut and afterwards the roots can be removed. If a length of row is involved, it should be possible after harvesting, to open the channel and to roll up root mats and debris to effect speedy removal from the channel.

Much greater difficulty may occur when a single plant is to be removed. Here the intertwining roots make it impossible to remove the plant complete with roots without disturbance to neighbouring plants. The best approach is to cut off the shoot and then snatch away the propagation block with a ripping action. Leave the remainder of the root in the channel where it will do no harm. If the plant is required with roots intact, the root mat should be cut through so a section can be removed. Plants so removed are easy to re-pot but they should be given a reasonable period to establish in good conditions before being exposed to a difficult environment. Where lettuce are harvested complete with roots, so as to be kept fresh at the point of use by sitting in a saucer of water, it is not necessary that all the root is removed undamaged. In fact, if only the propagation block and some root axes are removed, the technique is entirely effective, but if it is a commercial operation to produce and sell 'living lettuce' some effort should be made to recover more than the minimum of root so as to induce consumer confidence in the product.

Tough, unbreaking spreader mat may make removing root systems a little more difficult. However, it may also be advantageous when rolling up the roots as it binds the roll. The presence of spreader mat within the roots of plants to be re-potted is harmless.

In-Season Re-planting

If the plants from a single channel, or indeed from the lowest portion of any channel, are entirely removed it is easy and appropriate to sweep out the channel and remove all debris, taking care not to block the solution return system. Do not clean the channel with any strongly biologically active product as residues may subsequently contaminate the entire system with disastrous consequences. Re-plant exactly as at first setting-out.

Sometimes a small upstream area of channel may need to be re-planted following the removal of a group of plants. Again re-plant just as at the original setting-out after first removing noticeable pieces of loose debris. However, an occasional problem occurs if a large bulk of roots, occupying the channel downstream, act as a dam causing the solution to build up in the vacant area. Several procedures may be followed to eliminate this difficulty. Firstly, reduce the flow rate where there is sensible scope for doing so. This treatment alone may not entirely reduce the solution pool. Secondly, drain the excess solution by clearing a path through the blocking root mat, this is most easily achieved with flexible channelling by loosening the fastenings and allowing the channel to form a greater base before re-fastening. The method is illustrated in Figure 10/4.

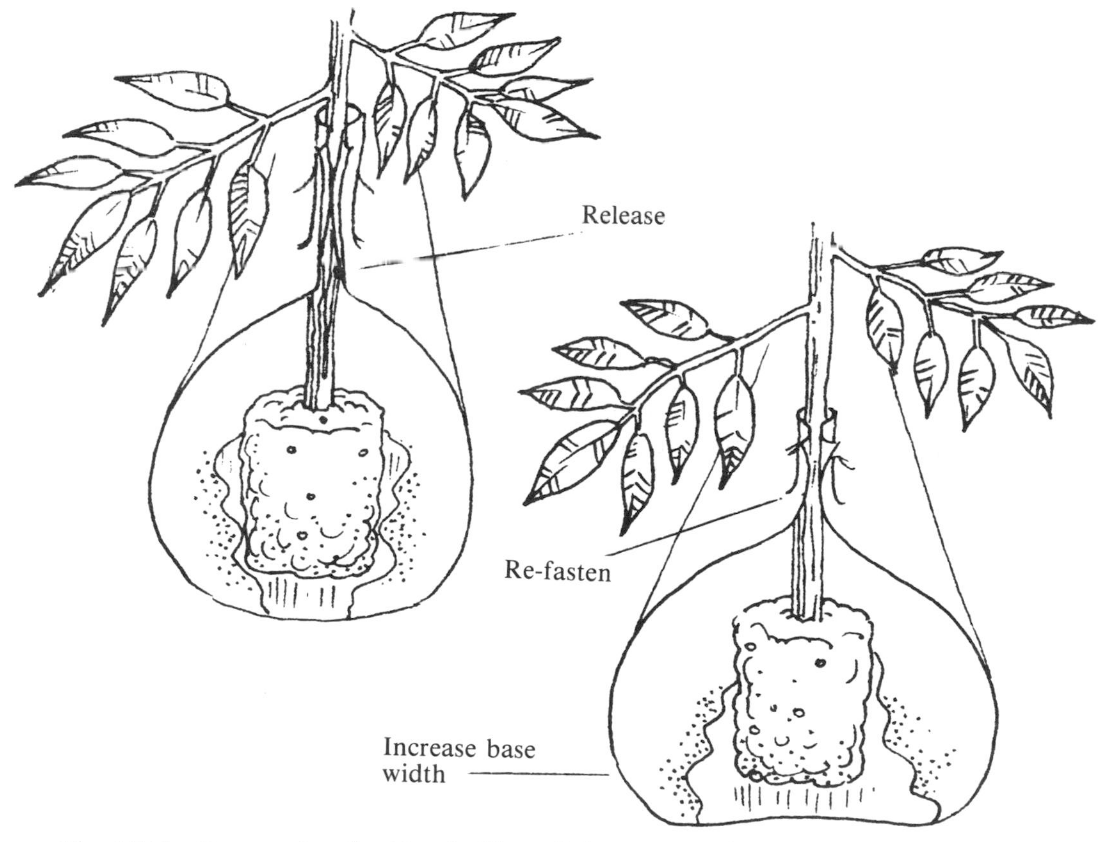

Fig. 10/4 Overcoming the 'dam' effect of the root mat by increasing the base width of flexible channel

In other cases, the root mat may be folded under at one edge, or a length of plastic pipe, 20-32mm dia., laid flat in the channel under the root mat to act as a drain. Normally if any of these techniques are followed, they need be extended only for a distance of equivalent length to the re-planting area.

Thirdly, the new transplants may be set out on raised blocks, possibly of polystyrene, complete with a spreader mat wick. Figure 10/5 shows this arrangement.

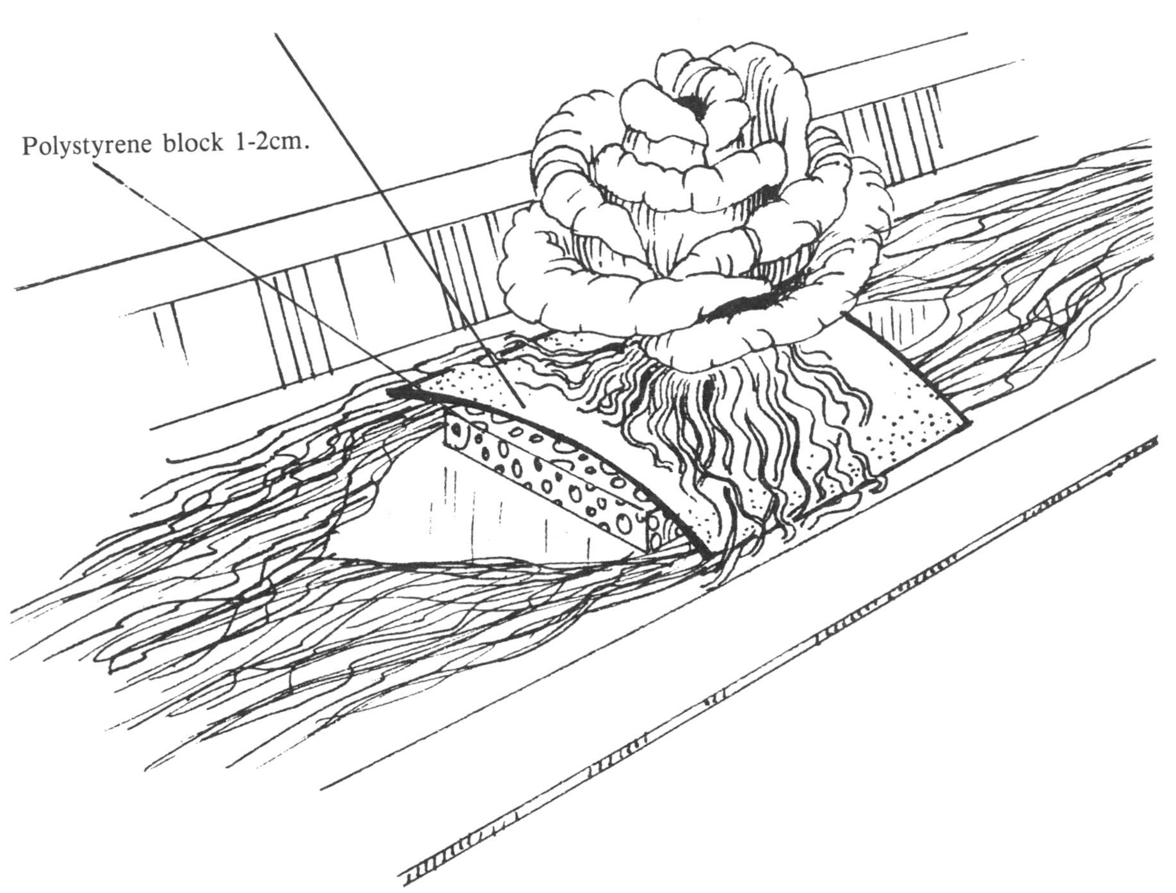

Fig. 10/5 Setting-out a transplant on a raised block with a spreader mat wick

Inspect new transplants for successful rooting just as at first setting-out and if necessary take measures to encourage rooting. If flow rate has been reduced re-instate the flow when the new transplants have become established.

Setting-out may also be made directly onto an existing root mat. Two situations occur. Firstly, where the existing root mat belongs to neighbouring plants in good health. Secondly, where the existing root mat belongs in whole or in part to plants, the shoots of which have been removed from the system. In either case surprisingly good results are obtained though in theory at least, the second case should not be so effective because bacterial activity in the decaying root may reduce oxygen levels in the locality. It is possible that this influence is entirely offset by the advantageous position of the propagation block and newly formed roots.

CHAPTER ELEVEN

GENERAL MANAGEMENT

DISEASES AND PESTS

At the outset it must be made clear that growing plants in NFT as opposed to conventional cultivation, has no significant influences on diseases and pests of the aerial parts of plants. Accordingly, whatever control measures are normally used to limit losses from these causes may be continued when adopting NFT. Additionally, if the change to NFT is to be profitable or rewarding, it is essential to undertake effective measures for the control of aerial diseases and pests as necessary, and sensibly, as preventative rather than curative treatments. This advice surely sounds obvious to experienced growers but it is a fact that NFT is attractive to newcomers to plant cultivation. It is essential that such persons should familiarise themselves with all common diseases and pests and appropriate control techniques before embarking on a venture into NFT, or else be prepared to face the certain prospect of rapid diminution of output.

Diseases

Growing plants in NFT does affect root disease incidence because it embodies a radically different root environment from that prevailing in conventional cultivation. Fairly extensive research into root disease in NFT has been undertaken in recent years at a number of establishments. Though there is no suggestion that this effort elucidates all but a small number of common situations, the results, on the whole are most encouraging.

The common root disease organisms which cause the symptoms colloquially known as "soil sickness" resulting in poor performance, accompanied by wilting, are not encouraged when plants are grown in NFT. Moreover, there is no obvious increase in alternative disease which could offset this gain. Accordingly plants grown in NFT are generally free from this one set of troubles which cause so much loss elsewhere. This optimistic situation should not be used as an excuse for shoddy practices, for in common with other techniques, the incidence of root disease is also closely related to the level of hygiene practised. It is prudent then not to introduce disease into the unit. Particular areas of attention are, not surprisingly, plant material and composts, where only disease-free materials should be used, and attention to end of season cleaning which is detailed later.

Particular disease problems are very few. Commercial lettuce growers may be concerned by a peculiar disorder known as lettuce big vein. This is transmitted by a fungus, known as *olpidium,* which is capable of surviving in water. Oddly it is controlled by the addition of a surfactant (wetting agent) to the solution. Details of control measures may be had from A.D.A.S. plant pathology officers. Although the disease may possibly be present on the non-commercial holding it will pass unnoticed and no control need be exercised.

Apart from lettuce big vein, only two serious diseases are thought to be readily transferred in NFT nutrient solutions. These are, a bacterial wilt of solanoceous plants including tomatoes, which anyway is not at all common in northern Europe, and a more widespread fungal induced wilt of carnations. Fortunately control of both of these, along with a range of other disease causing organisms, is achieved by sensible hygiene.

Root zone pests are fortunately of low occurrence. Some, such as carrot root fly, are almost certainly entirely inhibited when plants are grown in NFT, but others appear to have the same opportunity irrespective of the method of cultivation. One such, root aphid, has become a widespread prominent pest in recent years, especially on late summer crops of lettuce. The pest appears as woolly masses enclustered on exposed roots. The best control is effected by speedy removal of effected plants, and here NFT has the advantage because it offers the opportunity to inspect root zones and therefore to identify and remove affected plants more rapidly. Prevention, in situations where there is a known risk, may be effected if an appropriate long acting insecticide is mixed in with the propagation block compost.

Although NFT cultivation appears to be favourably placed in terms of root diseases and pests, there are still two questions which commonly arise when the subject is discussed. First, what are the prospects of inadvertently introducing a small piece of infected tissue into the unit and finding the disease spread throughout the system in the circulating solution? In fact the prospect is reasonably remote. Just such actions have been experimentally undertaken and it has been found that no common conditions spread rapidly in this manner. The most likely cause of inadvertent introduction of disease occurs when soil or field grown plants are set out in NFT. A particular example is strawberries when infected maiden runners are transferred to the channels. In this case wilt soon develops in the infected plants but does not spread within cropping time to neighbouring plants. Of course, the infected plants should be removed. This example emphasises the need to use only healthy stock and note that this argument is as applicable to ordinary cultivation techniques as it is to NFT.

Second, is it possible to add fungicides or insecticides to the nutrient solution to control diseases and pests? Some experimental work has been completed on this subject, and whilst it is true that there are certain fungicides which remain active in the nutrient solution for a reasonable period, their use is not recommended, because they all display a greater or lesser degree of plant toxicity at useful dose levels. Additionally, there are no insecticides for which recommendations for use as an additive to a circulating solution have been formulated, though there is some hope that this situation may not be irreversible. Accordingly, unless used under expert supervision, it is strongly advised that no fungicide or insecticide be applied to the circulating nutrient solution.

The toxic effect of fungicides shown by experimentation suggest that reasonable care should be exercised to prevent accidental contamination of the system when using these products in the normal manner. It seems improbable that spray drift will cause serious contamination, but if excess spray is applied at a single treatment, or if the droplet size is inordinately large, then sprayed fungicidal solution may run from the aerial parts of the plants, down the stem and into the nutrient solution. Apart from good spraying technique, minimise accidental contamination by ensuring that channels, and especially return ducts and circulation tanks, are covered at the time of spraying as far as is reasonably practicable to do so. Another sensible precaution, where appropriate, is to spray before a change of nutrient solution so that any contamination is quickly disposed of. Successive spraying as part of a controlled disease prevention programme should not pose a problem, because any slight contamination of the solution at one spraying will be deactivated in the solution before the next scheduled spray application. Smokes and fog systems of applying chemicals appear to have the advantage over spraying in terms of minimising contamination, but of course they are not always ideal on other more important criteria.

Pests

Not surprisingly a fair amount of animal life is attracted into a NFT unit. Amongst insects to be found are a large number of beetles, but damage attributable to them is unknown. Also widely occurring are colonies of the primitive bug *colembola* which are manifest as grey to pink sticky surface masses, but these again are entirely innocuous.

Of larger animals, frogs and toads are frequent. These chiefly inhabit the circulation tank, but they are also found within the channels. It is generally agreed that their presence can only be for the good as they feed, amongst other things, on slugs. In the same way as with garden ponds it is difficult to introduce frogs and toads unless they feel inclined themselves to stay. Conversely preventing unwanted settling in the system is equally difficult as they will constantly return if removed. Sometimes frogs and toads may drown in circulation tanks because they are unable to climb out up steep smooth sides. When this occurs their bodies rapidly putrify causing a highly undesirable situation. If a suitable ladder or ramp is fitted into the circulation tank, as shown in Figure 11/1, the problem is completely alleviated and the fitting of the escape does not appear to encourage inordinate numbers.

Fig. 11/1 Fitting a ramp allows frogs and toads to escape from the circulation tank

Only the ubiquitous slug of larger animals inhabiting the system can be regarded as a pest. Although conditions within the channels appear to be ideal for slugs, being both warm and moist with good protection, in fact they do not appear to be any more of a nuisance on NFT sites than elsewhere. Control is effected by usual means, mainly pellets placed outside the channels and on top of the propagation blocks. Slugs are very successfully trapped on interchannel pathways where these are constructed in stone or concrete. This construction may account for the surprisingly low numbers of slugs associated with some NFT sites, because it encourages a drier floor area and atmosphere compared to an earth floor. If, as is common, a single slug begins to cause damage, it may be found and eliminated during the day by opening the channel adjacent to the damage. Often it is possible to trace the culprit by following its slime path left on the channel.

PLANT SUPPORT

Strictly, plant support is hardly a subject which should be found in a book concerned solely with NFT, but in fact the question often arises; how do plants support themselves when they are not anchored in solid medium? Low growing bushy plants support themselves just as well as they do in conventional cultivation. Tall, top heavy plants need support in NFT just as they do elsewhere. In-between plants, for example fuchsias and geraniums benefit from support when grown in NFT and again this is very much in line with general practice. It is useful to consider the options for plant support with special reference to their use in NFT.

Staking

Small stakes make ideal plant supports when they can be inobtrusively inserted into the compost block holding the plant. In this way large numbers of smaller plants, as well as immature plants of taller species, may be adequately supported.

As the top load becomes greater, staking generally becomes less successful. Firstly, because branches and side shoots may need support, secondly, because the top weight simply overwhelms the stake and finally, because the stake is usually inadequately secured in loose soil or compost. This last difficulty may be overcome in NFT when channels are placed on strong supportive materials, such as wood or concrete, because accommodation holes may be drilled into the support to take the stake. In this way truly rigid support may be provided. The technique, shown in Figure 11/2, is especially useful to support specimen plants.

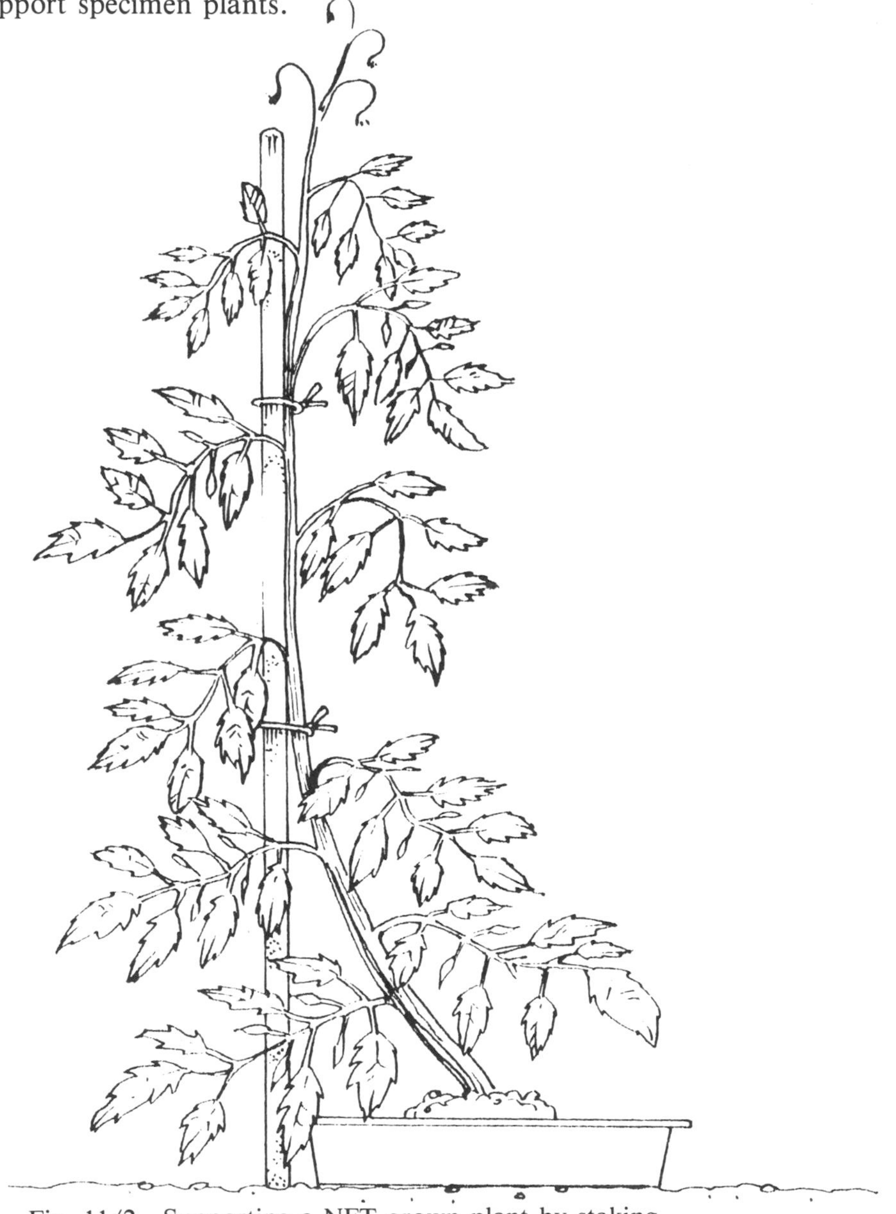

Fig. 11/2 Supporting a NFT grown plant by staking

Stringing

Stringing is a much more appropriate method of supporting long stemmed subjects than is staking. The preferred method has been developed with mainly crop plants especially tomatoes, cucumber, melons, aubergines and peppers, but any plant of roughly similar habit is easily supported by stringing. The basic technique is simple enough; using strong, thin string, preferably purpose made nylon, fasten a loose knot around the stem up to 250-300mm from the propagation block, but preferably not closer than 75mm. Tie the free end securely to a fixture high above the plant allowing the string to be a little lax. As the plant grows twist the leading shoot around the string.

In practice the method is much elaborated because stringing lends itself not only to supporting plants but also to training them. The usual adaptations are: Instead of tying the string to a roof member, tie it to a strong wire fitted parallel with the row at a convenient height. If the top wire is sited not directly above the plants, but to one side, then the row of plants is trained in the direction of the top wire. If now a second top wire is fitted similarly for an adjacent row, but training the plants in the opposite direction, then two distinct rows are produced. The technique can easily be adapted to form two rows from a single row of planting if alternate plants are trained to either side. This adaptation is used extensively in NFT when it is inconvenient to fit extra channels, thus compelling double planting in one channel where the roots are maintained in close proximity but the shoots are given the required air space.

If the string from each plant is tied to the top wire such that it can be readily untied, and if excess string is allowed, then plants held on the string can be formed into a gentle curve in the direction of the top wire, thereby increasing the separation of the rows and improving illumination. This modifed stringing technique is illustrated in Figure 11/3.

Finally, provided additional string is available, as the plant's leading shoot reaches the top of its string, more string can be released and the support string re-tied some distance along the top wire, thus providing string space for more top growth. In this case, each plant in turn is untied and re-tied so that successive spaces become available for all plants in the row. This complete technique is known as 'layering' and to facilitate it special hooks or reels are commercially available, but these can be home-fashioned from strong wire. Figure 11/4 shows this arrangement.

Layered plants, such as tomatoes, can be grown to quite phenomenal lengths when the weight of each plant complete with fruit, may become very heavy. Accordingly, special care must be taken to ensure that the top wire is sufficiently strong to support the combined weight of all the plants in the row. It helps if the top wire is supported along its length by attachment to the roof members.

Also, eventually some stem sections or fruit trusses may sag so that they come into contact with the ground. To prevent this a bottom wire about 37-45cm high may be fitted. To this wire layered stems may be secured. The bottom wire is rarely used in commercial horticulture because of the extra work involved, but in the private greenhouse it can much improve the neatness of the plants and keeps the channel tops free from obstruction.

Horizontal Supports

Two types of horizontal supports are found. Firstly, a mesh perhaps 100 × 100mm, though other sizes are used, and in sheet form of width about equal to the plant bed is fitted horizontally above the plants. The plants grow up through the mesh and are held in position. The mesh may be manufactured from flexible material such as polypropylene or of rigid material such as galvanised wire. Pig netting can easily be adapted for this purpose. Figure 11/5 illustrates the use of horizontal mesh in supporting plants in NFT.

Fig. 11/3 Supporting and training long stemmed plants by stringing

Meshes are usually supported in position with stout stakes at appropriate intervals on either side of the bed. For the small modern greenhouse, fastenings are available by which the mesh can be secured to the aluminium wall sections. Sometimes a second or even a third mesh is placed at appropriate height increments above the bed to increase support and allow for growth. Other times, the original mesh may be more than sufficient itself and still other times it may be raised, though this is often difficult because of side shoots.

Horizontal meshes are used commercially with many cut flower crops such as carnations and chrysanths, but they may also be used in mixed plantings.

The second horizontal support is the trestle designed for individual or small numbers of plants. In this case a horizontal mesh is supported above the plants by legs which are

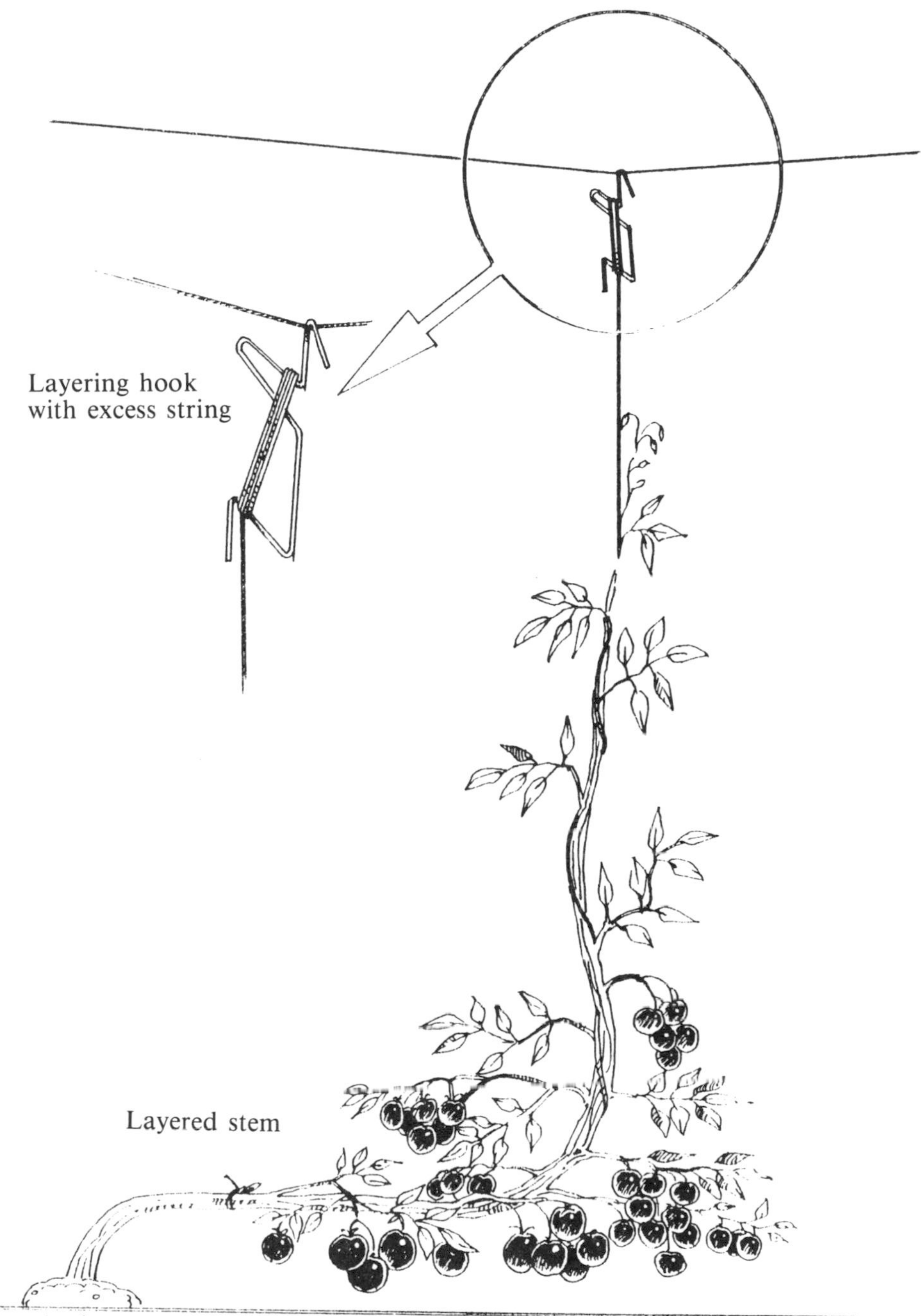

Fig. 11/4 A plant supported by stringing might be "layered" to allow for extra top growth

placed either side of the channel. These supports are available usually in plastic coated wire, but they can be home fabricated. An example is shown in Figure 11/6.

Other types of support

Some plants are best supported on enlarged propagation blocks. An example is onions where the bulb forms on top of the block and the larger than usual block allows continued support, even when the onion has become large. Note that this technique is only applicable to strong rooting plants where the block size is not a serious impediment to successful root emergence into the channel.

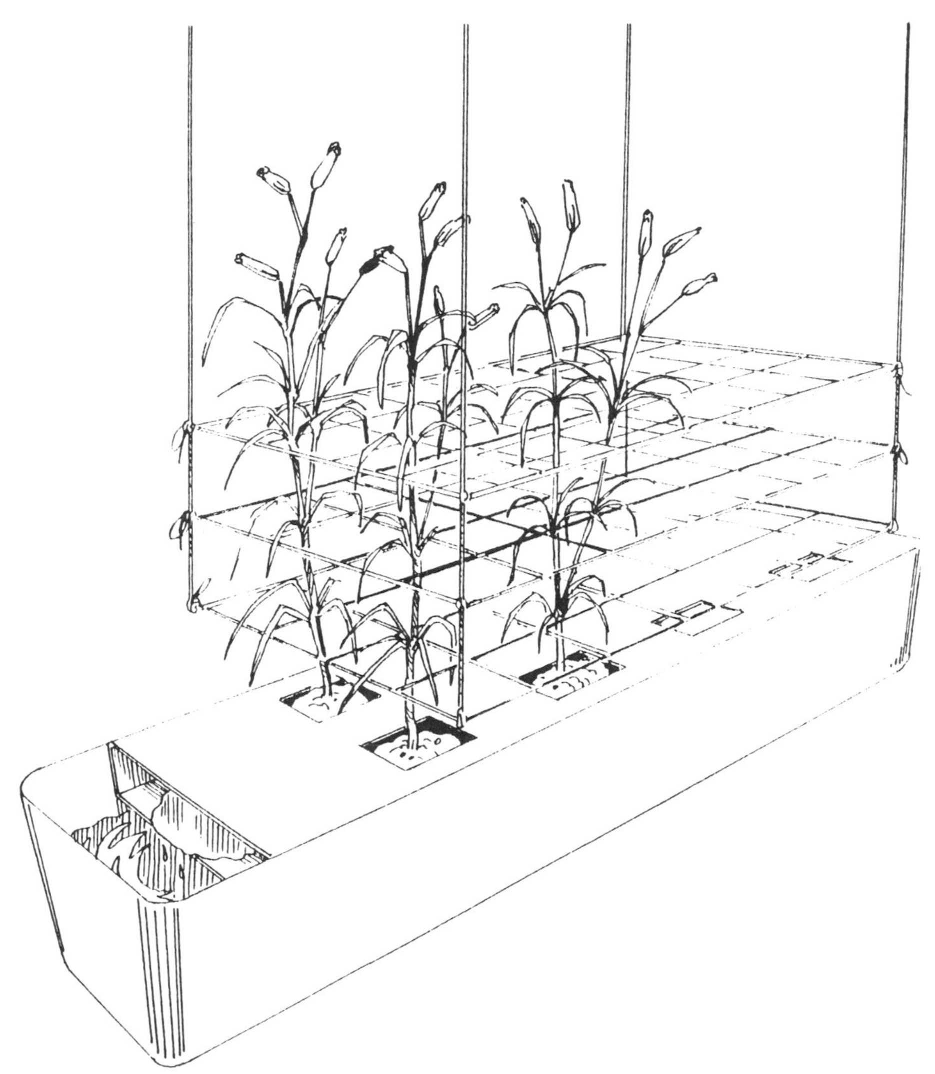

Fig. 11/5 Horizontal meshes in use as supports for plants grown in a NFT system

Plants which are not supported at all by propagation blocks, such as free rooted strawberries, may require external support to prevent them working free of the channels as shoot weight increases. In general this is achieved by keeping the crown well under the channel top plate, but in difficult cases it may be necessary to fit a support wire which normally would be about 75mm to the side of the plants at about 50mm height. This arrangement is shown in Figure 11/7.

RECORDS

Success with NFT is almost invariably associated with good attention to method and sensible pursuit of declared prescribed aims. To facilitate this, accurate information concerning procedures and results is desirable, though optionally it is possible to run any NFT system "by the book" and having regard only for the current state of plants in the unit. Few of us are capable, or would even aspire, to hold all the relevant information concerning a current cultivation programme within our heads, and certainly we would not expect to be able to recall with accuracy from season to season. Accordingly

Fig. 11/6 A trestle type mesh support

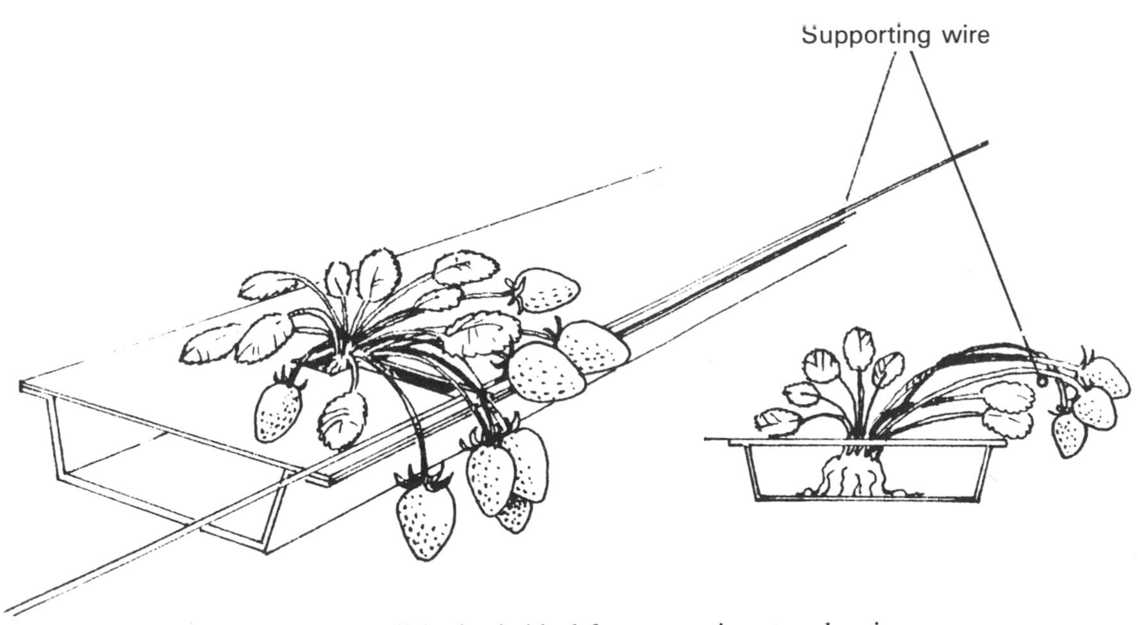

Fig. 11/7 A parallel wire is ideal for supporting strawberries

it is highly advantageous if a set of records are kept. In fact this situation is not dissimilar to that pertaining with ordinary cultivation, when almost without exception the best results are obtained by persons who keep at least a cursory record of their work.

For NFT growers there is certainly advantage in recording diary events such as date of setting out, date of first pick and accummulated yield totals, but more specific information concerning the day to day workings and results is beneficial. The most useful items of information are best recorded at a particular time each day so that daily variations are noted. For convenience it is usual to combine information collection with the demands of monitoring nutrient status. The suggested records include:

i. The CF of the solution.
ii. The pH of the solution.
iii. The amount of nutrients A & B added.
iv. The amount of acid added in the interval between recordings.
v. The quantity of water taken up by the plants.
vi. The temperature of the nutrient solution.
vii. A brief description of the weather - particularly approximate sunshine hours.
viii. Comments on the state of the plants.

It is readily appreciated that the complete information set is likely to be obtained only by the commercial or semi-commercial grower, but this does not absolve others from making an effort because even weekly compiled data sets are very useful, as indeed are data sets where particular items are missing. For example, many private gardeners would not be able to record solution CF. Further there is great advantage, in small scale NFT, of keeping a good set of information for only a limited period during which the workings and some inter-relationships of the system can be understood.

Use records in two ways. Firstly, in conjunction with guidance, set out in this book and elsewhere e.g., instructions accompanying manufactured nutrients, so as to assess the performance of the plants against reasonable targets. For example calculate the total weight of nutrient used per unit area cropped. Does it approach the expected? If not, why not? Do the water temperature records throw any light on this? Secondly, to assess current performance against previous performance. For example, is water uptake improving? Related to this is the assistance that records can give if, and when, trouble arises. Here, the daily observations provide an immediate commentary on the effectiveness of the remedial management since improving plants take up more water and more nutrients, whilst increasing stress on plants is shown by falling water and nutrient uptake. In the same way records showing a decrease of water and nutrient usage, which is not attributable to the environment, may induce the operator to discharge the solution. The effectiveness of this procedure will be shown by the records taken subsequently.

END OF SEASON PROCEDURE

Many NFT systems are partially planted for indefinite periods and in these cases no precise end of season can be identified. However, a more than adequate cleaning technique is available. At the time of least plant occupation, and after partially draining the system and switching off circulation, empty channels may be thoroughly washed down with hose or can and clean water raced through the return pipework. Afterwards, empty the circulation tank and remove all grit and dirt from the bottom. Partially refill with clean water and discharge this through the supply pipework. Drain to waste from the inlet tubes released from the channels. In this circumstance do not use a disinfectant. Replace channel base liners and flexible channels if their reliable life span is approximately complete. Note that many NFT growers prefer to replace base liners and flexible channels on an annual basis.

Only when there is a definite period of at least one week during which the NFT system is empty may a disinfectant be used. A commercial scale procedure is to circulate 2% formalin for 1 day before the old plants are removed. Then remove the plants complete with flexible channels and/or base liners and afterwards wash down channels and floors also with 2% formalin. Discharge any formalin solution from the tank and refill with clean water which is circulated, preferably warmed to up to 30°C, once base liners and flexible channels have been replaced. Several dischargings and refillings with clean water should be made to effect complete removal of formaldehyde fumes. After 2/3 days, more if cold water is circulated, and after a final discharge the system may be replanted.

This procedure is very often unsuitable for small scale work because of the danger of damaging neighbouring plants with formaldehyde fumes. A less hazardous method is to substitute a solution of proprietory sterilant such as is used in nursery and home brewing work. These solutions, as well as being very effective, are easy to use, odour free, quick acting and moreover residues are effectively removed without the need to circulate a heated solution.

The danger inherent in using strong disinfectants, namely the toxic effect of residues on replantings and neighbouring plants, suggests that it is preferable if disinfectant is not employed unless there is a particular reason to do so. Instead an excellent degree of cleaning can be attained simply by washing down the channels and components with clean water, in the manner set out previously, for use when the system was partially empty.

Also at the end of the season carry out essential maintenance. Likely areas of attention are slopes and channel outflows, tank insulation and regular pump maintenance. Remember that for many of the structural components this is the only opportunity with easy access to carry out detailed examination and improvement.